'African Potentials' for Wildlife Conservation and Natural Resource Management:
Against the Image of 'Deficiency' and Tyranny of 'Fortress'

Edited by

Toshio Meguro, Chihiro Ito and Kariuki Kirigia

In collaboration

Langaa RPCIG
Mankon Bamenda

CAAS
Kyoto University

Publisher:

Langaa RPCIG
Langaa Research & Publishing Common Initiative Group
P.O. Box 902 Mankon
Bamenda
North West Region
Cameroon
Langaagrp@gmail.com
www.langaa-rpcig.net

In Collaboration with
The Center for African Area Studies, Kyoto University, Japan

Distributed in and outside N. America by African Books Collective
orders@africanbookscollective.com
www.africanbookscollective.com

ISBN-10: 9956-552-85-2

ISBN-13: 978-9956-552-85-6

Notes on Contributors

Yuichiro FUJIOKA is Associate Professor at the Faculty of Social and Cultural Studies, Kyushu University, Japan. His main research fields in Africa are rural areas in northern Namibia and north-east South Africa. His main research topics are fluctuation of socio-ecosystem, agroecosystem and natural resource uses in rural Africa. His major works include: *Socio-Ecosystem of Savanna Agroforest*, Kyoto: Showado (2016, in Japanese) and 'Unique features of African agro-pastoralism: Adapting life and sharing wealth in fluid environment', in G. Hyden, K. Sugimura and T. Tsuruta (eds) *Rethinking African Agriculture*, London: Routledge, pp. 79–94 (2020).

Shinichiro ICHINO is Researcher at the Center for African Area Studies, Kyoto University, Japan. His research field is Madagascar. His research interests include lemur social evolution and lemur conservation. His major works include: 'Lifespan and reproductive senescence in a free-ranging ring-tailed lemur (*Lemur catta*) population at Berenty, Madagascar', *Folia Primatologica*, 86 (1-2), pp. 134–139 (2015) and 'Forest vertebrate fauna and local knowledge among the Tandroy people in Berenty Reserve, southern Madagascar: A preliminary study', *African Study Monographs, Supplemental Issue*, 54, pp. 115–135 (2018).

Taku IIDA is Professor of Ecological Anthropology at the National Museum of Ethnology, Osaka, Japan. His research interests include socio-economic changes in fishing communities, human abilities to develop fishing techniques and its relation to, as well as heritagisation of, rural life. He is the author of *Know-How to Survive on the Coast: An Eco-Anthropological Study in a Madagascar Fishing Village*, Kyoto: Sekaishisosha (2008, in Japanese) and the Chief Editing Secretary of *Handicrafting the Intangible: Zafimaniry Heritage in Madagascar*, Osaka: National Museum of Ethnology (2013).

Chihiro ITO is Associate Professor at the Faculty of Humanities, Fukuoka University, Japan. Her research fields are Zambia and Zimbabwe. Her research concerns rural livelihood, urban–rural interaction and political ecology. Her major works include: 'Development of fishing practices within commercial fisheries in

Lake Kariba, southern Africa', *African Study Monographs*, 41(1), pp.1–22 (2021), *Bridging Urban and Rural: People's Mobility and Livelihood Changes in Rural Zambia,* Tokyo: Sinsensha (2015, in Japanese) and 'The growth of "rural business" and its impact on local society in Zambia', in A. Takada, I. K. Nyamongo and K. Teshirogi (eds) *Exploring African Potentials: The Dynamics of Action, Living Strategy, and Social Order in Southern Africa (MILA Special Issue),* Nairobi: University of Nairobi, pp. 49–58 (2014).

Yukino IWAI is Associate Professor at the Hirayama Ikuo Volunteer Center, Waseda University, Japan. Her research concerns political ecology of wildlife conservation. She recently implemented a mitigation project of human–elephant conflict in the villages adjacent to the Serengeti National Park in Tanzania. Her major works include: 'Human–elephant conflict in the Serengeti: The side-effects of wildlife tourism', *global-e*, 11(53) (2018) available at <https://globalejournal.org/global-e/october-2018/human-elephant-conflict-serengeti-side-effects-wildlife-tourism>, and *Why Elephants Attack My Village?* Tokyo: Godo Shuppan (2017, in Japanese).

Daud KASSAM is Professor of Fisheries Biotechnology and Biodiversity Conservation in the Department of Aquaculture and Fisheries Science at the Lilongwe University of Agriculture and Natural Resources, Malawi, where he is responsible for fish genetics as well as fish biodiversity and conservation. He holds a PhD from Ehime University, Japan. His main research interests are in the fish population genetics and in the application of modern genetics and bioinformatics techniques in the conservation of aquatic biodiversity. Among his major research projects is the production of *Oreochromis* fish hybrids that are capable of outperforming locally available strains through the exploitation of different fish sex-determining systems.

Kariuki KIRIGIA is a PhD candidate in the Department of Anthropology at McGill University and an in-coming postdoctoral fellow at Concordia University in Montreal, Canada. His doctoral research, carried out under the supervision of Prof. John Galaty within the Institutional Canopy of Conservation (I-CAN) project, examines how capitalist relations penetrate an indigenous frontier in a postcolonial setting by studying shifts in land tenure and wildlife conservation initiatives. Kariuki's dissertation is informed by an ethnographic study of the politics and processes of dismantling the

Maasai commons of Olderkesi in Narok County, southern Kenya, and the creation of a wildlife conservancy in the area. At McGill University, Kariuki has taught 'Social Change in Modern Africa' and 'Swahili Language and Culture' courses.

Frank MATOSE is Associate Professor in the Department of Sociology and a Co-Director of the Environmental Humanities South Centre at the University of Cape Town, South Africa. His research interests are in environmental sociology with a particular focus on Southern Africa, placing emphasis on the intersection of local people, the state, capital, forest and resource conservation, and the political economy of protected areas. He is also a member of the International Sociological Association (ISA) in which he is active in the Research Committee on Environment and Society (RC24). He has a forthcoming monograph, titled *Politics of Chronic Liminality: Forests and the Power of the Marginalised in Southern Africa* and an edited volume, titled *The Violence of Conservation in Africa: State, Militarisation and Alternatives* (with M. Ramutsindela and T. Mushonga), Cheltenham: Edward Elgar Publishing. For his detailed profile: http://www.sociology.uct.ac.za/dr-frank-matose.

Motoji MATSUDA is Program Director at the Research Institute for Humanity and Nature, Kyoto, Japan. His research fields are Nairobi and Western Kenya. His research topics are urbanisation, migration and conflict. His major works include: *Urbanisation from Below*, Kyoto: Kyoto University Press (1998), *The Manifesto of Anthropology of the Everyday Life World*, Kyoto: Sekaishisosha (2008, in Japanese), *African Virtues in the Pursuit of Conviviality: Exploring Local Solutions in Light of Global Prescriptions* (co-edited with I. Ohta and Y. Gebre), Bamenda: Langaa RPCIG (2017) and *The Challenge of African Potentials: Conviviality, Informality and Futurity* (co-edited with Y. Ofosu-Kusi), Bamenda: Langaa RPCIG (2020).

Toshio MEGURO is Associate Professor at the Faculty of International Studies, Hiroshima City University, Japan. He has conducted fieldwork in southern Kenya. His research topics are community-based conservation, participatory development, environmental governance and changes in Maasai society. His major works include: 'The unchanged and unrepresented culture of respect in Maasai society', *African Study Monographs*, 40 (2-3), pp. 93–108 (2019) and 'Gaps between the innovativeness of the Maasai Olympics and the positionings of Maasai warriors', *Nilo-Ethiopian Studies*, 22, pp. 27–39 (2017).

Maxon NGOCHERA is Chief Fisheries Research Officer in the Department of Fisheries, Ministry of Forestry and Natural Resources, and Officer in-charge at the Monkey Bay Fisheries Research Station in Mangochi, Malawi. He holds a PhD in Freshwater Sciences from the School of Freshwater Sciences, University of Wisconsin-Milwaukee, USA. His research interests include tropical limnology, fisheries management, climate change and post-harvest loss and value addition. He is a recipient of the Fulbright Junior Development Program Scholarship (2003). His recent research work has been published in the journal of *Limnology and Oceanography*, 'Spatial and temporal dynamics of pCO_2 and CO_2 flux in tropical Lake Malawi' (2020, doi.org/10.1002/lno.11408, co-authored with Harvey A. Bootsma [email: hbootsma@uwm.edu]). Currently, Ngochera is responsible for overseeing research work in capture fisheries within the Malawian natural water bodies.

Nobuko NISHIZAKI is Professor at the Professional College of Arts and Tourism, Japan. Her research concerns African wildlife conservation and her main research area is Ethiopia. Recent major publications include: 'An Ethiopian alternative to "traditional" ethnic tourism', *global-e*, 12(1) (2019), available online at <https://globalejournal.org/global-e/january-2019/ethiopian-alternative-traditional-ethnic-tourism> and '"Neoliberal conservation" in Ethiopia: An analysis of current conflict in and around protected areas and their resolution', *African Study Monographs, Supplementary Issue*, 50: 191-205 (2015).

Tom G. ONDICHO is Associate Professor of Anthropology at the Institute of Anthropology, Gender and African Studies, University of Nairobi, Kenya. He holds a PhD in Anthropology from Massey University in New Zealand. His areas of specialisation include anthropology of tourism, community-based conservation, gender, violence and conflicts, and poverty. He is currently a Guest Editor of *African Journal of Gender, Society and Development* (AJGSD). His most recent works include: 'Impact of corona virus (COVID-19) pandemic and implications on tourism sector: The experience of Kenya', *Journal of African Interdisciplinary Studies*, 5(6), pp. 31–44 (co-authored with E. M. Irandu, 2021), 'A policy brief on the impact of

COVID-19 on tourism in Kenya: Strategies for recovery', *Kenya Policy Briefs*, 2(1), pp. 45–46 (2021), 'Students' perspectives on online learning at the University of Nairobi during COVID-19', in W. Shiino and I. Karusigarira (eds) *Youths in Struggles: Unemployment, Politics and Cultures in Contemporary Africa*, Fuchu: Tokyo University of Foreign Studies, pp. 233–250 (2021).

Kimaren Ole RIAMIT is an indigenous peoples' leader from the pastoral Maasai community in southern Kenya. He is the founder-director of Indigenous Livelihoods Enhancement Partners (ILEPA), a community-based indigenous peoples' organisation based in Kenya and working on indigenous pastoral communities' concerns. He is a holder of a Master of Arts Degree in Development Anthropology, a Post Graduate Diploma in Project Planning and Management, and a BSc. Degree in Foods, Nutrition and Dietetics. He is interested in anthropology of development, human rights and governance. He is primarily interested in the discourses of development, development institutions, how development is impacting grassroots communities in Africa and social movements that are challenging prevailing flawed development pathways, from an indigenous peoples' perspective, specifically, how property, rights to land and natural resources, decision-making arrangement interact to safeguard or impede rights to basic indigenous peoples' survival.

Bosco RUSUWA is Associate Professor in the Department of Biological Sciences at the University of Malawi, where he lectures in evolutionary biology, ecology and natural resource management. He holds a PhD in Biological Sciences from the University of Queensland, Australia. His main research interests lie in the understanding of fundamental evolutionary and ecological dynamics of aquatic ecosystems and their fauna. Among other projects, he has worked on the impact of sedimentation on rock-dwelling cichlid fish communities in Lake Malawi and is engaged in a collaborative research aimed at unravelling the genetic impact of strong fisheries-induced selection in natural populations of cichlid fishes of Lakes Malawi and Malombe (Malawi).

Samantha S. SITHOLE is a PhD student and is also working as a graduate assistant in the Institute of Geography and Sustainability at the University of Lausanne, Switzerland. She holds a MPhil in Development Studies from the University of Cape Town. Her research interests are in the militarisation of green or conservation spaces and the role of youth in conservation and how their livelihoods are affected in these contested green spaces.

Gen YAMAKOSHI is Professor at the Graduate School of Asian and African Area Studies, Kyoto University, Japan. His research topics are animal ecology, wildlife conservation, traditional ecological knowledge, landscape management and community-based conservation. He has conducted fieldwork mainly in forested Guinea, West Africa. His major works include: *Who Owns African Nature? African Perspectives on the Future of Community-Based Conservation* (edited with T. Meguro and T. Sato), Kyoto: Kyoto University Press (2016, in Japanese).

Yumi YAMANE is Specially Appointed Research Fellow at the Centre for African Area Studies, Kyoto University, and a Visiting Researcher at the Department of Tourism Science, Tokyo Metropolitan University, Japan. Her research topics are wildlife conservation within human-modified areas, especially the relationship between leopards (*Panthera pardus pardus*) and humans in Kenya. She launched the Madoadoa Project in 2020 which aims at conservation of felines and promotion of local employment. Her recent works include: *Conservation Ecology of Wild Leopard (*Panthera pardus pardus*) in and around Nairobi National Park,* Kyoto: Shokadoh (2020, in Japanese).

Table of Contents

African Potentials for Convivial World-Making

Motoji Matsuda

1. The Idea of 'African Potentials'

The *African Potentials* series is based on the findings since 2011 of the African Potentials research project, an international collaboration involving researchers based in Japan and Africa. This project examines how to tackle the challenges of today's world using the experiences and wisdom (ingenuity and responsiveness) of African society. It has identified field sites across a variety of social domains, including areas of conflict, conciliation, environmental degradation, conservation, social development and equality, and attempts to shed light on the potential of African society to address the problems therein. Naturally, such an inquiry is deeply intertwined with the political and economic systems that control the contemporary world, and with knowledge frameworks that have long dominated the perceptions and understanding of our world. Building on unique, long-standing collaborative relationships developed between researchers in Japan and Africa, the project suggests new ways to challenge the prevailing worldview on humans, society and history, enabling those worldviews to be relativised, decentred and pluralised.

After the rose-coloured dreams of the 1960s, African society entered an era of darkness in the 1980s and 1990s. It was beleaguered by problems that included civil conflict, military dictatorship, national economic collapse, commodity shortages, environmental degradation and destruction, over-urbanisation and rampant contagious disease. In the early 21st century, the fortunes of Africa were reversed as it underwent economic growth by leveraging its abundant natural resources. However, an unequal redistribution of wealth increased social disparities and led to the emergence of new forms of conflict

xiii

and discrimination. The challenges facing African society appear to be more profound than ever.

The governments of African states and the international community have attempted to resolve the many problems Africa has experienced. For example, the perpetrators of crimes during times of civil conflict have been punished by international tribunals, support for democratisation has been offered to states ruled by dictators and despots and environmental degradation has been tackled by scientific awareness campaigns conducted at huge expense.

Nonetheless, to us – the Japanese and African researchers engaging with African society in this era – the huge monetary and organisational resources expended, and scientifically grounded measures pursued, seem to have had little effect on the lives of ordinary people. The punishment of perpetrators did not consider the coexistence of perpetrators and victims, while the propagation of democratic ideals and training to raise scientific awareness was far removed from people's lived experiences. Nevertheless, while many of these 'top-down' measures prescribed to solve Africa's challenges proved ineffective, African society has found ways to heal post-conflict communities and to develop practices of political participation and environmental conservation.

Why did this happen? This question led us to examine ideas and practices African society has formulated for tackling the contemporary difficulties it has experienced. These were developed at sites where ordinary Africans live. 'African Potentials' is the name we gave to these home-grown ideas and the potential to engender them.

2. African Forum: A Unique Intellectual Collaboration between Japan and Africa

As the concept of African Potentials emerged, it required further reflection to develop ideas that could be applied in the humanities and social sciences. The context for these processes was the African Forum: a meeting held in a different part of Africa each year where African researchers from different regions and Japanese researchers studying in each of those regions came together to engage in frank discussion. The attendance of all core members of the project sympathetic to the idea of African Potentials ensured the continuity of the discussions at these African Forums. The core members who drove the project forward from the African side included Edward Kirumira (Uganda and South Africa), Kennedy Mkutu (Kenya), Yntiso Gebre (Ethiopia), the late Samson Wassara (South Sudan), the late Sam Moyo (Zimbabwe), Michael Neocosmos (South Africa), Francis B. Nyamnjoh (Cameroon and South Africa) and Yaw Ofosu-Kusi (Ghana). The researchers from Japan specialised in extremely diverse fields, including political science, sociology, anthropology, development economics, education, ecology and geography. As they built creative interdisciplinary spaces for interaction across fields over the course of a decade, project members have produced many major outcomes that serve as research models for intellectual and academic exchange between Japan and Africa, and experimental cases of educational practice in the mutual cultivation and guidance of young researchers.

African Forums have been held in Nairobi (2011), Harare (2012), Juba (2013), Yaoundé (2014), Addis Ababa (2015), Kampala (2016), Grahamstown (now Makhanda, 2017), Accra (2018) and Lusaka (2019). These meetings fostered deeper discussion of the conceptualisation and generalisation of African Potentials. This led to the development of a framework for approaching African Potentials and its distinguishing features.

3. What are African Potentials?

The first aim of African Potentials is to 'de-romanticise' the traditional values and institutions of Africa. For example, when studying conflict resolution, members of African Potentials are not interested in excessive idealisation of traditional means of conflict resolution and unconditional endorsement of a return to African traditions as an 'alternative' to modern Western conflict-resolution methods, because such ideas fix African Potentials in a static mode as they speak to a fantasy that ignores the complexities of the contemporary world; they are cognate with the mentality that depreciates African culture.

puts went on over the other

Rendering African culture static displaces it from its original context and uses it to fabricate 'African-flavoured' theatrical events, as we have seen in different conflict situations. Typical of this tendency is the 'theatre' of traditional dance by performers dressed in ethnic costume and the ceremonial slaughter of cows in an imitation of the rituals of mediation and reconciliation once observed in inter-ethnic conflicts. In our African Forums, we have criticised this tendency as the 'technologisation' and 'compartmentalisation' of traditional rituals.

Naturally, a stance that arbitrarily deems certain conflict-resolution cultures to be 'subaltern', 'backward' or 'uncivilised' needs to be critiqued and it is important to re-evaluate approaches that have been written off in this way. This does not mean that we should level unconditional praise on a fixed subject. With globalisation, African society is experiencing great changes brought about by the circulation of diverse ideas, institutions, information and physical goods. African Potentials can be found in the power to generate cultures of conflict-resolution autonomously under these fluid conditions, while re-aligning elements that were previously labelled 'traditional' and 'indigenous'. In the African Potentials project, we call this the power of 'interface function': the capacity to forge combinations and connections within assemblages of diverse values, ideas and practices that belong to disparate dimensions and different historical phases. In one sense, this is a kind of 'bricolage' created by dismantling pre-existing values and institutions and recombining them freely. It is also a convivial process in the sense that it involves enabling the coexistence of diverse, multi-dimensional elements to create new strengths that are used in contemporary society. The terms 'bricolage' and 'conviviality' are apt expressions characterising the 'interface functions' of African Potentials.

Following this outline, we can identify two features distinguishing African Potentials. First, African Potentials comprise not fixed, unchanging entities but, rather, an open process that is always dynamic and in flux. To treat African traditions and history as static is to fall into the trap of modernist thinking, in which Africa is scorned as barbaric and uncivilised, and the knowledge and practices generated there treated as subaltern and irrational – or a diametrically

xvi

[handwritten marginal note, left margin:] therefore used western intervention ⇒ colonialist

[handwritten note, bottom:] traditional knowledge is 'just as important'

opposed revivalist mindset that romanticises traditions unconditionally and imbues them with exaggerated significance.

The second feature of African Potentials is its aspiration to pluralism rather than unity. For example, a basic principle of modern civil society is that conflict resolution should occur in accordance with law and judicial process. This principle is deemed to be based on common sense in our society, which means that any resolution method that runs counter to the principle is regarded as 'mistaken' from the outset. This constitutes an aspiration toward unity. It supposes that there is a single way of thinking in relation to the achievement of justice and deems all other approaches peripheral, informal and inferior. The standpoint of Africa's cultural potential, however, renders untenable the idea of a single absolute approach that represents all others as mistaken or deserving of rejection. Here, we can identify a pluralist aspiration that embraces both legal/judicial approaches and extrajudicial solutions.

An aspiration to unity, reduced to the level of dogma, can find eventual culmination in beliefs about 'purity'. In other words, thoughts, values and methods can be regarded as an absolute good, while any attempt to incorporate other (impure) elements is stridently denounced as improper behaviour that compromises purity and perfection. In direct contrast, African Potentials affirm the complexity and multiplicity of a range of elements, and attach value to that which is incomplete. This signifies a more tolerant, open attitude to ideas and values, one that differs from those of the more developed world. African Potentials are grounded in this kind of openness and tolerance.

As we have seen, African cultural potentials are distinguished by their dynamism, flexibility, pluralism, complexity, tolerance and openness. These features are completely at odds with the notion that there is a perfect, pure, uniquely correct mode of existence that competes with others in a confrontational, non-conciliatory manner – one that repels, subordinates and controls them, and occupies the position of an absolute victor. African Potentials can lead us to worldviews on humans, society and history that differ from the hegemonic worldviews that dominate contemporary realms of knowledge.

4. The African Potentials Series

In this way, the concept of African Potentials has enabled researchers from Japan and Africa to organise themselves and pursue activities in multidisciplinary research teams. The products of these activities have been classified into seven different fields for publication in this series. The authors and editors were selected by and from both Japanese and African researchers, and the resulting publications advance the research that has grown out of discussion in the African Forums. The overall structure of the series is as follows:

Volume 1

Title: *African Politics of Survival: Extraversion and Informality in the Contemporary World*

Editors: Mitsugi Endo (The University of Tokyo), Ato Kwamena Onoma (CODESRIA) and Michael Neocosmos (Rhodes University)

Volume 2

Title: *Knowledge, Education and Social Structure in Africa*

Editors: Shoko Yamada (Nagoya University), Akira Takada (Kyoto University) and Shose Kessi (University of Cape Town)

Volume 3

Title: *People, Predicaments and Potentials in Africa*

Editors: Takehiko Ochiai (Ryukoku University), Misa Hirano-Nomoto (Kyoto University) and Daniel E. Agbiboa (Harvard University)

Volume 4

Title: *Development and Subsistence in Globalising Africa: Beyond the Dichotomy*

Editors: Motoki Takahashi (Kyoto University), Shuichi Oyama (Kyoto University) and Herinjatovo Aimé Ramiarison (University of Antananarivo)

Volume 5

Title: *Dynamism in African Languages and Literature: Towards Conceptualisation of African Potentials*

Editors: Keiko Takemura (Osaka University) and Francis B. Nyamnjoh (University of Cape Town)

Volume 6

Title: *'African Potentials' for Wildlife Conservation and Natural Resource Management: Against the Images of 'Deficiency' and Tyranny of 'Fortress'*

Editors: Toshio Meguro (Hiroshima City University), Chihiro Ito (Fukuoka University) and Kariuki Kirigia (McGill University)

Volume 7

Title: *Contemporary Gender and Sexuality in Africa: African-Japanese Anthropological Approach*

Editors: Wakana Shiino (Tokyo University of Foreign Studies) and Christine Mbabazi Mpyangu (Makerere University)

Acknowledgement

This publication is based on the research project supported by the JSPS KAKENHI grant number JP16H06318 'African Potential' and Overcoming the Difficulties of Modern World: Comprehensive Area Studies that will Provide a New Perspective for the Future of Humanity.

Introduction

'African Potentials' in the Context of Environmental Conservation and Human–Environment Interactions

Toshio Meguro

This book is the result of an international research project that spans Japan, Africa and the world. The project started in 2011 with 'African Potentials' as a keyword; the first phase lasted until March 2016, with the second phase beginning in April 2016.[1] The goal of the first phase was to elucidate the potential that African societies have to resolve conflicts and achieve the peaceful coexistence of others. By the end of the first phase, we had successfully confirmed the existence and several characteristics of what we call 'African Potentials' (Gebre et al. [eds] 2017a, Matsuda and Hirano-Nomoto [eds] 2016). During the second phase, the scope of the project was expanded; we began to examine the effectiveness of the idea of 'African Potentials' against various difficulties currently faced by African societies. Focused on environmental conservation, natural resource management, local livelihood and human–environment relationships, this book is one volume in a series that details the final results of this project.

This project adopted two basic stances. One was to attach importance to real-life experiences in Africa and face-to-face interaction with Africans. The other was to resolutely oppose any ideas that regarded Africa as having a status of 'deficiency' (Gebre et al. 2017b: 5), a term used to indicate that the continent has neither the ability nor the will to solve its problems, so that external intervention is the only path to resolution. Instead, by using the concept of 'African Potentials', we aimed to demonstrate the innate potential of African societies. This attitude stemmed from the actions taken by the local population and their willingness and ability to overcome various types of difficulties, as witnessed by all project members during fieldwork in Africa. While this perspective does not assume that Africa can solve any problem alone, Africans are not lethargic, nor are they passive recipients of external help. The purpose of this project was to adequately assess the reality of the actions of African societies towards their future.

The stances adopted in the project are significant in light of the subjects covered in this book. Today, it is rare for an environmental policy or conservation project not to declare sympathetic consideration for local people and communities. However, their valuation standards are basically modern and scientific, related to ecological sustainability, economic rationality and democratic procedures, among others. Such policies and projects are typically focused on governing local people's conducts to meet these objectives (Fletcher 2010). However, science offers only one way to understand nature (Goldman et al. [eds] 2010), and the perceptions and opinions of the African people are generally ignored. This globally dominant approach is, in fact, equivalent to regarding African societies as 'deficient'. In contrast to this approach, this book adopts the stance of 'African Potentials' and is based on fieldwork that has paid special attention to local practices, thoughts, institutions and relationships.

This introduction first presents discussions on 'African Potentials' to date. It then describes the results of the first phase of the project, particularly those concerning the subjects covered in this volume. Subsequently, it explains our strategy for the second phase and outlines each chapter in this book.

1. What Are 'African Potentials'?[2]

In these first two decades of the 21st century, Africa has faced as many as or more problems than in the previous century. Since the turn of the century, Africa has been at the forefront of investment for large-scale development in areas such as agriculture, oil and rare metals. In several African nations, large-scale development projects have been implemented and economic growth has been achieved. However, poverty and disparities have worsened in many countries, and several reports indicate that such projects have brought about conflict, oppression and loss for local residents. In the face of this

2

situation, the international community and global civil society continue to intervene in poverty reduction, violent conflicts and various kinds of humanitarian crises. However, it is premature to assume that the problems in Africa have been completely resolved.

Given this context, conflict resolution and peaceful coexistence became the theme of our project, and we first focused on the knowledge and institutions historically cultivated by African societies (Gebre et al. 2017b; Moyo and Mine 2016b). When this project started, 'African Potentials' were defined as 'philosophies, knowledge, institutions, values, and practices that African societies have developed, modified, and utilised in handling conflicts and achieving peaceful coexistence' (Gebre et al. 2017b: 3). We chose this as a starting point because the approach of the international community so far appears to have been based on Western-origin ideas, such as liberal democracy and the modern judicial system, while neglecting the manner of coexistence widely seen in African societies, which is based on dialogue and reconciliation rather than on judgement and punishment.

The purpose of the first phase of the project was to document the existence and characteristics of 'African Potentials'. Every year, an international forum is held to discuss these issues with Africans, from scholars to policy makers, activists and the representatives of local societies. As a result of the first phase, the following characteristics of 'African Potentials' were confirmed: the 'interface function' ('the ability to interweave and forge connections within assemblages of values, thoughts and practices that belong to disparate dimensions and different historical phases'), 'aspiration for pluralism', 'collective agency and networking', 'dynamism and flexibility', 'resilience and tolerance' and 'innovativeness and creative expression' (Gebre et al. 2017b: 19–26).

Based on these first-phase results, during the second phase, the scope of the project was expanded from conflicts to wider social issues. In doing so, the argument of 'incompleteness' and 'conviviality' by Francis Nyamnjoh, one of the core members of the project, came to attract attention. According to Motoji Matsuda, leader of the second phase of the project, 'African Potentials' not only consist of practical techniques for solving actual problems, but also include philosophical considerations or modes of knowledge that perceive human beings and the world in ways different from those of the modern Western world (Matsuda 2020). In reference to Nyamnjoh (2017a, 2019), Matsuda cites 'incompleteness', 'collectivity' and 'conviviality' as intellectual frameworks that characterise 'African Potentials' (Matsuda 2020: 237–252). In other words, Western modernity envisions a person as a being different from other creatures and independent of other humans, who has an orientation towards completeness in himself or herself. On the other hand, the knowledge of 'African Potentials' structures the world, which includes people and other beings, which, in turn, include natural and supernatural ones as well as organic and inorganic substances, as basically incomplete, and envisions, through collectivity and interactivity, a convivial life and the realisation of each latent potential. As people live everyday life on the basis of this implicit knowledge, the 'interface function' and other 'African Potentials' confirmed in the first phase are put into action and expressed.

It must be noted that the 'African Potentials' perspective does not view Western modernity as all-important, nor does it completely deny it. Instead, Western modernity is regarded as an incomplete idea with which one interacts and coexists in a collective and convivial manner, in this incomplete world. What should definitely be abandoned is not the knowledge of Western modernity, but the dichotomy that divides the world in a fixed and absolute manner in the form of 'Africa versus the West' or 'traditional versus modern' (Gebre et al. 2017b; Nyamnjoh 2017b).

2. 'African Potentials' in the Context of Environmental Conservation and Livelihood Activities

When the 'African Potentials' project began, our focus included not only national and international violent events, such as genocide in Rwanda, post-election violence in Kenya and civil war in South Sudan, but also cases of coexistence realised through face-to-face dialogue at the local level as an example of negotiations of bride-wealth between the relatives of two parties (Gebre et al. [eds] 2017a).

4

Conflicts over environmental conservation and livelihood activities were also addressed in the beginning of the project. This section expounds on the argument of 'African Potentials' in these contexts so far.

2-1. 'African Potentials' in the Politics of Environmental Conservation

In the 1990s, the paradigm of environmental conservation changed drastically (Child [ed.] 2004; Hulme and Murphree [eds] 2001; Western and Wright [eds] 1994). In Africa, the modern and mainstream approach to conservation known as 'fences and fines' or 'fortress conservation' has been adopted since colonisation. On the one hand, this perception saw wilderness as the ideal environment, while, on the other hand, it viewed the African people as spoilers and destroyers of such environment. Therefore, 'conservation' meant removing the local population from targeted areas and creating a space without humans, that is, wilderness. A typical example of this approach is the national park system, which originated with Yellowstone in the United States. Under this approach, many African communities have been deprived of land and access to natural resources without any consultation and compensation, all in the name of conservation.

Critics of 'fortress conservation' support a more 'community-based' approach, an idea based on experiences in the field of wildlife conservation in Africa that has spread worldwide since the 1990s (Suich et al. [eds] 2009; Western 2003; Western and Wright [eds] 1994). Advocates of this community-based approach emphasise the need to affirm the historical relationship between local societies and their natural environment, including wildlife, and aim at guaranteeing the benefits and rights of local people and promoting community participation and collaboration in conservation practices. While this approach is widespread in the fields of environmental conservation and natural resource management, during the first phase of this project, we focused on the case of wildlife conservation, which has received a high degree of global interest and intervention.

As a consequence of the paradigm shift, the majority of governments, aid agencies, NGOs and related companies have come to advocate for the 'community-based' idea. However, in reality,

5

criticisms of this approach have accumulated from political, economic, social and ecological perspectives. Many scholars have demonstrated that, despite the value of the idea, the guarantee of customary rights to resource use, the fair distribution of conservation benefits or the meaningful participation in conservation activities have not been achieved satisfactorily from the viewpoint of local people in several cases (Brockington et al. 2008; Büscher et al. [eds] 2014; Child [ed.] 2004; Nelson [ed.] 2010; Suich et al. [eds] 2009). At worst, it has been reported that the creation of protected areas in communal areas led by external powers has resulted in 'green grab', or the alienation of the local population from their land and the imposition of further burdens on them (e.g. Benjaminsen and Bryceson 2012).

During the first phase of the project, one of our focuses was to reassess conservation sites after the paradigm shift from the 'African Potentials' perspective. This was because, as we examined previous studies that criticised conservation policies and practices after the paradigm shift, we found that these critical studies adopted modern Western values, such as democracy, private property and sustainable use, as criteria, thus overlooking the perspectives of local populations. In other words, these recent studies present flaws similar to those that are the object of their criticism in that they do not incorporate local perspectives, as if they presume that African societies are in a state of 'deficiency'. Contrary to these studies, our work adhered to the idea of 'African Potentials' and focused on the daily actions, vernacular thoughts and indigenous interactions of local people.

Under such an approach, 'African Potentials' in the context of wildlife conservation were viewed as operating in two dimensions: increasing opportunities for the *arena* (a place for dialogue) and as 'something invisible and embedded in daily life' (Sato et al. 2016: 302–304). This perspective comes from case studies in various parts of Africa, such as Ethiopia, Kenya, Tanzania, Cameroon, Gabon, Democratic Republic of the Congo, Guinea, Senegal and Zimbabwe. We were able to confirm that opportunities for face-to-face dialogue between local people and outsiders who introduce and implement conservation were generally increasing in frequency due to the paradigm shift in conservation ideas.

At least 'fortress' is clearly morally wrong – 'community based' can hide these sins

Subsequently, the African people were able to demonstrate their ability to appropriately grasp the intentions and expectations of outsiders and change their words and deeds flexibly and strategically, depending on their resources and alternatives, in order to promote a more favourable relationship and obtain beneficial outcomes (Iwai 2017, 2018; Matsuura 2019; Matsuura et al. 2017; Meguro 2014, 2017; Nishizaki 2015). In reality, cases exist in which the 'community-based' approach is merely propaganda and, despite their resistance, local societies are deprived of their access to natural resources by the government and other powerful actors (Iwai 2017, 2018; Kirigia 2018; Nishizaki 2015). Therefore, while we cannot remain optimistic about the *arena*, we should be aware that, after the conservation paradigm shift, African societies are attempting to make good use of the increasing opportunity for communication and interaction with people from the outside world. *→ They want to be involved & would be very useful, but are not given the opportunity.*

too much money/power to resist

2-2. 'African Potentials' in the Context of Livelihood Activities

From the viewpoint of livelihood, in the first phase of the project, some of the contributors to this book focused on recent and common problems concerning natural resources and livelihood activities in rural areas, i.e. conflicts over land, which is collectively used and managed at the local level, regarding farming, livestock keeping and other livelihood activities.

The problems surrounding livelihood are diverse and multi-faceted. In Africa today, people, goods, services and capital are flowing from urban areas and foreign countries to rural areas in search of investment and business opportunities, while migration from rural to urban areas is steadily increasing. The problem of 'land grabbing' by national power and international capital that desire vast lands for large-scale agriculture, natural resources, such as oil and rare metals, and areas for high-end nature/wildlife tourism is discussed mainly from a macro perspective (e.g. Carmody 2016; Cotula 2013; Fairhead et al. 2012; Matondi et al. [eds] 2011; Nelson [ed.] 2010). On the other hand, in the first phase, one group of our project took a more micro-level perspective with the idea of 'African Potentials'. The central question was how the African people responded when competition and tension over the issues of land and other natural resources increased at the local level.

In the first phase, details of the ways in which local people use ecological environments and natural resources were examined through fieldwork, with case studies of countries such as Tanzania, Uganda, Cameroon, Ghana, Zambia and Namibia (Shigeta and Itani [eds] 2016). The key questions involved how local people collectively utilise resources with their neighbours, including those belonging to different villages and ethnic groups, but with whom they maintain daily interactions. We paid special attention to their behaviours when competition over resources increased, seeking hints for reflecting on 'African Potentials'. Although the literature points out that conflicts can occur when the population grows and competition for resources also increases (e.g. Goldstone 2002), the results of the first phase revealed 'African Potentials' that can ease tense relationships over land and livelihood. In other words, African societies possess 'indigenous knowledge' and adopt 'a manner of "not to compete" more than necessary with others and nature' (Shigeta 2016: 349–352; Shigeta and Kaneko 2017).

One important point is that, even if social changes widen the disparity between neighbouring people in terms of land, resources, income and opportunities, this does not necessarily cause conflict between them. In many cases, Africans avoid sowing discord and pursue ways to maintain coexistence without apparent conflict (Shigeta and Kaneko 2017; Yamamoto 2017). A typical example of this 'manner of "not to compete"' is the 'social levelling mechanism' observed in Zambia's Bemba society (Kakeya et al. 2006). In Bemba society, the distribution of wealth from the 'haves' to the 'have-nots' is incorporated as a matter of due expectation or ethical obligation. It does not reverse their hierarchical positions, but drives the redistribution of wealth and contributes to the survival of the poor and the maintenance of peaceful coexistence.

The other important point is that nature is also included among the targets of 'a manner of "not to compete" more than necessary'. Rather than seeking to manipulate and control nature completely at will, as with modern conservation and resource management, African societies are oriented towards acceptance and building a positive relationship with nature, even if inconvenient and uncontrollable aspects exist. This attitude is in line with the concept of 'African Potentials' that approve the 'incompleteness' of others and the world as well as with the ideals of 'collectivity' and 'conviviality'. Furthermore, when the importance of 'indigenous knowledge' is emphasised, one must remember that, while it is rooted in people's local and historical interactions with nature in a specific area, such knowledge is constantly updated and dynamically changing (Shigeta and Kaneko 2017). The word 'indigenous' means neither traditional nor modern; instead, it is a by-product of the interchange between Africa and the world – this is precisely the aspect that we have argued in terms of 'interface function'. Shigeta (2016) finally emphasises that 'African Potentials' are not something that can be materialised, but rather relational processes that approve of pluralistic values. These arguments are also consistent with the concepts of 'collectivity' and 'conviviality'.

3. Two Ways to Develop the Argument of 'African Potentials'

Based on the above-mentioned first-phase achievements, all contributors to this book share the premise that African societies have the potential to avoid violence and achieve coexistence with others (including nature) through interchange and interfacing, even if there are hidden disagreements, disparities and competitive interactions. However, in the first phase, we focused mostly on ascertaining the existence of 'African Potentials' and, therefore, we may not have fully examined what kind of results they have brought about. Such things are the targets for discussion in this book, and they are explained in detail below.

3-1. Investigation of the Actual Effectiveness of 'African Potentials'
The project's first issue was to examine whether the 'African Potentials' of local societies are realised and whether convivial coexistence is achieved in reality. Otherwise, the reasons why 'African Potentials' are not working or what suppresses their manifestation were investigated.

9

Throughout the first phase, we confirmed that many African societies have refrained from competing with others more than necessary and that the invisible potential of achieving a convivial coexistence through interaction and interfacing was embedded in their daily life. After the paradigm shift in conservation, local societies began to actively engage in using the newly established *arena* to communicate and negotiate with the outside world in order to improve their lives. We positively regarded this agency of local people as 'African Potentials'.

However, during the first phase, the power to suppress peoples' attempts to instigate social change and improve lives was already clear. In many cases of wildlife conservation, the local population was only allowed to participate and communicate in a way that did not conflict with the goals and plans previously set by outsiders. It is true that increasing opportunities for the *arena* were created as part of conservation policies and projects. However, the communication that actually took place did not involve interactive dialogue or reflective deliberations, but rather one-way statements, such as instruction, persuasion or education by outsiders who had the power to plan and implement projects. The majority of the local population had few opportunities to express their opinions or project their desires. These on-the-ground facts are usually not broadcast, and therefore remain unknown to global citizens.

The recent years have witnessed an ongoing debate over the neoliberalisation of environmental conservation and natural resource management, critically revealing the unaltered or aggravated oppression and alienation of local societies (Büscher et al. 2012; Holmes and Cavanagh 2016; Igoe and Brockington 2007). Studies have elucidated the actual conditions of oppression and alienation of local societies and of people's resistance to conservation initiatives. However, such research has not addressed the details of interaction between local societies and external actors on the ground and, thus, failed to discover either the positive potential of societies or the external hindrances to that potential. In this respect, we believe it is crucial to prioritise fieldwork as an academic method of understanding the actual situation.

During the second phase of the project, we conducted further fieldwork to examine the frontlines of wildlife conservation in Africa today, decades after the paradigm shift, while considering the real effectiveness of 'African Potentials'. Part one of this book discusses this issue.

3-2. Expansion of the Target Range of 'African Potentials'

The project's second issue was to expand the target range of our analysis. One direction of expansion was to include cases other than wildlife conservation in order to relativise the discussion. We agree to the opinion that the lessons learned from cases of wildlife conservation are applicable to other cases of environmental conservation and natural resource management (e.g. Child [ed.] 2004). However, it is also true that most of our studies during the first phase involved wildlife conservation, especially with regard to environmental conservation. When compared to other natural resources, such as plant and fishery resources, the degree of intervention by external actors appears to be much greater in the case of wildlife conservation (e.g. the fierce debate over the ivory trade and trophy hunting). Moreover, wildlife differs substantially from the forest and fishery resources in that daily consumptive use by the local population is generally prohibited.[3] Therefore, by covering various types of environmental conservation and natural resource management, we expected the applicability of our argument over 'African Potentials' so far to be examined.

The other key priority was to pay more attention to the multifaceted relationship and interactions between human societies, natural resources and the surrounding environment. On the one hand, this goal was rooted in the fact that our studies are related to nature, whereas the case studies of wildlife conservation conducted during the first phase focused mainly on the human side. Ecosystems and biodiversity are at stake as the human population grows and human activities expand throughout many areas of Africa. Therefore, conservation/management of the environment and human–environment interactions are urgent issues, which are addressed by several national, international and global movements. However, in the first phase of the project, little attention was paid to other

11

dimensions of nature and the relational process of human-environment interactions. In addition, while many project members studied the use of natural resources by the local population during the same period, their arguments were rarely situated in the context of environmental and/or aid politics management. There was little cross-reference between wildlife conservation studies and those on local livelihood. Thus, in the second phase, it became important to consider the outcomes of 'African Potentials' in non-human dimensions and from a relational perspective.

Furthermore, when natural resources that are consumed domestically or commercially are included as targets for case studies, the relationship between local societies and the market and political institutions that are under the influence of global dynamism also becomes a subject of discussion. This issue represents another aspect absent in the first phase. In that period, we focused on cases of wildlife conservation within rural communities rather than on the urban and commercial environment. Therefore, with the aim of developing arguments from a new dimension, the second part of this book presents articles that discuss natural resource uses in more modernised and commercialised settings.

4. Contents of This Book

Except for the Conclusion chapter, the remainder of this book is divided into two parts that address the two issues described in the previous section. Part I examines the reality of 'African Potentials' based on a series of studies on wildlife conservation, while Part II presents studies that focus on natural resources other than wildlife and/or analyse the human–environment relationship from a broader perspective. Throughout Parts I and II, many authors develop arguments in relation to 'African Potentials', while in the final chapter, Conclusion, specific insights into 'African Potentials' based on the results of each chapter in Parts I and II, are given full consideration. The following is an overview of each chapter.

4-1. Part I: 'African Potentials' at the Forefront of Wildlife Conservation

After this introduction, Chapter 1 touches upon the issue of human–elephant conflicts (HECs), a kind of human–wildlife conflicts. In Chapter 1, Yukino Iwai deals with HECs in an area around the Serengeti National Park in northern Tanzania, which is one of Africa's most famous national parks. Despite the park's significance, little is known about the recent increase in crop raids and human death by elephants in the area. Iwai reveals that, when little support was offered by the outside world, villagers created various countermeasures to mitigate the damage caused by elephants. Although some attempts, including a recent group patrolling initiative, have produced some significant results, the negative impact of elephants still persists. With specific examples, Iwai explains the seriousness of the HECs' visible and invisible impacts on villagers, as well as the ineffectiveness of national conservation policies in addressing this problem. Both local potentials and the power to suppress them are highlighted in this chapter.

Written by Samantha S. Sithole and Frank Matose, Chapter 2 presents a case study of a village adjacent to the world-renowned Kruger National Park, located in South Africa. First, Sithole and Matose review the recent argument about the 'militarisation' of conservation. Next, they elaborate on how the park came to implement militarised conservation. Subsequently, they give voice to local people who live in a village on the outskirts of the Kruger National Park. This chapter clarifies the negative impacts of militarisation, not only on natural resource use and livelihood activities, but also on the social relations of local people. With reference to studies on neoliberalism and governmentality, Sithole and Matose describe the violent and coercive aspects of today's wildlife conservation and the influence of global conservation movements, such as rhino anti-poaching.

Chapter 3 presents a case study of the Maasai Olympics, an athletic event held by a conservation NGO to stop lion hunting by young Maasai in southern Kenya. In this chapter, Toshio Meguro focuses on the representation of the Maasai people by the NGO, which exhibits a sympathetic attitude towards local culture in contrast to neoliberal conservation that typically ignores it. However, it is revealed that the NGO fabricated a fake traditional team for the event. Meguro argues that, when the NGO made a spectacle of the event, the local people became an object of the tourist gaze rather than a partner in dialogue within the *arena*. This situation highlights that neoliberal conservation continues to defy the idea of the new conservation paradigm (albeit in a different way from the previous chapter) and hinder 'African Potentials' found in Maasai.

In Chapter 4, Nobuko Nishizaki concentrates on park rangers/scouts. These conservation forces are the closest to the local population, and many scholars have discussed the progress of their militarisation and its negative impact on local people. After an explanation about park rangers in the USA and park scouts in Ethiopia, Nishizaki presents life experiences of Ethiopian scouts. It becomes clear that park scouts from rural areas have tried to connect local people and conservation authorities. Based on this result, Nishizaki proposes a different and overlooked role that park scouts can play: a communicator who has the 'interface function' and connects local societies and conservation institutions. Nishizaki draws attention to the fact that this ability is not formally acknowledged or institutionalised, and mentions 'associations' as an idea to break the status quo.

Chapter 5 presents a case study of community-based conservation (CBC) in the Amboseli area, the same area explored in Chapter 3. Tom G. Ondicho focuses on community-based tourism, which once gained global attention as a model of CBC. The case study involves a project aimed at establishing a protected area on communal land and developing tourism therein. As the land was communal, the project included various collective activities involving the local Maasai community. According to Ondicho, while the local majority approved of the project, inter-community politics may temper their motivation for conservation. This chapter demonstrates hetero-geneity and rivalry within a community, suggesting that several obstacles to 'African Potentials' can be found within local communities.

In Chapter 6, Kimaren Ole Riamit and Kariuki Kirigia focus on a Maasai community that lives around the Maasai Mara National Reserve, the most popular tourist destination in Kenya. As pastoralists, the Maasai people used land communally and coexisted with wildlife. However, since the 1960s, their communal land has been subdivided into smaller plots and private landownership has expanded. This measure was based on the assumption that sub-division would create a more favourable environment for economic development and sustainable natural resource management. However, it has imposed several injustices on the majority of the local population. Ole Riamit and Kirigia describe how local people have used state and non-state apparatuses to address such injustices. The role of indigenous 'organic intellectuals' as discussed by the authors resembles a number of characteristics of 'African Potentials'.

4-2. Part II: Re-Examination of 'African Potentials' in the Context of Human–Environment Interactions

Written by Gen Yamakoshi, Chapter 7 begins Part II of this book. Yamakoshi focuses on the anthropogenic landscapes, in this case patchy forests, in the southern part of the Republic of Guinea in West Africa. Yamakoshi clarifies the mechanisms by which the forests, where chimpanzees live, have grown as the local population has increased, pointing out that local people are not the obstacle to conservation. He discusses how the coexistence of local people and chimpanzees is achieved. When this chapter covers a wide range of topics including history, culture (not only human but also chimpanzees' one), ecology and politics, Yamakoshi intends to promote a reflection on the complexity and potentials of anthropogenic landscape, even if to find out the latter is not easy because of the former.

Chapter 8 explores the relationships between humans, wildlife and forests. Shinichiro Ichino presents a case study of the Gallery Forest in southern Madagascar, focusing on the Tandroy people, tamarind trees and lemurs. In Madagascar, the remaining forest fragments have become targets of national conservation policy, and the Gallery Forest is a vitally important habitat for lemurs, the world's most endangered mammal that lives only in southern Madagascar. In addition to the ecological relationship between lemurs and the forest, Ichino studies the Tandroy's customs regarding wildlife. Even though human–environment interactions have been examined since the first phase of this project, Ichino treats these three entities more equally in his analysis. In this respect, this chapter considers 'African Potentials' in a multi-faceted and more relational way.

In Chapter 9, Yuichiro Fujioka addresses a case of non-timber forest products (NTFPs), specifically on the fruits of marula trees in South Africa. In the 1980s, a brewery company started to produce a cream liqueur made with this fruit, which today is distributed worldwide. Fujioka explains the process of this commodification and its impact on local people. He reveals that, despite the increase in demand, the existence of traditional leaders has contributed to the management of this natural resource without obvious conflicts. Although the traditional authority exists, the study site and the human–environment relationship in this chapter are more urban and commercial compared to the previous chapters. Fujioka explains the historical events and various actors that have influenced the process of commodification in such an environment, in addition to discussing its outcomes, potentials and limitations.

In Chapter 10, Chihiro Ito presents another case study of an urban and commercial environment: the *kapenta* (small clupeids) fishery of Lake Kariba, which lies along the southeast border of Zambia. Lake Kariba is the world's largest man-made lake and its fisheries are important both locally and nationally. Since the late 1990s, Lake Kariba's problems have become increasingly apparent; while catches have decreased, the number of fishing boats and workers have increased rapidly, concomitantly with an upsurge in illegal activities. On one hand, Ito focuses on the political and economic environment affecting this natural resource; on the other hand, she examines how resource users have responded to local, national and international changes. Her intention is to understand the Kapenta fishery as a set of various dynamic human–environment interactions, taking into consideration the urban context.

Chapters 11 and 12 are also based on fieldwork in fishery-based societies. In Chapter 11, after the introduction of the history of local innovation in Africa, Bosco Rusuwa, Daud Kassam and Maxon Ngochera present the innovations of fishermen in the Makanjira area of Lake Malawi, in Malawi. In the country, overfishing has become rampant, and the sustainable management of fishery resources has become a priority. Then, Rusuwa et al. found that, without external support, fishermen with little education created artificial reefs, locally called *virundu*. The positive results of *virundu* described in this chapter demonstrate the existence of another example of 'African Potentials'. At the same time, however, the authors argue that the independence of the local population from macro-institutions remains a challenge for the future.

Taku Iida has studied the fishermen of Vezo in Madagascar for more than a quarter of a century. In Chapter 12, Iida discusses the limitations of the concept of 'sustainability' based on detailed data from a fishing village. As examples of the socio-economic changes observed, Iida shows data on price fluctuations for many commodities and population changes in the village. His explanation covers macro political and economic history, as well as local and individual practices, including active immigration/emigration. Subsequently, Iida argues how difficult it is to apply the concept of sustainability to social dimensions that change rapidly and unpredictably. While referring to the concept of 'Only One Earth', Iida further discusses perspectives and attitudes that are required for the future of human society and the global environment.

Chapter 13 presents a case study about wildlife in Kenya focused on the relationship between local people and wildlife rather than the outcomes of conservation policies and projects. Yumi Yamane concentrates on the distance between people and wildlife, specifically physical and psychological distance. She offers many examples of human–wildlife relationships in Kenya and clarifies that, while relationships differ among locations, people living modern and urban lives are generally concerned with the danger and damage inflicted by wildlife, i.e. human–wildlife conflicts. As explained in the other chapters, these conflicts are ongoing in various parts of Africa. Yamane compares many cases and outlines the key points to be addressed when considering the coexistence of humans and wildlife.

In the Conclusion, Toshio Meguro, Chihiro Ito and Kariuki Kirigia re-think the lessons one can learn from the results, discussions and conclusions from the previous chapters with the argument of 'African Potentials' in mind. First, the contents of the chapters in Part I are revisited, and the authors confirm the ground reality at the forefront of wildlife conservation. It is corroborated that, although local people are experiencing several problems while exerting certain 'African Potentials', it is difficult to say that the situation has improved significantly. The greatest problem appears to be the lack of *arenas*. Next, the chapters in Part II are reviewed in a similar way. It becomes clear that 'African Potentials' are found in the case of natural resources other than wildlife, although there are unresolved issues such as the discrepancy between individual and collective potentials, and the case of no traditional collectivity. In addition, the danger of assuming African societies as 'communities' and the importance of focusing on the relationships between people, nature and the environment is explained. Finally, after summarising these findings, the *arena* issue is presented as the most negative result.

Endnotes

[1] The first phase of the project was titled 'Comprehensive Area Studies on Coexistence and Conflict Resolution Realizing African Potentials' and the second phase was titled '"African Potentials" and Overcoming the Difficulties of a Modern World: Comprehensive Area Studies That Will Provide a New Perspective for the Future of Humanity'. The respective URLs of the official website of each phase are 'https://www.africapotential. africa.kyoto-u.ac.jp/en/index.html' and 'https://www.africapotential.africa. kyoto-u.ac.jp/mms/en/'.

[2] Unless otherwise stated, the descriptions in this section are based on Gebre et al. (eds) (2017a), Matsuda and Hirano-Nomoto (eds) (2016) and Moyo and Mine (eds) (2016a).

[3] In southern Africa, as part of community-based natural resource management (CBNRM), wildlife is consumptively used as a target for sport/trophy hunting in many countries, and such consumptive use is positively evaluated as sustainable natural resource management (Child [ed.] 2004; Child 2019; Suich et al. [eds] 2009). However, it must be noted that the majority of sport/trophy hunters who shoot game are rich white people, which makes the practice completely different from that related to the daily use of wildlife by Africans.

Acknowledgements

This work was supported by JSPS KAKENHI Grant Number JP16H06318.

References

Benjaminsen, T. A. and Bryceson, I. (2012) 'Conservation, green/blue grabbing and accumulation by dispossession in Tanzania', *The Journal of Peasant Studies*, Vol. 39, No. 2, pp. 335–355.

Brockington, D., Duffy, R. and Igoe, J. (2008) *Nature Unbound: Conservation, Capitalism and the Future of Protected Areas*, London: Earthscan.

Büscher, B., Dressler, W. and Fletcher, R. (eds) (2014) *Nature Inc.: Environmental Conservation in the Neoliberal Age*, Tucson: The University of Arizona Press.

Büscher, B., Sullivan, S., Neves, K., Igoe, J. and Brockington, D. (2012) 'Towards a synthesized critique of neoliberal biodiversity conservation', *Capitalism Nature Socialism*, Vol. 23, No. 2, pp. 4–30.

Carmody, P. (2016) *The New Scramble for Africa, 2nd Edition*, Cambridge: Polity Press.

Child, B. (ed.) (2004) *Parks in Transition: Biodiversity, Rural Development and the Bottom Line*, London: Earthscan.

————— (2019) *Sustainable Governance of Wildlife and Community-Based Natural Resource Management*, Oxon: Routledge.

Cotula, L. (2013) *The Great African Land Grab? Agricultural Investments and the Global Food System*, London: Zed Books.

Fairhead, J., Leach, M. and Scoones, I. (2012) 'Green grabbing: A new appropriation of nature', *The Journal of Peasant Studies*, Vol. 39, No. 2, pp. 237–261.

Fletcher, R. (2010) 'Neoliberal environmentality: Towards a poststructuralist political ecology of the conservation debate', *Conservation and Sociology*, Vol. 8, No. 3, pp. 171–181.

Gebre, Y., Ohta, I. and Matsuda, M. (eds) (2017a) *African Virtues in the Pursuit of Conviviality: Exploring Local Solutions in Light of Global Prescriptions*, Bamenda: Langaa RPCIG.

19

———— (2017b) 'Introduction: Achieving peace and coexistence through African potentials', in Y. Gebre, I. Ohta and M. Matsuda (eds) *African Virtues in the Pursuit of Conviviality: Exploring Local Solutions in Light of Global Prescriptions*, Bamenda: Langaa RPCIG, pp. 3–37.

Goldman, M. J., Nadasdy, P. and Turner, M. D. (eds) (2010) *Knowing Nature: Conservation at the Intersection of Political Ecology and Science Studies*, Chicago: The University of Chicago Press.

Goldstone, J. A. (2002) 'Population and security: How demographic change can lead to violent conflict', *Journal of International Affairs*, Vol. 56, No. 1, pp. 3–21.

Holmes, G. and Cavanagh, C. J. (2016) 'A review of the social impacts of neoliberal conservation: Formations, inequalities, contestations', *Geoforum*, Vol. 75, pp. 199–209.

Hulme, D. and Murphree, M. (eds) (2001) *African Wildlife and Livelihoods: The Promise and Performance of Community Conservation*, Oxford: James Currey; Cape Town: David Philips Publishers; Harare: Weaver Press; Zomba: Kachere Press; Nairobi: E.A.E.P.; Kampala: Fountain Publishers; Portsmouth, NH: Heinemann.

Igoe, J. and Brockington, D. (2007) 'Neoliberal conservation: A brief introduction', *Conservation and Society*, Vol. 5, No. 4, pp. 432–449.

Iwai, Y. (2017) 'Depriving tourism benefit of local communities: Betrayal of wildlife management areas in Tanzania', *Journal of African Studies (Africa-Kenkyu)*, Vol. 92, pp. 95–108 (in Japanese with English abstract).

———— (2018) 'Human-elephant conflict in the Serengeti: The side-effects of wildlife tourism', *Global-e*, Vol. 11, No. 53 (https://www.21global.ucsb.edu/global-e/october-2018/human-elephant-conflict-serengeti-side-effects-wildlife-tourism) (accessed: 30 June 2021).

Kakeya, M., Sugiyama, Y. and Oyama, S. (2006) 'The *citemene* system, social leveling mechanism, and agrarian changes in the Bemba villages of northern Zambia: An overview of 23 years of "fixed-point" research', *African Study Monographs*, Vol. 27, No. 1, pp. 27–38.

Kirigia, K. (2018) 'Land injustices in Kenya's wildlife conservancies', *Global-e*, Vol. 11, No. 50 (https://www.21global.ucsb.edu/global-

e/october-2018/land-injustices-kenya-s-wildlife-conservancies)
(accessed: 30 June 2021).

Matondi, P. B., Havnekij, K. and Beyene, A. (eds) (2011) *Biofuels, Land Grabbing and Food Security in Africa*, London: Zed Books.

Matsuda, M. and Hirano-Nomoto, M. (eds) (2016) *Cultural Creativity for Conflict Resolution and Coexistence: African Potentials as Practice of Incompleteness and Bricolage*, Kyoto: Kyoto University Press (in Japanese).

Matsuda, M. (2020) 'Creativity, collectivity and conviviality: Towards African Potentials', in Y. Ofosu-Kusi and M. Matsuda (eds) *The Challenge of African Potentials: Conviviality, Informality and Futurity*, Bamenda: Langaa RPCIG, pp. 229–254.

Matsuura, N. (2019) 'Community-based ecotourism in Gabon, Central Africa', *Global-e*, Vol. 12, No. 2 (https://www.21global. ucsb.edu/global-e/january-2019/community-based-ecotourism-gabon-central-africa) (accessed: 30 June 2021).

Matsuura, N., Ando, C., Shintani, M. and Takenoshita, Y. (2017) 'Bridging scientific research and local communities through ecotourism', *Journal of African Studies (Africa-Kenkyu)*, Vol. 92, pp. 109–121 (in Japanese with English abstract).

Meguro, T. (2014) 'Becoming conservationists, concealing victims: Conflict and positionings of Maasai, regarding wildlife conservation in Kenya', *African Study Monographs, Supplementary Issue*, Vol. 50, pp. 155–172.

———— (2017) 'Gaps between the innovativeness of the Maasai Olympics and the positionings of Maasai warriors', *Nilo-Ethiopian Studies*, Vol. 22, pp. 27–39.

Moyo, S. and Mine, Y. (eds) (2016a) *What Colonialism Ignored: 'African Potentials' for Resolving Conflicts in Southern Africa*, Bamenda: Langaa RPCIG.

———— (2016b) 'Introduction: African Potentials for conflict resolution and transformation', in S. Moyo and Y. Mine (eds) *What Colonialism Ignored: 'African Potentials' for Resolving Conflicts in Southern Africa*, Bamenda: Langaa RPCIG, pp. 1–33.

Nelson, F. (ed.) (2010) *Community Rights, Conservation and Contested Land: The Politics of Natural Resources Governance in Africa*, Oxon: Earthscan.

Nishizaki, N. (2015) '"Neoliberal conservation" in Ethiopia: An analysis of current conflict in and around protected areas and their resolution', *African Study Monographs, Supplementary Issue*, Vol. 50, pp. 191–205.

Nyamnjoh, F. B. (2017a) 'Incompleteness: Frontier Africa and the currency of conviviality', *Journal of Asian and African Studies*, Vol. 52, No. 3, pp. 253–270.

———— (2017b) 'Incompleteness and conviviality: A reflection on international research collaboration from an African perspective', in Y. Gebre, I. Ohta and M. Matsuda (eds) *African Virtues in the Pursuit of Conviviality: Exploring Local Solutions in Light of Global Prescriptions*, Bamenda: Langaa RPCIG, pp. 339–378.

———— (2019) 'Ubuntuism and Africa: Actualised, misappropriated, endangered and reappraised Africa Day memorial lecture', Bloemfontein: University of Free State.

Sato, T., Meguro, T. and Yamakoshi, G. (2016) 'Place and future of African Potentials in the practice of nature protection activities', in G. Yamakoshi, T. Meguro and T. Sato (eds) *Who Owns African Nature? African Perspectives on the Future of Community-Based Conservation*, Kyoto: Kyoto University Press, pp. 295–305 (in Japanese).

Shigeta, M. (2016) 'Manner to avoid conflict: Potentials about subsistence and ecology', in M. Shigeta and J. Itani (eds) *How People Can Achieve Coexistence through the Sound Use of Ecological Resources*, Kyoto: Kyoto University Press, pp. 331–353 (in Japanese).

Shigeta, M. and Itani, J. (2016) (eds) *How People Can Achieve Coexistence through the Sound Use of Ecological Resources*, Kyoto: Kyoto University Press (in Japanese).

Shigeta, M. and Kaneko, M. (2017) '*Zairaichi* (local knowledge) as the manners of co-existence: Encounters between the Aari farmers in southwestern Ethiopia and the "Other"', in Y. Gebre, I. Ohta and M. Matsuda (eds) *African Virtues in the Pursuit of Conviviality: Exploring Local Solutions in Light of Global Prescriptions*, Bamenda: Langaa RPCIG, pp. 311–338.

Suich, H., Child, B. and Spenceley, A. (eds) (2009) *Evolution and Innovation in Wildlife Conservation: Parks and Game Ranches to Transfrontier Conservation Areas*, London: Earthscan.

Western, D. (2003) 'Conservation science in Africa and the role of international collaboration', *Conservation Biology*, Vol. 17, No. 1, pp. 11–19.

Western, D. and Wright, M. (eds) (1994) *Natural Connections: Perspectives in Community-Based Conservation*, Washington DC: Island Press.

Yamamoto, K. (2017) 'Renewing herds through livestock trades: Changes in cattle keeping under population pressure in the Mbozi plateau, Tanzania', *African Study Monographs*, Vol. 38, No. 1, pp. 38–51.

Part I

'African Potentials' at the Forefront

of Wildlife Conservation

Chapter 1

Listening for Elephants in the Dark: Hidden Impacts of Human–Elephant Conflict in the Serengeti District, Tanzania

Yukino Iwai

1. Introduction

It is a cloudy, dark and moonless night. Twelve men have gathered and are standing on the rocks of Copier, listening to sounds from the plains of the Serengeti. They usually talk loudly, but no one speaks now. They turn off their torches so no one knows they are here. They stand still so as not to make footsteps.

They are listening for elephants.

Snap, crinkle, rustle ... there are distant sounds of broken branches and rubbing leaves. It is the elephants! They are in the bush along a depression in the game reserve that is about 500 m away from the border of a village.

'Two elephants. The same two I saw yesterday. They have returned and are approaching the village', says Wambura, the leader of the elephant patrol team. However, no matter how much I listen, I cannot hear the elephants. These men have lived here their entire lives, working on the land, farming, grazing livestock and collecting water and firewood. They are familiar with the ecosystem and regularly encounter wildlife, which is why they can hear the faint sounds of the elephants moving (Figure 1).

Misseke Village is near the Serengeti National Park in the Serengeti District of Mara Region, Tanzania. The elephant patrol team chases away elephants that enter the village to eat the crops. Elephants can cause food shortages by devastating crop fields. The members gather every night to guard the border between the village and wildlife protected areas. However, scaring elephants is dangerous

27

Figure 1. Misseke villagers listening for the elephants

and can result in an elephant attack, which can be fatal. Elephants kill several residents of the Serengeti District each year. The team assumes this risk because human–elephant conflict (HEC) has been increasing for about 15 years in Tanzania and other African countries (Gross 2019).

Those living near the elephants mitigate the HEC damage themselves and do not wait for external support. The Misseke villagers have succeeded in controlling a large part of the damage by cooperating and inventing new methods to alleviate HEC. Such innovative and flexible ingenuity is a good example of 'African potential' (Gebre et al. 2017). However, this success is not without the sacrifice of enduring the damage and other hidden impacts of HEC.

HEC is one type of human–wildlife conflict and is a critical conservation issue in Africa (Woodroffe et al. 2005). This chapter discusses HEC particularly in the Misseke Village, Serengeti District of Mara Region, Tanzania, and is focused on the hidden impacts of HEC. Most studies on HEC are narrowly focused on the visible impacts, such as crop damage or human injuries and fatalities (Hoare 2000; Naughton-Treves and Treves 2005; Mduma et al. 2010). The hidden impacts of HEC are poorly studied and may include emotional stress, restricted movement and the opportunity cost of mitigation activities (Dickman 2010; Barua et al. 2013; Mayberry et al. 2017). When considering compensation for HEC, only the visible damage is considered (Jackson et al. 2008). To develop a proper long-term mitigation strategy, hidden impacts should also be assessed (Barua et al. 2013; Mayberry et al. 2017; Shaffer et al. 2019).

I have visited the Serengeti District annually since the mid-1990s for research, staying twice a year for two weeks each visit, and once for ten months. This chapter includes data from the interviews and participatory observations conducted during fieldwork. The names of the people in this chapter are all pseudonyms.

2. Background of Human–Elephant Conflict in Tanzania

Elephants fascinate people around the world. African elephants (*Loxodonta* spp.) are the most popular animals among tourists and are a pivotal resource in the tourism industry. As an umbrella species, elephants are also important for their ecosystems. However, elephants have experienced population declines and regional extinction largely due to overhunting for the ivory trade. Therefore, African elephants became a protected species when the Convention on the International Trade in Endangered Species of Wild Fauna and Flora (CITES) prohibited international ivory trade in 1989.

Despite their international conservation status, elephants have been described as problem animals by local residents, due to a rise in the incidence of HEC such as the destruction of crops and elephant-related farmer deaths (Hoare 2000). Tanzania, Botswana, and Zimbabwe have the highest elephant populations in Africa (UNEP et al. 2013). In Tanzania, elephants live in conservation areas all over the country, and elephant damage occurs around their habitat. A survey conducted in Tanzania between 2007–2009 found that 60 of the 87 participating districts (69 per cent) had reported incidents of HEC (Mduma et al. 2010). According to these reports, 30–40 people are injured and 40–50 are killed by elephants annually (Mduma et al. 2010). Most of these injuries occur when elephants enter the farms and damage crops. Many international tourists may expect this damage to occur because of elephant habitat destruction or expanding elephant populations, but the true cause is not so simple.

29

While HEC is increasing throughout Tanzania, elephant population trends vary by area. Elephant populations are increasing in northern Tanzania but declining in southern Tanzania. The elephant population in the Serengeti National Park (SNP) in northern Tanzania doubled between 2006 and 2014, and there are currently 7,500 elephants there (WWF 2014). At the same time, the elephant population in the Selous Game Reserve in southern Tanzania decreased by 79 per cent from 70,000 to 15,000 (TAWIRI 2019). Despite this population decline, however, elephant damage remains prevalent in the villages around Selous (Smit et al. 2017). In addition, the SNP staff have reported that there is no remarkable vegetation deterioration in the surrounding areas.

Studies on human–wildlife conflicts in Japan have found that animals that damage farms recognise farmlands as a safe environment with crops to forage. They have become accustomed to human habitats without fear (Ueda et al. 2018), as may be the case with elephants that invade farms.

3. Visible and Invisible Impacts of Human–Elephant Conflict in the Serengeti

3-1. Study Area: Misseke Village, Serengeti District, Tanzania

The SNP was established in 1951. With a large land area of 15,000 km^2 and its spectacular savannah ecosystem, it is also famous as a World Heritage Site. The park's annual tourist income has been estimated at 800 million US dollars (World Bank 2015), and elephants are an important factor for tourists. In Tanzania, poaching has reduced the elephant population by 68 per cent, from 135,000 in 2006 to 43,000 in 2014 (TAWIRI 2015). Fortunately, due to the efforts of the Tanzanian government and international organisations, poaching levels have dropped (TAWIRI 2019). Despite the elephant population crisis of Tanzania, the elephant population in the Serengeti continues to increase due to strict poaching regulations.

The Serengeti District neighbours the SNP, the Ikorongo Game Reserve, and the Grumeti Game Reserve. There are about 250,000 people in the district (2012 census). Since the beginning of the 2000s,

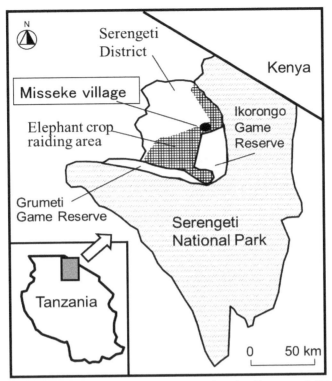

Figure 2. Crop areas raided by elephants in the Serengeti District, Tanzania

HEC has increased and threatens about 80,000 local residents of 30 villages (Figure 2).

Misseke Village has a population of approximately 3,000 people. Agriculture and livestock keeping are the main livelihoods; the average cultivation area is five acres per household and the primary crops include maize, sorghum and cassava. The village shares an 8-kilometre border with the Ikorongo Game Reserve, which is adjacent to the SNP. This border is not fenced and, therefore, animals can move freely between the game reserve, the national park and the village.

Elephants began causing damage in Misseke Village around 2005. Initially, a small number of elephants would enter the village a few times a year, but the herd size and frequency of visits increased over time. They began causing severe damage in 2010.

3-2. Crop Damage and Field Invasions

Once an elephant herd enters a field, they can eat all the crops within a few hours. The farmers become angry and disappointed at the loss of their yield, especially if the raid occurs just before the harvest. Farming requires daily labour, often in extreme heat. The residents then suffer food shortages and have less income for things such as their children's education or medical expenses. Indeed, the quality of life significantly deteriorates because of the elephant raids.

Between March 2017 and February 2018, there were 134 elephant intrusions in Misseke Village (Figure 3). The intrusions occurred every 2–3 days on average, threatening the everyday lives of the villagers. The herds averaged 15 individuals, but herd size ranged from 1 to 120 individuals. Even one elephant on a rampage can be dangerous, so as many as 100 elephants in a village can cause despair. As an example of crop damage, Shatana is an avid farmer in Misseke Village:

Case Study 1: Elephant Damage on Shatana's Farm

Shatana has a wife and six children. In 1997 he moved to Misseke Village from Morotonga Village to purchase farmland and bought a number of fields that were 5–10 acres in size. Shatana cultivated maize, sorghum and millet, which are the staple crops of the region. They can be harvested twice per year: during the rainy season (February to June) and during the dry season (September to January). Table 1 shows Shatana's 2013–2017 farming records. In 2013, the damage to Shatana's farms became severe; ten acres of crops were eaten by elephants in three days. He then had no harvest for two years. In 2015, he left Misseke Village and returned to Morotonga, where the elephants do not raid because it does not border protected areas. Shatana was only able to harvest two acres of crops in Morotonga due to a shortage of land. This small harvest was not enough to develop his life.

In 2015 a wire fence was set up in Misseke and the villagers began to drive elephants away from the village. As a result, elephant damage was reduced. In 2016, Shatana and his family returned to Misseke. During the growing season of February to June 2016, he successfully

32

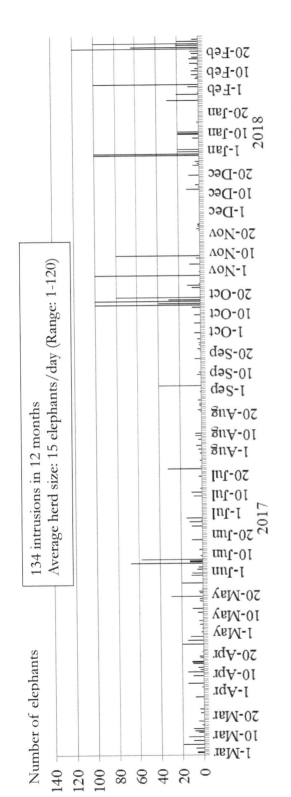

Figure 3. The number of elephants that invaded Misseke Village between March 2017 and February 2018 (The data were collected by the Misseke elephant patrol team)

Table 1. Farming record of Shatana, 2013–2017

Year	Agriculture season	Area cultivated (acre)	Area raid by elephants (acre)	Ratio of the harvested area (%)	
2013	Sep. - Jan.	10	10	0	
2014	Feb. - Jun.	7	7	0	
	Sep. - Jan.	5	5	0	
2015	In another village	2	0	100	In Morotonga Village
2016	Feb. - Jun.	5	0	100	
	Sep. - Jan.	7	7	0	
2017	Feb. - Jun.	2	0	100	
	Sep. - Jan.	7	3	14	3 acres were dried up by the sun

harvested five acres of crops. However, elephants intruded three times from September to January of 2016 and consumed all the crops. In 2017, Shatana had a successful harvest because the elephant patrol team protected his fields. However, from September to January 2017, some crops died from drought and others were consumed by elephants. That season, only one acre of crops was harvested.

Because elephant invasions are unpredictable, the Misseke farmers are constantly worried. A field requires approximately 180 days of care before harvest. However, the elephants can eat an entire field in just an hour. If their crops are eaten just before the harvest, there could be up to 179 days of labour wasted with no yield.

In years of little or no harvest, the villagers must lower their quality of life to survive. For example, Shatana sold his goats and cows, then harvested and sold the trees on his land as timber. His children were transferred from a private school to a government school with lower tuition and a lower quality of education. He also reduced the quality of his family's diet and decreased the frequency of their meals. Moreover, he did not seek any medical care or use a mobile phone.

Shatana family's quality of life deteriorated in various ways as he tried to overcome the loss of his harvest.

Making charcoal is an alternative way to earn income from agriculture; when elephants destroy crops, more households rely on making charcoal for income. Making charcoal requires firewood and leads to deforestation and environmental degradation.[1] Fortunately, since elephant damage was reduced in 2016, crops were harvested and deforestation also declined.[2]

Relocating to another village is not a practical solution for most Misseke farmers. Obtaining land in Tanzania is difficult and expensive, and most average farmers cannot afford to move. Changing to a different swathe of land is also difficult for farmers because crop growth varies depending on soil conditions and microtopography; a successful harvest requires knowledge of the land from several years of continuous cultivation. Shatana was unusually lucky because he had access to farmland in another village and could return to Misseke again without selling his land. There have been other households that could not find an alternative farm, and the family members had to disperse due to poverty caused by an elephant raid. Thus, elephant crop damage leads to deterioration in the quality of life by increasing deforestation and decreasing the victims' nutritional status, education quality, and medical care.

3-3. Human Fatalities Caused by Elephants

Encounters with the elephants can become deadly; the highest number of fatalities occurred in 2019, when seven people were killed in the Serengeti District (Figure 4; Table 2). Most fatalities occurred in the villages adjacent to the protected areas, east of Serengeti District (Figure 5). There is no pattern to the accidents; the sex and age of the victims, as well as the time of day and circumstances leading to death, are variable. The detailed situation of one fatality is described below.

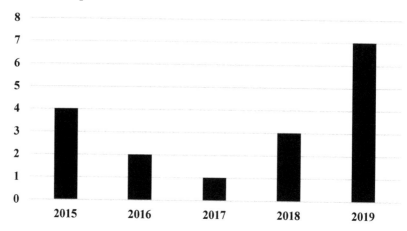

Number of persons

Figure 4. Human fatalities caused by elephants in the Serengeti District, Tanzania

Table 2. Sexes and ages of victims killed by elephants in the Serengeti District, Tanzania, in 2019 (The data were collected through interviews with Serengeti District game officers)

Case	Month	Village	Sex	Age
1	May	Merenga	M	58
2	June	Machochuwe	M	n.d.
3	July	Mbalibali	F	40
4	July	Bokore	F	n.d.
5	August	Bonchugu	M	19
6	September	Bonchugu	M	20s
7	September	Bwitengi	M	60s

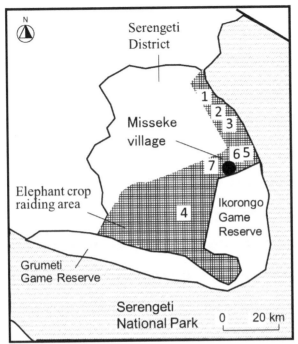

Figure 5. The locations of elephant-caused human fatalities in the Serengeti District, 2019 (The numbers of each case correspond to those in Table 2)

Case Study 2: The Death of Mr Chacha in Bonchugu Village

Chacha was 19 years of age and a second-year secondary school student. At 20:00 on 24 August 2019, he was attacked by an elephant near his home and died. Earlier that day, Chacha's mother had asked him to go to a store in the village centre. Chacha spent some time talking with his friends and it was dark by the time he left the village centre. He and his neighbour walked toward their homes, which were about 4 km from the centre of the village and very close to the border of the game reserve. Chacha said goodbye to the neighbour at their house and walked the remaining distance to his house alone. It had been a cloudy day and the moon was not visible. Chacha did not have a torch or a mobile phone, so he walked in darkness. When he had walked about 20 m from his neighbour's house, an elephant suddenly attacked him from behind. Chacha desperately tried to escape. He sprinted away at full speed, but the elephant was too fast to escape. He ran about 30 m but was caught and thrown by the elephant's

37

trunk. The elephant then pierced Chacha with his tusks and trampled him to death.

The attack occurred only about 100 m from his home. Although a neighbour's house was nearby, the family were terrified of the elephant and could do nothing to help. They stayed in the house and listened to the terrifying trumpet of the elephant and the screams of Chacha. There were traces of blood and pieces of tusk in the soil, and buttons from Chacha's clothes that had been torn off during the attack laid on the ground when I visited the site two days after the incident. It was a miserable scene.

I attended Chacha's funeral (Figure 6). Unsurprisingly, his mother's sadness was unbearable. She couldn't even say a final goodbye to her son but cried in her room with close relatives. There were 50 classmates from his secondary school at his funeral, and they were all crying. Relatives travelled from afar and many villagers also came, so about four hundred people attended his last farewell. Chacha was a devout Seventh-day Adventist believer and was enthusiastic about church activities. I hope that the choir hymns sung at his funeral reached him in heaven. His father was working in Dar es Salaam, a large city 1,500 km away, so he could not attend the funeral. He had suddenly lost his son and could not say a last goodbye.

Figure 6. The funeral of Chacha on 26 August 2019

At the funeral, the village chairman told the attendants to avoid going out after dark and said that children should avoid walking to school early in the morning[3] to prevent another tragedy.

It was unusual that three government officers from Serengeti District and the game reserve attended the funeral.[4] These officers expressed their condolences but did not mention specific preventive measures against elephant invasion. They only mentioned the possibility of receiving financial compensation by applying for a wildlife damage compensation scheme (described in the next section), which is unlikely to be paid.

The bereaved families cannot be compensated for the mental, emotional and economic loss caused by the elephant attacks. HEC has both visible and invisible negative impacts, and elephants limit the villagers' daily activities. People fear for their lives even in their home village. In such a situation, it is inevitable that the villagers will come to hate the elephants.

4. Ineffective Support by the Government of Tanzania

4-1. Ineffective Compensation Scheme

The government of Tanzania established a wildlife damage compensation programme in 2011. Victims receive up to 100,000 Tanzania shillings (Tsh; 1 US dollar is about 2,000 Tsh in 2020) for every acre of field damage. However, this system is ineffective. The first payment from the government was made in 2018, several years after the application was submitted. To date, only five villages have received compensation. There are 25 other villages still waiting for compensation, including the Misseke Village. Moreover, 100,000 Tsh per acre is not enough to cover the damage. Maize seeds (8 kg) for a 1-acre farm cost 30,000 Tsh and cultivating a field using cows costs 30,000 Tsh. Furthermore, it is expensive to apply for compensation: the applicant must travel to see the district officer, which costs time and money; the officer must then visit the field to assess the damage and to prepare documents and the applicant must pay for the officer's meals and travel. Therefore, even if the farmer is awarded the compensation, it is not enough money to reimburse the farmer's expenses, labour and time. In many cases, the farmer is never compensated. After a fatal elephant attack, the victim's family is eligible to receive 1 million Tsh per person. However, this process requires a lot of bureaucratic effort, and many families are not aware of this reimbursement option. To my knowledge, no family has successfully received this compensation.

District officers and wildlife officials tout this compensation programme as the government's response to HEC. A district game officer explained to me that, 'The HEC compensation office in Dar es Salaam is piled up with application documents from all over the country, that is the reason why the screening is delayed.' These officers frequently recommend this compensation programme at the village farmer's meetings, although they are not sure when it will be paid.

4-2. Growth in Tourism Revenue, but Little Benefit-Sharing

One possible solution is for tourism income to be used for mitigating HEC, but this has not occurred. Tourism is a growing industry in Tanzania. In 2017, tourism revenue reached 4.7 billion US dollars, around 9 per cent of Tanzania's GDP (World Travel and Tourism Council 2018). While tourism revenue has been increasing, most of the people living around the Serengeti National Park are burdened by the costs of wildlife tourism without seeing the benefits. Some communities originally lived on the land now covered by the park, but were forced to relocate in 1951. With the establishment of the park, hunting and the consumption of wildlife meat were forbidden, taking away a key form of local livelihood. At the same time, local residents find it difficult to get employment in the tourism industry. Townsfolk with schooling are mostly hired while local residents are generally offered short-term, lower-paid employment.

In an attempt toward equity, the Tanzanian government introduced a system called Wildlife Management Areas (WMAs), which is often highlighted as the best example of community-based conservation in Tanzania (WWF 2014), in 2006. A WMA is an area of communal land set aside exclusively as habitat for wildlife by member villages, in which the local communities have the right to lease the area to tourism operators to generate revenue. However, this system has not been functioning effectively in many WMAs

(Benjaminsen and Bryceson 2012; WWF 2014). In the Serengeti District, IKONA WMA was established and achieved the sum of 500,000 US dollars in 2012 (WWF 2014). However, its earnings are distributed to only five member villages. Twenty-five other villages affected by elephants in the district are not members of the WMA because their land is inadequate for wildlife habitation and they are far from the main tourist infrastructure. Ironically, it is these 25 villages – with a human population of around 70,000 – that are heavily affected by elephants' crop raiding. Furthermore, 35 per cent of tourism revenue goes to the government, and the foreign tourism enterprises running the hotels in WMA are making large profits. Given this, the WMA's benefits are limited, both in terms of the revenue generated and the land area covered.

5. Villagers' Efforts to Mitigate Elephant Raids

5-1. Prohibited Traditional Bow and Arrow

HEC is a complex issue. Tanzanian law strictly protects elephants. The villagers seek to protect their crops by driving elephants away from their fields, and they risk their lives in such efforts. Elephants are 4–5 m tall and weigh as much as 6–7 tonnes. The villagers have tried different approaches to find an effective strategy.

In the past, the Misseke villagers used bows and arrows to hunt and for self-defence. During one incident, farmers carrying bows and arrows for self-defence chased away elephants, but were arrested by the game scouts and accused of being poachers. Yet, the elephants had invaded and eaten the crops from a section of the village. The farmers had risked their lives to protect their livelihoods, but the scouts arrested them for carrying bows and arrows rather than offer to help them drive away the elephants. Since this event, farmers have been forbidden to use bows and arrows to drive away elephants. Although the elephants may turn to attack the farmers in these encounters, under the current regulations, there is no option but to be killed by the elephants.

41

The farmers have continued to devise methods of scaring the elephants without hurting them. Torches used to be an effective tool to deter night-time elephant raids. However, by 2014 and after three years of success, the elephants became habituated to the torches and no longer feared them.

In 2015, the farmers introduced a non-electric wire fence made of a single wire (Figure 7). The fence is 8 km long and sits along the boundary of the Ikorongo Game Reserve and Misseke Village. It is effective because most elephants are wary of the wire. In 2016, the villagers successfully harvested 80 per cent of their crops, which was the largest harvest in five years.

Figure 7. Fixing the wire fence

However, for the fence to remain effective the wire needs continuous maintenance because it is often broken. Cattle sometimes break the wire while grazing, because the wire is at the same height as their horns. Some elephants are not afraid of the wire and intrude into the village. The wooden fence posts also need maintenance because they can fall down, rot, get eaten by termites or get swept away by a tropical squall.

Checking and repairing the fence daily is a burden for farmers, who do not have much free time. They are busy with daily routines such as farming and grazing, collecting water and firewood, taking care of their family, and so on. Sometimes they need to travel into town to bring a sick family member to the hospital or visit the district office to arrange higher education for their children. As such, maintenance of the wire fence is often neglected. However, the Misseke villagers work together to complete the daily fence checks. They now use living trees as fence posts and keep the wire fence effective with their ingenuity and cooperation.

6. Elephant Patrol Teams as a Villager-Oriented Mitigation Measure

6-1. How to Listen for Elephants

Although the crop damage has been reduced by the wire fences, the farmers still worry that the elephants will break the wire and raid the village. Elephants are smart, and they sniff around the wire. If they sense no danger, they will break the wire and enter the village. Therefore, to maintain the effectiveness of the wire, it is necessary for the farmers to chase the elephants away from the wire, and drive them back into the game reserve. There was no support from the district government or the game reserve. Only the internal efforts of the community were available to protect the wire. Under such a circumstance, an elephant patrol team was organised in 2016. In this section, while describing the details of the patrol team's activities, the hidden consequences are analysed.

Initially, the team was disorganised with no formal membership. Currently, there are about 60 members on the patrol team, including a chairman, a secretary and an accountant. The team created watch points along the wire fence, where they look for elephants getting close to the village each night. They remain at their posts overnight regardless of weather, often carrying torches and wearing raincoats and boots. However, many members cannot buy raincoats or boots because of economic limitations.

There are four watch points set up along every 2 km of the fence. When the sun goes down around 17:00, the patrol members gather at their respective watch points. Before the sun goes down, they look for any approaching elephants. It is helpful to see the number and demographics of an elephant herd before they arrive at the village. If the patrol team does not see any approaching elephants, they must remain vigilant by 'listening for elephants'. Elephants are difficult to track at night because they are smart and will stop moving if they detect that a human is approaching. The patrol members must keep quiet to hear the sounds of elephants stepping on branches, scratching trees, rubbing leaves, eating or growling. Skilled patrol members can detect elephants even a several hundred meters away and can tell how many elephants are in the herd. These skills protect members from surprise elephant attacks.

Nights in the Serengeti District are cold, and members lie on the rocks of Copier, which retain warmth from the sun, to keep warm while listening for the elephants (Figure 8).

Figure 8. Lying on the rocks of Copier

If the members detect approaching elephants, they continue to listen for about 30 minutes to observe how many individuals are in the herd, in which direction they are moving and how the herd is spreading. It is important for the patrol members to know how many elephants are in a herd and the position of each individual so that there are no omissions. It is also necessary to clarify where the elephants have broken the wire to enter the village, because the elephants usually exit from the same place they entered.

44

If there are not enough patrol members to surround the herd, they must gather more members to form a team of 20–30 people. However, calling members by mobile phone can be difficult. Not all patrol members can afford a mobile phone. The cellular signal is weak and there is often no connection. Furthermore, there is no electricity in Misseke Village, so the batteries of mobile phones must be charged by going to a charging shop in town or visiting a neighbour with a solar panel. So, if backup patrol members cannot be reached by telephone, the guards must run to the next watch point to ask for support. Running is usually the quickest and most reliable method to gather crew members.

6-2. How to Chase Elephants Away

Once the team members are gathered and have information on the number and location of the elephants, they start the repatriation by positioning themselves into a V-shaped formation. They surround the elephant herd and use firecrackers to scare the elephants away (Figure 9). This operation needs close cooperation; if one member makes a noise earlier than the others, the elephants could rush to attack. To prevent this, the team always makes sure everyone is ready for placement before starting the repatriation.

Chasing the elephants away is much easier if they haven't yet reached the farm. Once they are in the farm, the temptation to eat the crops is too strong and they do not leave. Even if the elephants are displaced, they may return to the village again; or, a different herd may infiltrate. So, the patrol crew must guard the border throughout the night.

The firecracker, or *baruti* in Swahili, is a tool invented by a villager that is powerful enough to scare elephants without injuring them. The *baruti* is a tool that can be filled with gunpowder and, when struck, makes a sound like a gunshot that is loud enough to rupture human eardrums. Although the *baruti* is effective at scaring elephants, their use is burdensome to the patrol. The gunpowder is gathered by scraping off the powder from the tips of matches (Figure 10). The crew has to buy dozens of matchboxes and work to scrape off the gunpowder, which is costly, time consuming and labour intensive. A crew member will often need to rush to an elephant intrusion without

45

Figure 9. Firecracker called a *baruti*

gunpowder because he hasn't had enough time to prepare it. Moreover, the *baruti* is so loud that it scares elephants from dozens of meters away, yet the patrol must listen to it at arm's length. This can cause noise-induced hearing loss. Other tools such as guns, helicopters and drones are also effective at repelling elephants but are expensive or illegal for the villagers.

Figure 10. Scraping off the match tips to use for *baruti* gunpowder

Elephant repatriation often results in injuries. The patrol members have to run at their maximum speed through thorny bushes in the darkness. There are no paved roads or footpaths, and the stones, rocks and tree roots on the ground are obstacles. The acacia trees have many thorns that can be stepped on. Many patrol members wear slippers because they cannot afford boots with thick soles. They can stumble, twist an ankle or get scratched. They have to pay for treatment costs out of pocket. In addition, during the day, they participate in cultivation, grazing livestock and other subsistence activities. As a result, they don't get much sleep, which makes them weak and easily sick. The poor health of the patrol team is one of the hidden impacts of HEC. Also, patrolling on rainy days can reduce their physical fitness and increases their risk of contracting infectious diseases. It is common to be absent due to illness or injury.

The patrol member's families must bear the anxiety, which affects mental health. For example, if a father is injured and cannot work, the entire family can lose their income and livelihood. Villagers in the Serengeti District rely on the ability to perform labour for their income.

The need for villagers to carry a torch is another burden. Prior to the HEC increase in 2010, they were not needed. The large torches that are needed to find elephants in the distance are expensive, 15,000 Tsh (7 US dollars), which represents a high cost to the villagers. The batteries are difficult to charge and easily deteriorate, and a new one is needed every six months.

There is also an opportunity cost of the elephant patrol and the hidden impact of HEC. The repatriation leader Wambura said, 'Without elephant patrols, I could have done other income-generating activities. I would have worked hard to sell agricultural products at a higher rate, to do small businesses while travelling to and from the town, or to support my wife's business. But the patrols take my time and effort, then I cannot do anything to develop my own life.' If the members could, instead, spend their patrol time on doing something toward their personal development, they could increase their standard of living.

There are concerns that the elephants might become accustomed to the wire fence and the *baruti*. They do not fear the *baruti* as much;

they used to quickly run to the reserve once they heard the *baruti*, but now they stop running after about 50 m to see if they are being followed. Also, more elephants are attempting to break the fence. Elephants are very smart and may become accustomed to the countermeasures. The patrol is reducing their use of the *baruti* to prevent the elephants from becoming habituated to it.

Although the elephant repatriation activities produce a hidden impact on the team members and their families, Misseke Village has reduced its HEC since 2016. Nevertheless, some damage still remains. The Serengeti villagers continue to patrol and repatriate the elephants, which is effective but requires the self-sacrifice of members. Such hidden impacts and villagers' sacrifice are overlooked by the government, international NGOs and international media.

7. Conclusion: Hidden Impacts of HEC

I have described the hidden impacts that accompany the visible damage caused by elephants, and also the hidden impacts that occur during the implementation of mitigation measures against visible damage (Table 3).

Many HEC studies have focused on visible damage such as crop destruction and human fatalities (Hoare 2000; Naughton-Treves and Treves 2005; Mduma et al. 2010). However, as described in this chapter, various types of invisible impacts accompany the visible damage. The loss of agricultural income has led to an overall decline in quality of life, with negative consequences for children's future due to poor health and a lower quality of education. Furthermore, charcoal production to supplement income increases deforestation.

Regarding the fatalities, the impact of the loss of a person on families and communities has not been considered. It becomes clear that the negative psychological and economic impacts on the families of those killed, and the fear of the entire community, deprived of a free and secure life, are a great burden. Although visible damage can be reduced by implementing deterrents, these countermeasures cause

Table 3. A summary of hidden impacts of elephant damage and their mitigation measures in Serengeti District

		Hidden impacts
Visible damage	Crop damage	- Disruption of livelihood: education, medical treatment, housing and nutritional status - Forest degradation caused by charcoal production - Transaction cost of bureaucratic compensation scheme
	Fatalities	- Psychological and economic burden to family - Fear, restricted mobility, loss of freedom in residential area for community
Mitigation measures for visible damage	Wire fence	- Construction, daily check and maintenance labour cost
	Patrolling and chasing elephants	- Lack of sleep, - Risk of injury and disease - Psychological and economic burden to family - Economic and labour cost of mobile phone, torch, charging electricity, *baruti* and gunpowder - Opportunity cost of other economic activities

other hidden impacts including injury, illness, equipment cost, family members' anxiety and opportunity costs.

The Misseke villagers have demonstrated characteristics of 'African potential', such as resilience, tolerance, innovativeness and collective agency (Gebre et al. 2017). They have invented several different types of HEC mitigation using their own resources, without institutional or governmental assistance. However, HEC continues to cause hidden impacts that threaten a sustainable human–elephant coexistence.

To achieve a sustainable coexistence, elephant intrusions must be prevented. Some HEC studies point out the importance of tackling the human–human conflict over resources (Shaffer et al. 2019; Gross 2019). In the Serengeti region, the villagers were originally forced to seize land when the national park was established and hunting became prohibited, which made the villagers dissatisfied with the government. The villagers recognise elephants as government property and believe that the government of Tanzania should initiate a long-term, comprehensive strategy for HEC.

However, the government does not take proper action. Since the 1990s, conservation policy in Africa has taken a community-based natural resource management (CBNRM) approach that was also launched by the Tanzanian government. However, the governmental damage compensation scheme is not working effectively for people affected by elephants. Meanwhile, the system that redistributes tourism benefits to the community (IKONA WMA) does not have enough income to compensate for elephant damage. To make matters worse, the WMA has been accused of seizing communal land (Iwai 2017; Green and Adams 2015; Benjaminsen and Bryceson 2012). The elephants that should remain in the national parks and governmental game reserves are entering villages and causing problems. There is a strong demand to reform the current injustice of requiring the victims to solve the issue.

Endnotes

[1] To make charcoal officially, the villagers must purchase a permit from a government office. However, many people do not comply as the permit fee is expensive.

[2] Another effect of reducing elephant damage was a housing boom. Houses in this region are often built with burnt bricks, which villagers cannot afford if there is elephant damage. When income from their crops began to increase in 2016, the villagers had the time to work on housing repairs and construction.

3. Children in Tanzania's primary schools arrive at school at 07:00. The children who live far away usually leave their house before sunrise.

4 A government officer is supposed to attend the funeral of an elephant attack victim as the elephant came from the protected area managed by the government. However, this does not always happen.

Acknowledgements

This work was supported by JSPS KAKENHI Grant Number JP16H06318, 17H01637, 17H01937 and 16H02039.

References

Barua, M., Bhagwat, S. A. and Jadhav, S. (2013) 'The hidden dimensions of human–wildlife conflict: Health impacts, opportunity and transaction costs', *Biological Conservation*, Vol. 157, pp. 309–316.

Benjaminsen, T. A. and Bryceson, I. (2012) 'Conservation, green/blue grabbing and accumulation by dispossession in Tanzania', *Journal of Peasant Studies*, Vol. 39, No. 2, pp. 335–355.

Dickman, A. J. (2010) 'Complexities of conflict: The importance of considering social factors for effectively resolving human–wildlife conflict', *Animal Conservation*, Vol. 13, No. 5, pp. 458–466.

Gebre, Y., Ohta, I. and Matsuda, M. (2017) 'Introduction: Achieving peace and coexistence through African Potentials', in Y. Gebre, I. Ohta, and M. Matsuda (eds) *African Virtues in the Pursuit of Conviviality: Exploring Local Solutions in Light of Global Prescriptions*, Bamenda: Langaa RPCIG, pp. 3–37.

Green, K. E. and Adams, W. M. (2015) 'Green grabbing and the dynamics of local-level engagement with neoliberalization in Tanzania's wildlife management areas', *Journal of Peasant Studies*, Vol. 42, No. 1, pp. 97–117.

Gross, E. M. (2019) *Tackling Routes to Coexistence: Human-Elephant Conflict in Sub-Saharan Africa*, Bonn: Deutsche Gesellschaftfür für Internationale Zusammenarbeit (GIZ) GmbH.

Hoare, R. (2000) 'African elephants and humans in conflict: The outlook for co-existence', *Oryx*, Vol. 34, Issue 1, pp. 34–38.

Iwai, Y. (2017) 'Depriving tourism benefit of local communities', *Journal of African Studies*, Vol. 92, pp. 95–108.

Jackson, T. P., Mosojane, S., Ferreira, S. M. and Van Aarde, R. J. (2008) 'Solutions for elephant *Loxodonta africana* crop raiding in northern Botswana: Moving away from symptomatic approaches', *Oryx*, Vol. 42, No. 1, pp. 83–91.

Mayberry, A. L., Hovorka, A. J. and Evans, K. E. (2017) 'Well-being impacts of human-elephant conflict in Khumaga, Botswana: Exploring visible and hidden dimensions', *Conservation and Society*, Vol. 15, Issue 3, pp. 280–291.

Mduma, S., Lobora, A., Foley, C. and Jones, T. (2010) *Tanzania Elephant Management Plan 2010–2015*, Arusha: Tanzania Wildlife Research Institute.

Naughton-Treves, L. and Treves, A. (2005) 'Socio-ecological factors shaping local support for wildlife: Crop-Raiding by elephants and other wildlife in Africa', *Conservation Biology Series-Cambridge*, Vol. 9, p. 252.

Shaffer, L. J., Khadka, K. K., Van Den Hoek, J. and Naithani, K. J. (2019) 'Human-Elephant conflict: A review of current management strategies and future directions', *Frontiers in Ecology and Evolution*, Vol. 6, p. 235.

Smit, J., Pozo, R., Cusack, J., Nowak, K. and Jones, T. (2017) 'Using camera traps to study the age-sex structure and behaviour of crop-using elephants in Udzungwa Mountains National Park, Tanzania', *Oryx*, Vol. 53, No. 2, pp. 368–376.

TAWIRI (Tanzania Wildlife Research Institute) (2015) *Population Status of Elephant in Tanzania 2014*, Arusha: TAWIRI.

———— (2019) *Aerial Wildlife Survey of Large Animals and Human Activities in the Selous-Mikumi Ecosystem, Dry Season 2018, TAWIRI Aerial Survey Report*, Arusha: TAWIRI.

Ueda, Y., Kiyono, M., Nagano, T., Mochizuki, S. and Murakami, T. (2018) 'Damage control strategies affecting crop-raiding Japanese macaque behaviors in a farming community', *Human Ecology*, Vol. 46, No. 2, pp. 259–268.

UNEP, CITES, IUCN and Traffic (2013) *Elephants in the Dust - The*

African Elephant Crisis. A Rapid Response Assessment, United Nations Environment Programme GRID-Arendal (www.grida.no) (accessed: 15 February 2021).

Woodroffe, R., Thirgood, S. and Rabinowitz, A. (2005) 'The impact of human-wildlife conflict on natural systems', in R. Woodroffe, S. Thirgood and A. Rabinowitz (eds) *People and Wildlife: Conflict or Coexistence?* Cambridge: Cambridge University Press, pp. 1–12.

World Bank (2015) *Tanzania's Tourism Futures: Harnessing Natural Assets,* Washington DC: World Bank Group.

World Travel and Tourism Council (2018) *Travel and Tourism Economic Impact 2018 Tanzania,* London: World Travel and Tourism Council.

WWF (2014) *Tanzania's Wildlife Management Areas: A 2012 Status Report,* Dar es Salaam: World Wildlife Fund for Nature Tanzania.

Chapter 2

'Where Did Our Nature Go?' Situating Voices of Local Communities around Conservation Violence

Samantha S. Sithole and Frank Matose

1. Introduction

From bumper stickers of 'save-the-rhino' on motor vehicles and store fronts to gruesome pictures of slaughtered rhino on social media, the telling tale of rhino poaching is both visually heartrending and distressing. Since the ban on the trading and selling of rhino horn in 1977, a significant number of resources has been spent on environmental campaigns to raise awareness on poaching of the dwindling rhino population and, recently, social media campaigns on platforms that include Facebook and Twitter, constantly chant the slogans of 'good versus evil' when relating the rhino to poachers (Büscher 2016: 987). The violent rhetoric against poaching has spurred a campaign that has humanised the rhino and dehumanised 'the poacher'. Within the Kruger National Park (KNP) in South Africa, responses have been centred on eradicating rhino poaching by adopting military-style tactical operations and ranger training. The increase in arms and the securitised response in protected areas such as KNP have been widely termed the militarisation of conservation.

The coercive response to combat poaching by the South African state and South African National Parks (SANParks) is termed by Büscher and Ramutsindela (2015) as 'Green Violence'. Whilst Lunstrum (2014) coined it as 'Green Militarisation'. Annecke and Masubelele (2016) say that there is little to no inclusion of one key major group in discussions on how to stop poaching. This group is comprised of the communities that have neighboured the Kruger since its establishment in 1926. Conservation as practice has arguably always embodied exclusionary principles from its antecedent

55

approaches of fortress conservation to its most recent militarisation. Murombedzi (1999) argues that the discipline of conservation is therefore for nature without people. These debates are anchored in discussions on the commercialisation of natural resources like wildlife, where tourism is acceptable and local access is not (Murombedzi 1999). This study seeks to argue that if conservation was a shovel that dug out a trench between local communities and natural spaces, then militarisation is the excavator that does a more efficient job of creating a crater between the two.

This chapter therefore seeks to situate the debate of militarised conservation in the community of Justicia, in the greater KNP area. It will, firstly, delve into the current debates around conservation and the war on poaching using Foucault's theory of governmentality. Thereafter, it will contextualise these debates through the lens of the KNP and the historical violent nature of the KNP and, lastly, it will narrate the lived experiences of those from the Justicia community.

2. Understanding Militarisation: A Tool Used to Enforce Conservation

The practice and enforcement of conservation in the global south is based in the American constructivist view of nature as pristine, sublime and untouched by humans (Büscher and Dietz 2005). The practice is often called 'fences and fines approach' or 'fortress conservation', and is highly exclusionary and implemented with the view that indigenous communities are not good stewards of nature and therefore needed to be removed from it in order to protect it (Dowie 2009). As such, militarisation, as a model for or a tool to implement conservation, not only reinforces a colonial precedent but also perpetuates continuous productions of violence and marginalisation due to the way in which the spaces of conservation are then governed using this tool in and around protected areas. Büscher and Fletcher (2018: 106) argue that there is a growing caucus that advocates for the extreme forms of punishment and the 'the increasingly violent defence of (certain forms of) nature, so as to ensure its conservation and preservation'. As a result, militarisation is argued to be modelled using military-style approaches that involve the use of paramilitary tactics as well as violent means to enforcing conservation in protected areas (Duffy et al. 2019: 66). In the context of the KNP, it is to reduce and ultimately stop rhino poaching to save the species from extinction.

These spaces have and continue to embody the discussions on the role of power and how it influences human interaction and behaviour around the natural environment (Bryant and Bailey 1997). As a result, the lens of governmentality and neoliberalism presented by Foucault (1997, 2008) are pertinent to illuminate how militarisation is used to advance conservation goals and as a tool for social control. Foucault argues, in his investigations of political power, that governance is an 'activity that undertakes to conduct individual's behaviour throughout their lives by placing them under the authority of a guide responsible for what they do and for what happens to them' (Foucault 1997: 82).

Foucault also uses the lens of political power which he believed to work towards strategic reasoning within government of actions that would be directed towards a specific end (Rose et al. 2006). Foucault believes that all political forms of action and planning are being overcome by a specific mentality or way of thinking, which inform institutions and bodies that are part of the governing process. This mentality, which he named 'governmentality' was responsible for the imposition of obligations and conceptions or ways of living and interacting that created and regulated relations between 'people and people, people and things and people and events' (Rose et al. 2006: 11).

Foucault states that free market needs rigorous and consistent government intervention and regulation (Fletcher 2010). This is because the market is not viewed as a sphere that exists naturally, but instead, as an 'artificial construct that has to be maintained through diverse forms of governance' (Fletcher 2010: 173). In order to effectively monitor and manage the market and market conditions, the state has to establish market parameters through state intervention in two ways: regulatory and organising actions (Fletcher 2010). Briefly explained, regulatory actions encompass the stabilisation of prices through inflation control for example, whereas organising actions require intensified government intervention because they operate in conditions surrounding the market (Fletcher 2010). In this way, the market influences not only the economic realm but also the socio-political realm, and subjects or the governed are guided and regulated by the techniques and ideals engrained in political institutions as well as the market (Fletcher 2010). Neoliberal governmentality is thus an important tool through which to view the 'invisible' arm of the state, the market, social institutions, economic and historical processes which affect the natural environment and those who utilise it (Rogers 2002). Using governmentality through a neoliberal lens, one can view how militarisation is implemented as way to control behaviour that falls outside of the framework of conservation.

Duffy et al. (2015: 346) rightfully state that militarised approaches 'escalate conflict between rangers and poachers and also lead to the alienation of communities'. Local communities, as the least powerful actors, are left marginalised and are obligated to reorganise their lives and utilise this space within the confines of the militarised conservation model. This therefore leads us to the question of what kind of lived realities of local communities are in light of the militarisation model being enforced in the KNP due to increased rhino poaching since 2008. However, before expanding more on the local level experiences, this chapter will situate militarisation and its history in the greater KNP area through apartheid and now recently to combat rhino poaching.

3. Historical Background of the Violent and Military Nature of the Kruger

Given its apartheid legacy, Humphreys and Smith (2014) argue the 'rhinofication' of security within conservation in South Africa further highlights the socio-economic divisions that already existed. Carruthers (1995: 88) argues that the establishment of apartheid in 1948 saw the wildlife conservation being directed towards the 'Afrikaner republic moral', dominated by Afrikaner bureaucrats and scientists. Lunstrum (2015) argues that the KNP's militarisation was a result of the National Party's (NP) need for self-preservation against anti-colonial and apartheid hostilities that began in the 1960s.

Given that a large expanse of the KNP borders Mozambique, liberation fighters, Umkhonto we Sizwe (MK) which was sheltered by Frelimo[9] (Front for the Liberation of Mozambique), utilised the strategic location of the KNP (Lunstrum 2015: 360). The KNP was the frontline as Mozambique neared its independence in the 1970s, and thus became a military stronghold. Lunstrum (2015) states that in 1973 the apartheid regime manifested its military presence by deploying the SADF (South African Defence Force) which established a Kruger Park Commando (KPC), as a regional defence strategy. The deployment of the SADF to tactically monitor and defend the border, resulted in three outcomes. These outcomes have arguably led to what is now termed the 'fortress Kruger'.

Firstly, the establishment of the KPC resulted in the meshing of rangers and the military. Lunstrum states that rangers began patrolling the border and this resulted in the blurring of ranger, conservation and military duties (Lunstrum 2015). 1977 saw the deployment of soldiers, the fencing of the border and the construction of the Sisal Line[1] along the international border (Lunstrum 2015). This led to the entire park being enclosed with a fence in order to protect wildlife by limiting its movement into Mozambique and preventing hostile elements from crossing the international border (Lunstrum 2015). The creation of the Sisal Line shows how the apartheid forces harnessed nature to achieve military ends.

The second outcome is the creation of a conflict/war zone within the park which has resulted in the coercive control of space. As a result of the MK's alliance with Frelimo, the apartheid state aided the guerrilla organisation, Renamo (Mozambican National Resistance) and further instructed the SADF to occupy bases that were managed by the South African Police Service (SAPS) and ranger stations, thus fortifying Kruger and strengthening the park and military relationship (Lunstrum 2015). The ranger force became and remained para-militarised and was now centred on anti-poaching efforts in the 1980s (Lunstrum 2015). Lunstrum states that 'Kruger's ranger corps was thus reinvented from a colonial style conservation force into ... a paramilitary force equipped to take on well trained elephant poachers' (2015: 363).

The third outcome argued by Lunstrum (2015) is the exclusion and impoverishment African villages across the border of the KNP in South Africa and Mozambique. 'Renamo troops destroyed villages and livelihoods as part of their destabilisation campaign' and this resulted in poverty that, she contends, has come to shape rhino poaching, especially within Mozambique (Lunstrum 2015: 365). The militarisation of this space arose from the strategies used to remove and exclude local communities which they felt were not suitable stewards of nature. Established in 1926, the Kruger was originally recognised in line with the model that encouraged the 'romanticisation' of the frontier experience and the promotion of national pride (Carruthers 1995). As such, the creation was to unify the English-speaking and Afrikaans-speaking cultural groups while excluding Africans and non-whites (Carruthers 1995). It was thus established on the moral ground of white perceptions and values of wildlife and how they could strengthen their national unity through it.

The increase in rhino poaching from the year 2008 resulted in the state shifting conservation strategies from purely ecological, to rhino poaching prevention. Annecke and Masubelele (2016: 196) state that the social media reports of the gruesome images of de-horned rhinos and distressed calves resulted in a public outrage that channelled the efforts of NGO's and public campaigns to 'raise funds and exert considerable pressure on the South African government ... to act forcefully against rhino poaching'. They argue that this global campaign against rhino poaching resulted in the militarised response and the fortification of the KNP (Annecke and Masubele 2016). Büscher (2016) further states that the militarisation has also been shaped by white-dominated conservation groups' fear of losing control over conservation spaces that represented white ideals for generations. Therefore, the rhino crisis has been escalated from an ecological issue to a national security issue, where the South African government has had to respond in a visible and strong way in order to protect the integrity of its national heritage. This study argues that the shift from incorporated conservation to a militarised and controlled framework is a result of socio-political hysteria that was generated as a response to the crisis surrounding rhinos and the rate of poaching.

This section has provided a background to the historical and current factors that influence the implementation of militarised conservation in the KNP in South Africa. The next section will discuss the findings of the fieldwork conducted within two communities that neighbour the KNP. This will allow the debates discussed in this chapter to be situated on a practical level using the narratives of people on the ground.

4. The Case Study of Justicia

4-1. Overview

Justicia is a village located on the periphery of the KNP (Figure 1). It is part of the Bushbuckridge district (Ngwato 2012). It directly neighbours the Sabi Sands Game Reserve (SSGR) and predominantly comprises black/African populations of the Tsonga and Shangaan ethnic and language groups, as well as Mozambique migrants who settled in the area as early as the 1800s and during the civil war from the mid-1980s (Ngwato 2012). Justicia is made of two sub-settlements: Justicia A, the original village and Justicia B established in 1987 to accommodate first and second-generation families of Mozambican heritage. In 2016 (when the study was conducted) there were 1,503 households in the village of Justicia with a population of 7,313 people (both men and women – Table 1).

The community is made up of several employees of the SSGR who are employed as kitchen staff, ground maintenance and game drivers and guides. The narratives from Justicia will be based on the relationship it has with the SSGR. Due to its extremely close proximity to the fence, the village is at the heart of issues that deal with conservation and park militarisation strategies. This section will therefore shed light on the narratives of the participants interviewed during fieldwork in this area in an effort to answer the main thesis question.

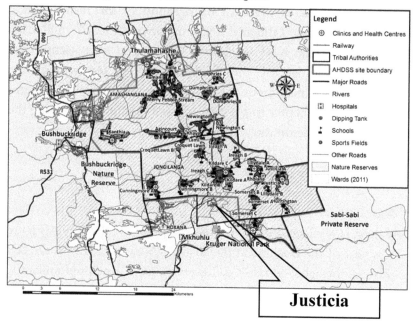

Figure 1. Map and location of Justicia

Source: MRC/Wits Rural Public Health and Health Transitions Unit (Agincourt 2017)

Table 1. Mid-year figures of Justicia, 2016

Households	1,503
Population	7,313
Male	3,390
Female	3,923
Children under 5	853
Children of school-going age (5-19)	2,335

Source: Agincourt (2017)

4-2. How Increased Surveillance and Security by the SSGR Affects the Community of Justicia

The effect of increased security in the game reserve is not visible upon arrival to the village. The SSGR has tightened its levels of security and surveillance within the reserve and within the village. This section will illustrate through narratives how this has created internal social strife between neighbours in the village, disturbed business operations for local business owners and has established a tense atmosphere for staff within the lodges of the SSGR. In order to experience narratives of the participants further, this section will be sub-divided into two themes (4-2-1) and (4-2-2) the breakdown of social cohesion and securitisation of the work place.

The fence, which separates the village from the reserve and wildlife, is not the only security measure that has been employed to stop people from illegally entering the park and reserve. The adoption of stringent security measures by the SSGR has increased due the rhino-poaching crisis. The SSGR has employed various measures to collect information and establish pre-emptive response measures to catch people suspected of poaching. This has arguably deepened the fracture that exists within the relationship the SSGR has with the community of Justicia. It is important to note that the narratives and experiences under the following themes overlap and are interlinked.

4-2-1. The Breakdown of Social Cohesion

The Sabi Sands has reportedly hired or makes use of a private security company that helps in the policing of Justicia and neighbouring villages. Similar to the accounts reported in Werlverdiend (see Sithole 2018), Justicia experiences cases of violence towards community members when a rhino has been killed or poachers have been spotted in the reserve or park. J5 states that the presence of security agencies and police should be increased to deter people from thinking about jumping the fence to hunt illegally or even rhino poaching.[2] J1 stated that the game reserve has a helicopter that goes on random patrol to survey and monitor the village from the sky. He shrugged that 'those who are poachers complain about the noise and that the sound cracks the walls and windows of their houses'. As such, he stated that the reserve needs to protect the animals using whatever means necessary. He recalled a story of a suspected poacher and his family:

> A guy who was a suspect was tracked down by the security. When they went to his house and couldn't find him, they 'beat-up' the whole family because they wouldn't reveal his location. Men like that don't deserve to be in this village (Respondent-J1).[3]

J1 believes that people in Justicia should embrace conservation and rhino protection for their own safety because, 'the park means business'. He stated this because he argued that the SSGR is profit-making game reserve and they will protect their animals using whatever means necessary. When asked a follow-up question, how the SSGR would protect wildlife he pointed out that,

> People who buy cars and extend their houses with rooms or new furniture are suspected of poaching because this (Justicia) is a poor village so one needs to be able to account for their cash (Respondents-J1).

SSGR has a twenty-four-hour poaching hotline that people can telephone when they suspect poaching activity. The callers are allowed to remain anonymous when giving out information.

J7 states that 'the more police we have, the more likely they (poachers) will get caught'. The security he states, is a necessary emergency measure and is not meant to be permanent. However, he argues that the level at which the private security companies operate in the village is intimidating.

> The way they are trying to combat rhino poaching in this village has elements of oppression or oppressive tendencies. For instance, I was personally harassed by the police or private security …
>
> I don't even know which they are. I am a businessman and because I have more than others (property and money), they come here looking for rhino, rifles and money. They suspected me of poaching (Respondent- J7).[4]

He stated that the incidences of harassment went beyond the physical damage it caused to his household and work equipment. His neighbours started suspecting him of engaging in illegal activity even despite the fact that they knew he was a successful businessman. He recalled that his business activity had to halt for a week in order for the pressure and tension to dissipate. He believed that someone in the village had called the police and had identified him as a suspect because of his success.

> This idea that you can call a number and report your neighbour, even when you have no evidence of criminal behaviour, is unfair. They (his neighbours) do not trust me and I do not trust them. I do not know who is trying to destroy my company (Respondent-J8).[5]

He acknowledged the decrease in the trust that he had in his neighbours. He strongly believed he was harassed as a suspect because someone was jealous of his success as a businessman in Justicia. The internal village surveillance networks may have the potential to increase the probability of the private security and police catching a potential poacher. J5 argued that the relationship between SSGR and the community is generally respectable and is healthy.

> The people who were sought after by security has resulted in speculation and a disturbing scenario that has led to other people not being honest and others not being respected (Respondent- J5).

Community members that are under surveillance are viewed differently and they lose the respect of their neighbours because they are perceived as criminals. He went on to state that the presence of the military does not destabilise the unity in the village because they are carrying out their investigations. He and J1 believe that the only people who are disturbed by the actions taken by the SSGR are those who have something to fear. Justicia 6 (J6) on the other hand, states that the SSGR promised people, who give information to the police or private security (whether the information is false or true), a financial gift for their 'help'. J6 states that some people in the village had begun to take advantage of this fact and had started to blackmail people they suspected of poaching in order to get money.

> For those who are suspected correctly, the security will come with SAPS, even if they don't find anything, the helicopter will be hovering over their house daily. It is very disruptive way of saying we suspect you. This happens when a rhino is killed – because if a rhino is killed, the helicopter flies around the community for about 3 days to intimidate everyone (Respondent- J6).[6]

The levels of intimidation escalate depending on the level of the threat. The first intermediary level is when a person is suspected of poaching. J6 explained that the private security officers will visit the village to make their presence known. He states that they will not harass anyone at this stage. He believes that they come to the village to remind people that they are being watched – particularly those who are under suspicion. The second level, is when the person has been identified and there is hard or physical evidence that could implicate the person of being involved in poaching. For example, the purchase of a new car or the refurbishment of their household or the purchase of new items of furniture. J5 states that when poachers get money from a job, they are believed to enjoy flaunting their wealth to their neighbours. Thus, those who purchase or add to their household, immediately become suspects. At this stage, the police and private security will visit the person at their home and will ransack and physically harass them in an effort to find evidence like money, rifles or weapons, rhino horn or animal products, to implicate them in a crime. The third level is a combination of level two and the presence of the helicopter. When a rhino is killed, the helicopter hovers over the village in order to intimidate people. If someone is named as a suspect, the helicopter will hover over their homestead for several days and they will receive random visits from the police and security, until they can get the person to talk and identify any other members involved. J5 states that the village complained to the Community Development Forum (CDF), about the presence of the helicopter. He also revealed that the SSGR wanted to establish a 'spy operation' named Operation PIMPA. Operation PIMPA is a secret organisation that would allow residents to become informants and receive protection from rangers for providing information. J6 argues that this would have put the lives of informants in danger because this would have allowed residents to enter their neighbour's compounds and question them about their personal activities and financial status. Operation PIMPA has the potential to destabilise the whole community because the community would begin to divide itself between the informants and the suspects, causing increased friction between SSGR employees like rangers and business owners in the village. J6 argued the following:

> This community does not support rhino poaching. We even tried to hold mass meetings to address people to stop rhino poaching. We had a direct focus on awareness of the impact it will have on tourism. Tourism is the lifeline of this village. The Kruger is our natural resource. If visitors don't come it will be worse for us than it is for these private reserves (Respondent- J6).

J6 went on to argue that the lodges within SSGR are not consistently assisting with the facilitation of awareness about rhino poaching yet they attract millions of rands from donors around the world.

He argues that 'the surveillance and security is the primary measure that we have seen them implement. So they are the facilitators of poaching in retrospect – they deliberately ignore the community and implement policing instead of active engagement'. The unintended consequences therefore include the degeneration of the relationships between families and households.

The relationship between the SSGR and Justicia is strained. Although some residents feel the measures (anonymous hotline and Operation PIMPA) are necessary to deter people from poaching, others believe that it is fracturing the way in which the village views SSGR and causes mistrust.

4-2-2. Securitisation of the Workspace

The erosion of community and family level relationships does not only happen because of the increased surveillance and public harassment and humiliation. It has also emerged within employee relations with their families. Employees of the park also experience a breakdown in their personal relationships with their families because of the employment regulations within the SSGR game lodges. The securitisation of the workspace is experienced when employees enter and leave the workspace. J9 states that the employee's private belongings are searched at the gate. Women are searched by women and men by men. Employees have restricted levels of communication with their families because they cannot leave the reserve during a work cycle and, thirdly, the level of mistrust that SSGR has with its employees from the villages, impedes the ability of employees to experience a vertical progression up the company ranks.

J5 and J3 stated that the regulations stipulated that employees work twenty-one day shifts with no access to cell phones and without permission to leave the park within that period. They are then given seven days off work and then the cycle begins again. J5 argues that the SSGR stopped employees from using cell phones and leaving the reserve during work cycles because they do not want them spreading information about where rhinos can be found to potential poachers. There is a high level of mistrust that stems from the management with regards to honesty of their employees. The level of mistrust has restricted the employee's access to opportunities for promotion, especially if they do not seem trustworthy. J6 and J9 argued that mistrust is based on whether the employee has information or is involved in any way in rhino poaching. J9 argued that trust is not based on how long the person has worked there or how good they are at their job. She stated that when an employee is suspected of being involved in poaching, he or she is continuously questioned and shadowed at work, making the working environment uncomfortable for the employees. She revealed that employees' trustworthiness is based on polygraph tests (lie-detector tests) that are held at the lodges and a questionnaire that asks employees if they know anyone involved in poaching.

You (as an employee) are compelled to take that test as long as you are an employee there. You are strapped onto a machine. The machine works like it is a chair and has belts like in an aeroplane. They'll ask you

68

if you have a friend or know someone who poaches. If you say no and are lying, the machine will say yes (and vice versa). They are only interested in what the machine is telling them about your answers. If the machine says 'yes' you are involved in poaching, they'll arrest you immediately and you'll lose your job! (Respondent-J9).[7]

She further explained that the SSGR lodges were running this operation with a private company and when the polygraph is taking place, employees are obligated to speak to two white men that they are not familiar with. J10, another employee, stated that the polygraph process commenced in May of 2016 and is ongoing. He begrudgingly stated that '*if you refuse to take the lie-test, they'll say you are a poacher and either arrest you immediately or fire you first*'. He stated that he and his colleagues are not happy in their workspace because they are under constant surveillance with regards to what they are saying and how they behave.

Other people I know have fainted or have had problems breathing because of the test. If that happens to you, they tell you to come back next week or they wait to calm down. It is very frustrating because I personally don't know anything about the rhino ... I don't know how they walk — ask me about pots, pans and food because that's what I know (Respondent- J10).

The word 'poacher' in her workplace is considered taboo, similar to how the word 'bomb' in an airport is treated as a threat (similar to the account of W6 in Werlverdiend). Lastly, he stated that for over four months out of the year the management of most lodges live in Johannesburg or Cape Town. Due to this fact, the managers believe that employees will misbehave and take advantage of the manager's absence and guide poachers into the park, where the rhinos are.

In addition, J6 stated that employees of lodges in the SSGR come under a lot of pressure when someone in the village is suspected of poaching. He states that the workers are expected to give information on those suspected of poaching in the village and if they fail to do so, they are not trusted, victimised and/or dismissed. J6 strongly argued that the SSGR are intent on controlling their employees' behaviour by '… telling them that conservation of the rhino and protecting it at all costs is more important than maintaining relationships with their community. It is colonisation of the mind through conservation'. He argued that the life of employees in the village is not to protect the rhino, but to provide for their families' well-being. Lastly, he stated that the impact of securitisation in the workplace is felt within the family because the lodges allow employees to fraternise with each other. He argued that workers engage in extramarital sexual activity because they are not allowed visitors during their work cycles. Furthermore, he believes that this will harm the community at large because it promotes the spread of diseases like HIV and AIDS, '… diseases like that break down families and orphan children – imagine what will happen to this community in the next ten years'. SSGR regulations have manifested in ways that resemble the migrant worker policies experienced during apartheid. It is therefore important to continue exploring how militarisation has affected the way specific groups of people in the community carry out their activities.

5. Discussion: Conservation Being Viewed as Rhino Anti-Poaching

The understanding of wildlife conservation and environmental protection on the community level is closely tied to rhino anti-poaching. Wildlife conservation, as understood by academics, practitioners in the field and the government, strongly influences the perception of those at the local community level. The question that needs to be probed in order to situate the missing link is:

> Where is the disjuncture in the wildlife conservation knowledge framework between SANParks' approach to wildlife protection and the community's understanding of wildlife protection and conservation of endangered fauna?

This is important because the narratives of individuals in Justicia assume that the discourse surrounding rhino anti-poaching efforts defines what conservation is and how it should be approached.

The understanding of any form of conservation, despite the level of engagement or position from which one may try to assess it, is strongly influenced by powerful actors and the interests that conservation represents to that organisation or individual. Rhino anti-poaching efforts are centred on the fact that the mega-fauna is endangered and is also of high commercial value in the tourism market. Therefore, the interest of powerful actors such as SANParks and the SSGR would lie in the protection of the rhino. According to Parks and Gowdy (2013) the commercial value would be closely tied to how popular or endangered the natural attraction is. In the case of the rhino, international attention to its endangered status and the moral panic built around the high levels of poaching, have arguably triggered a supply and demand chain, whereby the fewer rhinos left because of poaching, the higher the demand to see them.

This commodification of wildlife protection (which is rooted in the neo-liberalisation of nature), makes the rhino supersede other mega-fauna that are endangered (for example, the elephant). As a result, the importance of wildlife and nature to people on the grassroots level in Justicia is closely linked to this commercialised view. The case study of Justicia showed how individuals within the community understand the draw that the rhino has within the tourism industry. The higher the levels of poaching of the rhino, the more attention these communities receive from conservation groups and tourists. As such, the understanding of conservation, as a practice, is strongly influenced by the interests of more powerful actors who have channelled a lot of resources to see to rhino protection.

If mega-fauna such as rhino were no longer existent in the wild, the impact on village tourism would be negative because the number of tourists would dwindle and the village's significance would arguably cease. As such, some members of the community view conservation as rhino anti-poaching and, as a result of the acclaim the rhino has received through eco-tourism, they argue that any means the park is ready to employ in order to protect the rhino is justified. The understanding of wildlife conservation, in this regard, is similar to what Dowie (2009) terms the social construction of nature which ties into the Parks and Gowdy (2013) argument of the commercialisation of endangered species like the rhino. This understanding of wildlife conservation is arguably rooted in the commodification of nature and the ideals of the neo-liberalisation of conservation. Najam (2005), Dhandapani (2015) and Brockington et al. (2008) all argue that protection of nature is a result of its commodification through eco-tourism and, as such, wildlife conservation under this guise serves as a commodity for the revenue it generates.

Ergo, the view of large endangered mammals like the rhino is considered to profitable and beneficial. Therefore, discussions and campaigns are focused on nurturing animals that are most profitable and this arguably trickles down from the most powerful stakeholder group to the least powerful (Büscher 2016). Justicia illustrates a more conflictual relationship between it and the Sabi Sands Game Reserve (SSGR) which was created because of how wildlife conservation, as a practice, is perceived and enacted.

Justicia's relationship with the game reserve that governs its relationship with the natural environment is highly contentious. As was shown in the previous chapter, respondents in Justicia's understanding of wildlife conservation were similar to that of other villages, where the views of the SSGR and SANParks framed how they perceived wildlife conservation. The SSGR in this regard carries out its activities with the village using the rhino anti-poaching rhetoric. The anti-poaching discourse arguably sets precedence for environmental activities such as education initiatives, campaigns and NGO activities for awareness. Conservation is seen as a necessary tool for understanding nature and generating revenue for benefit-sharing within the community. Thus, accepting wildlife conservation for Justicia is illustrated when respondents show that wildlife protection is the driving force in their relationship with the park and game reserves. The understanding of wildlife conservation is also firmly rooted in its monetary and commercial value. It is understood in terms of employment and tourism which highlights a transactional relationship that both communities have with nature conservation and their respective neighbours. However, the results show that the SSGR was selling nature at the cost of residents of Justicia and as a result nature stewardship was pressed as a mandate on locals because of the crisis of rhino poaching.

Respondents noted that the acceleration of anti-poaching campaigns between SSGR and group/individual interaction with them, either in spaces of employment or schools, has done more harm than good for the villagers. Poaching created mistrust between the SSGR and the community, especially for those who were employed within lodges in the SSGR. Therefore, respondents in Justicia highlighted that wildlife conservation was imposed on them and it was understood as a forced process by the SSGR because they heavily rely on them for employment and tourism opportunities.

In light of this, Lunstrum's (2014) argument that the production of different forms of violence to combat poaching has been transferred from the park itself to civilian spaces is warranted. This production of violence closely ties in with what Büscher and Ramustindela (2015) argued as 'Green Violence'. This argument encompasses the various forms of violence that were being enacted on local communities through militarised conservation. The form of violence discussed by Büscher and Ramustindela (2015), which speaks to the experiences of locals with regard to the construction of rhino anti-poaching as the hegemon in wildlife conservation, is social violence. They argue that social violence is the use of social power in protected spaces (not visible yet powerful) and it manifests in the controlling of circulation of ideas (Büscher and Ramutsindela 2015). It has emerged in Justicia through the hegemon of rhino poaching or anti-poaching within environmental and conservation discussions with locals. It has ultimately shaped and contained the way locals think about nature or conservation and this is controlled through the use of social violence (Büscher and Ramutsindela 2015). As such, the flow of information and knowledge from powerful conservation actors, such as the SANParks or the SSGR, to the community implies a level of control that is perpetrated to advance conservation goals such as anti-poaching but not with the community as a partner, but the community as a tool to achieve an end.

Knowledge creation and the hegemonic discourse surrounding wildlife protection, therefore, influence the grassroots level view and approach towards wildlife conservation. As a result, when coercive or forceful methods (securitisation of protected arenas) are implemented, they are seen by locals as a necessary intervention which is for the good of the environment. Lastly, it can be interpreted that the community's importance to the park and game reserves is emphasised when they (SANParks and SSGR) need help with or need to ensure wildlife protection. This discussion feeds into the next section where the means of violence through securitisation or militarisation are enacted by the government, through SANParks and game reserves, on the community as a means to control behaviour through restricted access and movement.

6. Conclusion

In this chapter, we have made attempts to situate the voices of different people living around Kruger National Park in the context of militarised conservation space or arenas. In the process we have examined the meanings such people attach to nature in relation to the neoliberal environmentality and violence being perpetrated over them by the state and conservation actors in pursuit of the protection of rhino species and other mega fauna. From the narratives, voices and storytelling of local populations we can make the case as argued by Fletcher (2010) of viewing the complicity of conservation arenas in advancing neoliberal environmentality amongst populations adjacent to them. The Kruger National Park and its ancillary private game reserves are marketed to tourists as spaces to encounter endangered mega-fauna, including the rhino. This has consequences for how such arenas are governed, and regulate behaviour of local populations as witnessed in the case presented here.

Endnotes

[1] Sisal is a plant that was strategically planted along the border in order to create rough foliage that was regarded as impenetrable and would make it difficult for the Frelimo and MK forces to cross into the KNP (Lunstrum 2015).

[2] Interviews conducted with J5 in Justicia in July 2016.

[3] Interviews conducted with J1 in Justicia in July 2016.

[4] Interviews conducted with J7 in Justicia in July 2016.

5 Interviews conducted with J8 in Justicia in July 2016.
6 Interviews conducted with J6 in Justicia in July 2016.
7 Interviews conducted with J9 in Justicia in July 2016.

Acknowledgements

Funding for this research is gratefully acknowledged from the Andrew W. Mellon Foundation to the Environmental Humanities South graduate programme of the University of Cape Town (2014-2017) and the National Research Foundation of South Africa (rating support 2015-2020).

References

Annecke, W. and Masubelele, M. (2016) 'A review of the impact of militarisation: The case of rhino poaching in Kruger National Park, South Africa', *Conservation and Society*, Vol. 14, Issue 3, pp. 195–204.

Agincourt (MRC/Wits Rural Public Health and Health Transitions Research Unit) (2017) *Justicia Village Fact Sheet (Unpublished)*, Johannesburg: Agincourt

Brockington, D., Duffy, R. and Igoe, J. (2008) *Nature Unbound: Conservation, Capitalism and the Future of Protected Areas*, London: Earthscan.

Bryant, R. L. and Bailey, S. (1997) *Third World Political Ecology*, London: Psychology Press.

Büscher, B. (2016) 'Reassessing fortress conservation: New media and the politics of distinction in Kruger National Park', *Annals of the Association of American Geographers*, Vol. 106, Issue 1, pp. 114–129.

Büscher, B. and Dietz, T. (2005) 'Conjunctions of governance: The state and the conservation-development nexus in Southern Africa', *The Journal of Transdisciplinary Environmental Studies*, Vol. 4, No. 2, pp. 1–15.

Büscher, B. and Fletcher, R. (2018) 'Under pressure: Conceptualising political ecologies of green wars', *Conservation and Society*, Vol. 16,

Issue 2, pp. 105–113.

Büscher, B. and Ramutsindela, M. (2015) 'Green violence: Rhino poaching and the war to save Southern Africa's peace parks', *African Affairs*, Vol. 115, No. 458, pp. 1–22.

Carruthers, J. (1995) *The Kruger National Park: A Social and Political History*, Durban: University of Natal Press.

Dhandapani, S. (2015) 'Neo-liberal capitalistic policies in modern conservation and the ultimate commodification of nature', *Journal of Ecosystem and Ecography*, Vol. 5, Issue 2, pp. 2–6.

Dowie, M. (2009) *Conservation Refugees: The Hundred-Year Conflict between Global Conservation and Native Peoples*, Cambridge: MIT Press.

Duffy, R., St. John, F., Büscher, B. and Brockington, D. (2015) 'The militarisation of anti-poaching: Undermining long term goals?', *Environmental Conservation*, Vol. 42, No.4, pp. 345–348.

Duffy, R., Massé, F., Smidt, E., Marijnen, E., Büscher, B., Verweijen, J., Ramutsindela, M., Simlai, T., Joanny, L. and Lunstrum, E. (2019) 'Why we must question the militarisation of conservation', *Biological Conservation*, Vol. 232, pp. 66–73.

Fletcher, R. (2010) 'Neoliberal environmentality: Towards a poststructuralist political ecology of the conservation debate', *Conservation and Society*, Vol. 8, Issue 3, pp. 171–181.

Foucault, M. (1997) *Ethics: Subjectivity and Truth*, New York: The New Press.

————— (2008) *The Birth of Biopolitics*, New York: Palgrave Macmillan.

Humphreys, J. and Smith, M. L. R. (2014) 'The "Rhinofication" of South African security', *International Affairs*, Vol. 90, Issue 4, pp. 795–818.

Lunstrum, E. (2014) 'Green militarisation: Anti-poaching efforts and the spatial contours of Kruger National Park', *Annals of the Association of American Geographers*, Vol. 104, Issue 4, pp. 816–832.

————— (2015) 'Conservation meets militarisation in Kruger National Park: Historical encounters and complex legacies', *Conservation and Society*, Vol. 13, Issue 4, pp. 816–832.

Murombedzi, J. (1999) 'Devolution and stewardship in Zimbabwe's CAMPFIRE Program', *Journal of International Development*, Vol. 11, Issue 2, pp. 287–293.

Najam, A. (2005) 'Developing countries and global environmental governance: From contestation to participation to engagement', *International Environmental Agreements: Politics, Law and Economics*, Vol. 5, Issue 3, pp. 303–321.

Ngwato, T. P. (2012) 'Together apart: Migration, integration and spatialised identities in South African border villages', *Geoforum*, Vol. 43, No. 3, pp. 561–572.

Parks, S. and Gowdy, J. (2013) 'What have economists learned about valuing nature? A review essay', *Ecosystems Services*, Vol. 3, pp. 1–10.

Rogers, P. J. (2002) 'Governance/governmentality, wildlife conservation and protected area management: A comparative study of Eastern and Southern Africa', *Proceedings of the African Studies Association 45th Annual Meeting*, 5 December 2002, Washington DC: Bates College.

Rose, N., O'Malley, P. and Valverde, M. (2006) 'Governmentality', *Annual Review of Law and Social Science*, Vol. 2, pp. 83–104.

Sithole, S. S. (2018) 'Understanding the impact of militarised conservation on communities neighbouring the Kruger National Park, South Africa', Master's thesis, University of Cape Town.

Chapter 3

Neoliberalisation of Environmental Conservation through Spectacularisation and Eventisation: The Case of the Maasai Olympics in Southern Kenya

Toshio Meguro

1. Introduction

1-1. Neoliberal Conservation and the Spectacle

As explained in the Introduction, the paradigm of conservation changed around the 1990s. By the 1990s, a conventional top-down, technocratic conservation approach had become criticised for ignoring local people, and a new approach came to the fore, which took a serious view of local benefits, rights and livelihoods, and dialogue and collaboration with local people. As a result of this change, the possibility of creating an *arena*, a place for local people and those who practise conservation to have a dialogue, has increased (Yamakoshi et al. [eds] 2016). Meanwhile, in the 2000s, the neoliberalisation[1] of environmental conservation attracted a growing interest among scholars, and its impact on local people became a matter of concern.

Although neoliberal approaches often insist that they are taking a line of 'community-based' (e.g. Barnes and Child [eds] 2014; Child [ed.] 2004, 2019; Suich et al. [eds] 2009), it is argued that the permeation of neoliberalism into the realm of conservation, like ecotourism, enabled several contradictions to occur, such as the commodification of nature and alienation of local people from it, the global circulation of capital and a widening gap between the rich and the poor, and the rise of an anti-politics of neoliberal ideology that idealises neoliberalism as the sole solution to contemporary environmental problems (Büscher et al. [eds] 2014; Büscher et al. 2012; Holmes and Cavanagh 2016). Also, the problem of the representation of nature has been argued to be an issue strongly related to the contradictions above.

Jim Igoe has led the discussion about representation in neoliberal conservation. Following Debord (1995), Igoe (2010: 376) defines *spectacle* as 'the mediation of relationships between people and the environment by images', and argues that, because of the exacerbation of emergent information technologies, an increasing number of images of 'the spectacle of nature' are circulating globally. The examples of 'the spectacle of nature' by Igoe (2010) include documentary films depicting African national parks as 'wild paradises'; popular and emotional wildlife stories and images circulated by conservation NGOs, tourism companies and various famous and influential individuals through the Internet and social network services; and various campaigns developed by global companies like McDonald's, Dream Works, Coca-Cola in developed countries.

'The spectacle of nature' is imaginary, but it makes an impact on environmental politics and human–environment relationships in the real world (Igoe 2010). On one hand, when it is a carefully elaborated 'spectacle', people believe that it is a reality and will have a sense of connections to nature. However, it is the image and not the reality. A typical example of such a misunderstanding is that all local people living there are 'ecologically noble savages', who are natural conservationists prioritising the inheritance of tradition and environ-mental conservation over modern development. In this way, it exacerbates the 'separation'[2] of people from the actual nature. On the other hand, when 'the spectacle of nature' is a co-product of conservation, consumerism, and entertainment, it excites those who receive and enjoy the images to neoliberal practices such as purchasing campaign commodities and other 'eco/green' goods and services.

1-2. Maasai Olympics as Spectacle

In the 21st century, media coverage of Africa has changed drastically (Bunce et al. [eds] 2017a; Gallagher [ed.] 2015). On the one hand, Bunce et al. (2017b) explain that, because of the increase in local employment in the media industry and the development of information technologies, there has been a dramatic increase in the amount of information provided by African people. On the other hand, Igoe (2010) concludes that the representation of nature is governed by global powers via the continuing alienation of local people. Both are similar in recognising that the media representation of Africa is changing and increasing, but there is a sharp contrast between these two articles regarding whether the recent media images of Africa are produced increasingly by local people or still dominated by global actors.

In light of these discussions, this chapter takes the case of the 'Maasai Olympics', a sporting event held by a conservation NGO in southern Kenya. This is an event that involves 'spectacle' and has attracted global attention and financial support so far. Recently, it has been changing so as to enhance the degree of spectacles. This chapter focuses on such changes and aims at examining what points and forms today's neoliberalisation of environmental conservation has reached. Additionally, this chapter considers such changes from the perspective of 'African Potentials'.

In the following section, the outline of the target case and region will be explained. Next, based on observations from the second (2014) to the fourth event (2018),[3] the changes in the Maasai Olympics over time are summarised. Then, the meaning of such changes is examined through the lens of spectacle and event. The final section examines how neoliberalism is present in the spectacularisation and eventisation of the Maasai Olympics, as well as whether it unleashes or suppresses the potentials of the Maasai people.

2. Outline of Case and Target[4]

2-1. Outline of the Case: 'An Innovative Conservation Strategy'

The Maasai Olympics is a sporting event for the Maasai 'warriors', who are often associated with the image of traditional lion killers by the mass media. It is held by a conservation NGO, Big Life Foundation (BLF), which is active around Amboseli area in southern Kenya. The venue is the Sidai Oleng Wildlife Sanctuary located on the south-eastern part of that area. Since the first Maasai Olympics held on 15 December 2012, it has been held on a weekend in

81

December every other year. It is named 'Olympics', but it has not obtained permission to use that name from the International Olympic Committee. According to a staff member of the BLF, at the time this event was being planned, the 30th Olympic Games was being held in London, which inspired the use of the term 'Olympics' in naming the event.

The purpose of this event is to have the Maasai people stop lion hunting. In Maasai society, unmarried adult men (*ilmurran*) could gain lifelong fame by hunting male lions. To cease this customary practice, the Maasai Olympics has been held as an alternative competition and an opportunity for honour. There are six events: 200-m run, 800-m run, 5,000-m run, javelin throw, club throw and high jump. Around 20 to 30 young Maasai men take part in each event: in total, there are over one hundred participants in the six events. They compete in four teams organised on the basis of four traditional villages (*imanyat*). The first to third placed players in each event are awarded gold, silver or bronze medals, together with monetary prizes. The team to which the prizewinner belongs is given a score according to the ranking, and the team with the largest total wins. The winning team will be awarded a trophy and bulls worth several thousand US dollars. In addition, there are several prizes for individuals and teams.

Figure 1. Scene of 5,000-m run (10 December 2016)

Figure 2. Scene of high jump (10 December 2016)

On the website, it is described as 'an innovative conservation strategy'. The 'innovative' aspects of this strategy consist in usage of new methods in the context of conservation, namely sports, and in an attempt to change the tradition of Maasai society. While the BLF expressly denies that lion hunting is 'no longer culturally acceptable', the Maasai Olympics is explained as 'an organised Maasai sports competition based upon traditional warrior skills' and will lead to the protection and inheritance of Maasai's 'noble way of life, traditional land, and ancient culture'. Igoe and Brockington (2007: 442) explain that 'neoliberalised conservation often devalues local environmental knowledge and undermines local environmental initiatives'. The positive attitude of the BLF towards the Maasai's tradition, except lion hunting, presents a stark contrast to such a negative evaluation generally found in neoliberal conservation.

The Maasai Olympics is open to the public. It is free to watch and, in addition to the guests invited by the BLF and the press members who come to report, the local Maasai people and other Kenyans (both the Maasai and the non-Maasai) who live near the venue gather at the Olympics site. Photography and videography are also free, and the news of the Maasai Olympics is broadcast by a global news networks based in the United States, United Kingdom, France, Qatar, China and so on.

2-2-1. Maasai and Amboseli

The Maasai Olympics targets Maasai 'warriors' living in the Amboseli area. The Maasai is an ethnic group whose primary settlement is in arid and semi-arid areas extending from central Kenya to northern Tanzania in East Africa. They have been cattle pastoralists, and their livelihood activities are diversifying today. The fact that the Maasai society is organised on the basis of an age system – consisting of age grades and age groups – remains the same today. Generally, Maasai men are divided into three age grades: boys (who have not yet undergone adult rituals and have not formed an age group), youths (who have experienced the adult rituals but are in the process of organising an age group and contraindicated in marriage) and elders (who have formally formed an age group and are usually married).

The word 'warriors' is applied to the youth grade. By convention, they have been tasked with protecting their community from external enemies and have hunted wild animals that harm humans and livestock. The lion is a special animal in Maasai culture, and the first man to throw a spear to a quarry during a collective hunt has earned a lifetime honour. However, hunting is extremely rare in Kenya today, including in the Amboseli area, as a result of strict poaching crackdowns and the spread of school education as well as changes in the Maasai society.

In this chapter, 'Amboseli area' refers to the South Kajiado Constituency (6,356.3 km²) in Kajiado County, located in southern Kenya. The constituency is equivalent to the territory that one Maasai group called Loitokitok has laid out. Most of the area is arid and semi-arid, with an average annual rainfall of less than 400 mm. Around the centre of the area, Amboseli National Park was established in 1974 despite the objection and resistance by local people. It covers 390.2 km², surrounding Amboseli Swamp, where water is not depleted year-round. It is a habitat for a variety of wildlife, including African elephants, and thus wildlife conservation and tourism development have been promoted throughout the 20th century.

2-2-2. BLF Active in Amboseli Area

The BLF, the organiser of the Maasai Olympics, is a conservation NGO founded in 2010, with headquarters in the Amboseli area and branch offices in the United States, Canada and the United Kingdom. The co-founders were three Caucasians, one of whom started conservation activities in the Amboseli area in the 1990s and opened a luxury ecolodge in the 2000s. He was recognised for his many years of work and was awarded the Prince William Award for Conservation in Africa in 2006. Another is a New York-based male social entrepreneur who has been helping the first co-founder's conservation activities for more than 20 years. The third, a world-renowned photographer and film and music director, visited the Amboseli area for a photoshoot and learned about the problem of poaching of African elephants. It led to the foundation of the BLF.

The mission of the BLF is 'On the ground in Africa, partnering with communities to protect the nature for the benefit of all', obviously in line with the new paradigm of community-based approaches. The main activities and achievements are crackdown on elephant poaching. Other areas of activities are such as bush meat, wildlife damage and community-support initiatives (scholarships, employment opportunities, school facilities, etc.). The Maasai Olympics is one such community-support activity.

The presence of the BLF is extremely strong in the Amboseli area. In Kenya, the Kenya Wildlife Service (KWS) is responsible for national parks and wildlife. However, in the Amboseli area, the KWS routinely covers only national parks; thus, the BLF is conducting patrols and other conservation activities outside the park, the land where local Maasai people live their daily life; according to its annual report of 2019 (BLF n.a.), the BLF covers 16 million acres (around 650 million km^2). The KWS has only a few dozen employees and a few vehicles, while the BLF has 269 rangers, 14 vehicles and two aeroplanes. Such substantial equipment depends on the size of its income.[5] In other words, under a globally recognisable co-founder, the BLF is raising funds on a global scale and trying to put local areas not under the jurisdiction of public authorities but under their own control.

When the Maasai Olympics is featured in various media, its 'innovative' features – to praise the Maasai tradition and help them to carry it on while abandoning hunting alone as an unacceptable culture – have been emphasised following the explanation of the BLF. In such an explanation, the local Maasai community is described as assenting to wildlife conservation and cultural change, and is credited with initiating the Maasai Olympics.

However, local facts that are contrary to such popular accounts have already been identified by preceding studies. For example, Meguro (2017) reveals the fact that while the local Maasai youths represent themselves in public as traditional animal lovers who approve the Maasai Olympics, it is their strategy in order to obtain benefits.

Also, Meguro (2019) examines whether BLF's explanation of the Maasai culture and the Maasai Olympics reflects local opinion. According to Meguro (2019: 100–102), claims on the official website of the Maasai Olympics are summarised into four points: (1) Lion hunting is a rite of passage, (2) the Maasai Olympics is a project based on the community and its tradition, (3) the local community accept the Maasai Olympics as their culture, and (4) without conserving wildlife, it is impossible for the Maasai people to maintain their culture. All four of these have been rejected outright by local leaders.

To begin, both the leaders of youths and elders were not aware of what kind of description the BLF had given on the website. After learning the BLF's explanation, they unanimously stated that (1) lion hunting is neither a rite of passage nor an obligatory practice for Maasai youths, (2) the Maasai Olympics does not follow the traditional procedures of the Maasai society (especially in terms of consensus building through dialogue), (3) the Maasai Olympics does not have the same importance as traditional rites of passage (e.g. *enkipaata*, *eunoto*, and *olngesher*), and (4) they (the Maasai people in the Amboseli area) do not maintain their culture for the good of wildlife. Their opinion was that the Maasai Olympics was initiated by the BLF and some elders, and no community-wide discussions and agreements have been made on the abolition of lion hunting, nor has the local community recognised any particular cultural significance in the Maasai Olympics and, what is more, they never admitted that there is any relationship between the preservation and inheritance of tradition and the conservation of wildlife.

It is common for today's Amboseli area to support the importance of wildlife conservation and the potential for tourism development as claimed by the BLF (Meguro 2014, 2019). Elders are positive about the changes in Maasai culture, calling Christianity, schooling and the market economy 'development'. Meanwhile, youths want to continue the Maasai Olympics, but the primary motivation for youths to take part in the event is prize money, not conservation (Meguro 2017, 2019). The youths do not think the stoppage of lion hunting is due to the Maasai Olympics. Their understanding is that as a result of severe crackdown activities by the KWS and the BLF and the spread of school education since the 1990s, local youths had come to find no meaning in spending time and labour in traditional hunting even before the beginning of the Maasai Olympics (Meguro 2019). They join the Maasai Olympics not because the event is based on their initiatives and they are eager for conservation but because they are invited by its organiser and aspire to win prizes.

3. Changes of Maasai Olympics

Among the constants of the five Maasai Olympics thus far, such things that have not been changed are the timing, period and place of the event, the six-event and four-team format of competition, the medal and prize money for the top three participants of each event and the trophy and bulls for the winning team. On the other hand, there have been many changes. Here, four changes are discussed that are considered important in relation to the subject of this chapter. They are explained in order: (1) increasing the amount and types of prize money with the acquisition of large sponsors, (2) establishing a new 'best dress award' that exudes 'traditional' attire, (3) changing the layout of the high jump competition to take into account the sight of invited guests, and (4) replacement of participating teams due to conflicts over the distribution of conservation benefits.

3-1. Change (1): Increase in Prizes

The amount and type of prize money have increased significantly since the fourth Maasai Olympics in 2018. The prize money awarded to the first to third placed players in each event used to be Ksh. (Kenya Shillings) 20,000, Ksh. 15,000, and Ksh. 10,000, respectively.[6] In the fourth Maasai Olympics, the prize money for all places increased by Ksh. 5,000. In addition, for the same event, Ksh. 100,000 is awarded to all four teams as a prize for participation, and Ksh. 100,000 is awarded as the best dress award to one team and a female, respectively, who wears the most 'traditional' and beautiful outfit. Maasai youths are especially happy about the participation award, because, until it was instituted, if they failed to reach the third place as an individual or win the first place as a team, they gained no benefits despite spending their time and effort training. The youths were, in fact, quite dissatisfied with the previous situation.

The reason why prize money could be expanded is the acquisition of new large sponsors. When the first Maasai Olympics was held, the BLF stated that it would host the Maasai Olympics every year. However, because funding was not raised at the expected level, the second Maasai Olympics was held two years later. Except for a handful of sponsors, such as the Chester Zoo and the National Geographic Society, many sponsors had changed. Under such a circumstance, it was impossible for the BLF to increase the prize. However, the Disney Conservation Fund and the Born Free Foundation joined the sponsorship in the fourth event.

The Disney Conservation Fund is a division of the world-class entertainment company, the Walt Disney Company, and the Born Free Foundation, which is originated from the movie *Born Free*, is an NGO focusing on animal welfare and reintroduction with global influence (cf. Martin 2012). A banner of the Born Free Foundation was set up at the venue of the fourth event, and representatives of both organisations had the opportunity to speak during the award ceremony. It is unclear how these organisations became aware of the Maasai Olympics, but it can be said that the addition of two large sponsors was the outcome of increased media exposure to date[7] and led to an increase in prize money.

3-2. Change (2): Best Dress Award

When the prizes increased in the fourth event, the best dress award was particularly apparent from the perspective of spectacle. Of the four teams that participated in the fourth Maasai Olympics, one team wore red cloth and ornaments sewn with a large number of colourful beads. Such attire had never been seen before, and for this they received the best dress award. Since their entry in the Maasai Olympics' opening parade, that team was frequently photographed by many people and also received many camera shots during the commendation ceremony. In addition, a small girl who was selected as a woman's best dress award winner also had a decorated cloth and accessories with a large number of beads that I had never seen in my fieldwork so far. She was selected at the awards ceremony by a European woman, an individual large sponsor of the event.

Figure 3. Winners of the best dress award (15 December 2018)

Players wear bibs in the colours (red, yellow, green, blue) determined for each team. On this occasion, some players wore beaded jewellery on top of them for the competition, but many of them wore only bibs. For the award ceremony, many players changed their dress from bibs to Western clothing such as jerseys and T-shirts. Such Western-style athletes could be the subject of photography, but the sheer number of photographs taken of the winner of the best dress award demonstrated that their appearance attracted many more spectators. Since the best dress award was first set up in the fourth Maasai Olympics, it can be said that a new spectacle was born there.

3-3. Change (3): Change of High Jump Layout

In Maasai society, young men used to sing and dance in a circle, come forth to its centre and jump high in turn as an everyday form of entertainment as well as a collective and physical act generating intense excitement during important rituals. Even now, it is often practised in traditional villages. It is called the 'Maasai Jump' or 'Maasai Dance' by mass media, and has become a stereotypical image of Maasai. The high jump event at the Maasai Olympics – in which players jump on the spot and compete for how high the head can touch a string that is stretched overhead between two wooden poles – is based on it. It excites not only outsiders but also Maasai people. Since the first time, it has been the last event, and has shaped the climax of the Maasai Olympics.

Until the third Maasai Olympics, there was no clear boundary between the audience and the athletes. Therefore, the crowd, comprising mainly Maasai people, was able to come as close as just next to the high jump players to cheer them on. The BLF staff members ordered the audience to step back many times, but they soon returned to close proximity. These audience members often blocked the view of others.

From the third Maasai Olympics, a fence was set up several metres around the competition space, and the general public was barred from entering it. This measure was intended to ensure that guests sitting in chairs in tents could comfortably watch the game. The BLF set up tents in the venue, and many chairs underneath them were reserved for invited guests. The guests here included those who were (potential) sponsors and supporters of the Maasai Olympics and the BLF, both foreigners and Kenyans serving on BLF committees, those who became sponsors of the Maasai Olympics as individuals or with organisations, representatives of organisations working for conservation and tourism in the Amboseli area and Kenyan political elites such as local and national politicians. Along with the installation of the fence, the place and direction of jumping were adjusted so that the guests sitting in chairs could see the event from a shorter distance and directly in front.

Figure 4. Scene of high jump in the fourth Maasai Olympics (15 December 2018)

While this change guaranteed a comfortable viewing for the guests, it deprived the local people of enjoyment and excitement. At the third and fourth Maasai Olympics, only a few people could secure space around the guest tent during the high jump. Because of the fence, it was difficult for the rest of the audience not only to see the participants' leaps well but also to hear youths singing traditional songs that encourage players. Beforehand, the audience had the sense of unity with the competitors as they stood close and listened to the songs. However, such an experience became impossible. During the high jump at the fourth Maasai Olympics, many Maasai audience members just leaned against the fence, not knowing what to do with their hands. Changes in the high jump competition layout clearly put guests' gaze and enjoyment ahead of those of community.

3-4. Change (4): Participating Teams

The last change differs from (1) to (3) in that it was made in secret. Since the first Maasai Olympics, the four teams were formed according to the four traditional villages that had historically been established in the east, west, north and south of the Amboseli area based on clan affiliations. These traditional villages are places where Maasai youths live together and have been considered eminently important in Maasai culture. Today, an increasing number of youths go to school instead of living in the villages. However, the tradition of establishing four villages has been inherited till now, and tens of young people are living there. Also, when there is an important meeting and ritual, the majority of youth gather there, and those who attend school live with their peers in the villages during long holidays. Because the competition involving the four teams is based on such traditional villages, not only young people but also women and elders cheer on their clan team, rejoicing in the results.

At the fourth Maasai Olympics, one of the participating teams was different from the original four. One of the four original teams ceased to participate owing to conflict between a political leader in the area, called Olgulului, where their traditional village is located, and the BLF over the sharing of conservation benefits. Consequently, that political leader banned the BLF from operating in the area. Therefore, the BLF was unable to visit the traditional village in that area, and the team of Olgulului was unable to participate in the fourth Maasai Olympics. In response to this situation, the BLF had formed a new team with young people living in Eselenkei, a remote area where there was no traditional village, and held the fourth Olympics as a four-team competition as before. As a Maasai tradition, youths in the Eselenkei area also belong to one of four traditional villages, and some of them had joined the Maasai Olympics as members of those teams. This was not publicly explained and the newly entered Eselenkei team, which was not rooted in the traditional village, was awarded the best dress award for their most 'traditional' appearance by the BLF.

According to the leader of youths in the Amboseli area, the change in participating teams is not problematic. Rather, he said that it was good because this was the first time for the most members of the Eselenkei team to join the Maasai Olympics. He meant that it was better to hold the fourth Maasai Olympics with four teams including Eselenkei rather than to have it with the original three teams, because more youths could join it. On one hand, the youth leader, who belongs to the traditional village of Olgulului, resolutely opposed the idea of establishing a new village in Eselenkei because it was against their tradition. On the other hand, he expressed no criticism of the BLF's formation of a new team without consulting him or of its participation and reception of the best dress award.

He understood that youths in the Eselenkei area also wanted to join the Maasai Olympics, and he did not think it was a problem to form a new team regardless of the traditional villages. Therefore, he did not find any fault in the BLF's response to the nonparticipation of the Olgulului team. He placed priority on giving more youths an opportunity to take part in the event rather than organising it just based on the four villages. However, it must be remembered that the BLF, who continues to publicly lay emphasis on the traditionality and 'innovativeness' of the Maasai Olympics, concealed both the existence of a conservation-related friction with a local community and the non-traditionality and artificiality of the team that won the best dress award.

4. Spectacularisation and Eventisation of Maasai Olympics

4-1. Further Spectacularisation of Maasai Olympics

The Maasai Olympics is an athletic competition or sporting event. According to Besnier et al. (2017: 3), record breaking is the core of the modern sports, and thus good performance and record updates are essential for the satisfaction of audiences and the success of an event. From this point of view, it is doubtful whether the Maasai Olympics is regarded as a successful event because it is hard to say that the records of the Maasai youth are so wonderful. For example, when the championship records of 200-m run, 800-m run and javelin throw of the IAAF World Youth Championships in Athletics are 20" 34, 1' 44" 08 and 83.16 m, the records of the winner of these events in the second Maasai Olympics are 24" 31, 2' 10" and 52.90 m (Meguro 2017). Despite the name of Olympics, records are not at world-class level.

However, the fact remains that the Maasai Olympics has gained global attention and financial support. One obvious reason is that it is a sport event of Maasai, who are globally known as a symbol of

Africa, or 'the most beautiful, noble, martial, endangered, and animal-like' tribe (Hughes 2006: 288). In truth, one foreign reporter visiting the Maasai Olympics said, 'this is [an event of] Maasai. So, if I can take a good photo, it will be an article'. His statement suggests that because such an image of Maasai people is spread worldwide, even one photo of 'traditional Maasai warriors' is enough to attract attention and satisfy the curiosity of global citizens. Or, the fact is that few media describe the records of Maasai youths although almost all reports have the pictures of 'traditional Maasai warriors'.

'Traditional Maasai warriors', wearing red cloth and ornaments decorated with colourful beads constitute a spectacle. Many of the audience members at the Maasai Olympics, including foreigners, tourists and press as well as Kenyans and local Maasai people used mobile phones and smartphones to take a picture of the dynamic and lively motion of the 'traditional Maasai warriors'. Their behaviour clearly showed that the Maasai Olympics is an amazing spectacle. On top of that, as written in the previous section, the Maasai Olympics is becoming more spectacular, and it is important to note that such spectacularisation is advanced by the host of the event, bearing the gaze of the guest in mind.

In that process, the 'Maasai tradition', the core of the spectacle, is manipulated by the same host, not by the Maasai people themselves. Among the changes seen in the previous section, (3) changing the layout of the high jump competition is a measure that allows the guest to gaze at the spectacle clearly and comfortably. In addition, while (2) the new establishment of the best dress award is being rolled out as a new spectacle, the fact that (4) the team that won the award was newly built with the replacement of the original team, and is not based on the traditional villages as others is concealed. Here, the visible 'Maasai tradition' of dressing is recognised and praised as a spectacle, while the invisible 'Maasai tradition' of the clannism is ignored.

This 'spectacularisation of tradition' with the guest in mind is a sort of 'appropriation of representation' (Büscher et al. 2012; Holmes and Cavanagh 2016), and a form of alienation of the 'community'. However, when the funds collected are used as an award for participation, the Maasai youths did not regard the joining of a new team that was not based on a traditional village and its winning of the best dress award as problematic. In other words, they did not give a first priority to hold an event based on their tradition. Rather, they understood that outsiders were expecting 'Maasai tradition', and accepted the way the BLF organised the Maasai Olympics and represented the Maasai people as traditional 'spectacle' as long as it brought them benefits.

4-2. Eventisation of Maasai Olympics as Spectacle

The website of the BLF has a number of spectacle images, such as artistic photos of wildlife and landscapes, pictures of (body parts from) wildlife killed by poachers and the smiles of children receiving support from the BLF. Besides them, there are many pictures of the Maasai Olympics, and thus one can get information on that website. Under such circumstances, the BLF has established a new website solely for publicisation of the Maasai Olympics. This website offers detailed information and many more pictures of the event. By such a measure, the BLF progresses the spectacularisation of the Maasai Olympics; simultaneously, the Maasai Olympics is becoming an established event for guests and spectators alike.

Here, the word *event* is introduced from the argument of 'mega-events' (Roche 2000) in the research area of sociology of sport. Roche (2000: 1) defines *mega-events* as 'modern society's great "parades" and "shows"'. Roche speaks of 'large-scale cultural (including commercial and sporting) events which have a dramatic character, mass popular appeal and international significance' (Roche 2000: 1). As examples of mega-events, Roche (2000) mentions the Modern Olympic Games, World Fairs and FIFA World Cups. In the context of conservation, the Maasai Olympics cannot be said to have a global recognition of its 'international importance'. However, the fact is that public attention and financial support are gained globally, demonstrating its spectacle image has 'a dramatic character [and] mass popular appeal'. Also, the use of the name Olympics certainly has the power to create the impression that the Maasai Olympics is a 'large-scale cultural event' (cf. Horne and Whannel 2016; Roche 2000, 2017).

The important point here is that a mega-event has a *host*. A mega-event is an opportunity to provide some sort of spectacle, and thus its host carefully prepares and aims to provide the guest with the best experience. There, the aim is to provide or experience spectacles, and a 'host–guest' relationship is a major premise that is rarely seen (or needed) in other conservation activities. According to Besnier et al. (2017: 195), becoming a host of the modern Olympic Games is a 'self-conscious cultural performance'. To host a mega-event entails incurring vast expenditure and, therefore, it is criticised as being economically irrational. However, Besnier et al. (2017: 195) stress the fact that it is based on the logic of the gift economy rather than the market. When the host provides dedicated hospitality to the guest in fulfilling its role, it consequently indicates that the host deserves a 'world-class' status. If successful, it will be possible to raise capital globally after the event.

In the case of the Maasai Olympics, the BLF treats the guests in various ways to facilitate their enjoyment of the games. It does not immediately make corresponding profits, but gathering a large number of guests will not only bolster the prestige of the BLF as the host and the Maasai Olympics itself; it will also allow the BLF to have the expectation that if it show guests hospitality, they might give a return present in some ways. At the fourth Maasai Olympics, the person who selected a winner of the best dress award for a female was an elderly European woman who continued to be a large individual sponsor. The event organiser suddenly called and asked her to select the most beautiful woman in the award ceremony. In doing this, she suddenly gained the public's attention, her dedication was praised and she was instantly positioned at the centre of the spectacle in the form of a winner selector. This may encourage further gifts or reciprocity from the guest who received psychological and intangible reward (for her contribution) of being put under the spotlight in the spectacle by the host. When the Maasai Olympics becomes more of a spectacle, from a different point of view, it becomes an event that assumes the presence of guests.[8]

4-3. Neoliberalness of Maasai Olympics

The Maasai Olympics is a spectacle event that both overlaps and does not overlap with 'the spectacle of nature' discussed in previous studies. First, the difference is that the most often referred to 'spectacle of nature' is the commodification of nature for the international tourism industry (Igoe 2010). The Maasai Olympics, on the other hand, can be described as a 'spectacle of culture' or a 'spectacle of tradition', which asks for charitable contribution but do not entail any direct commercial and instant profit-making activities. Second, when nature became the target of neoliberal conservation, historical connections between local societies and their environments are generally ignored or, worse, disapproved of (Büscher et al. 2012; Holmes and Cavanagh 2016). Contrary to such a negative attitude towards localness, the Maasai Olympics admits that the co-existence of the lion and the Maasai people on the same land is a historical relationship that should be maintained from the past to the future. Focusing on these points, the Maasai Olympics can be said to be different from 'the spectacle of nature' that involves the alienation of local people.

On the other hand, the Maasai Olympics includes phenomena that characterise neoliberal conservation. In other words, the acceleration and expansion of the global capital flow by taking advantage of the spectacle, the arbitral manipulation of local representation and the dissimulation of its contradiction and deceitful self-esteem that it is the only solution to the conservation problem (Büscher et al. [eds] 2014; Büscher et al. 2012; Holmes and Cavanagh 2016). As a further consideration, it must be remembered that one of the co-founders of the BLF who has long been involved in conservation activities runs a luxury eco-lodge in the Amboseli area; thus, it is difficult to completely separate the BLF's conservation activities from the business of wildlife-based tourism there. Today, the link between philanthropical celebrities and the private sector is increasing in relation to environmental conservation, dynamism that accelerates global flows of capital and creates new economic opportunities (Brockington 2009, 2014).

Neoliberalism is usually defined in strong relation to market dynamics. However, it includes various processes beside marketisation (Holmes and Cavanagh 2016) and its influences reach political, social and ecological dimensions (Büscher et al. 2012), some of which are the results of 'the spectacle of nature' (Igoe 2010). To analyse the Maasai Olympics with reference to these processes and effects, and to consider the relationship between the element of market economy in an international tourism business and that of gift economy in NGO activities, is a future project.

5. Concluding Remarks from the Perspective of African Potentials

The Maasai Olympics is an event with a spectacle representation, and the spectacle was strengthened in the past while attracting global attention and support. In this chapter, such changes are considered as owing to the process of spectacularisation and eventisation, and the Maasai Olympics is compared with the discussion in the previous studies, especially about 'the spectacle of nature'. As a result, it is confirmed that, at first glance, there is a contrast in terms of commercialisation and alienation, but it is possible to point out the Maasai Olympics has such features noted for neoliberal conservation as the acceleration of global capital flow, the appropriation of local representation, the concealment of contradictions on the ground and the forming of alliances with celebrities. When the concept of neoliberalism is controversial, some may find it uncomfortable to discuss the Maasai Olympics as an example of neoliberal conservation. In response, I would like to note the fact that the BLF is no less than a conservation NGO, and it clearly states that the Maasai Olympics is 'conservation through sports' and 'innovative conservation strategies'. In other words, today's neoliberal conservation is trying to accelerate the global capital circulation by calling these not-conservation-like activities 'conservation'.

Finally, I would like to consider the case of the Maasai Olympics from the perspective of 'African Potentials'. Yamakoshi et al. (eds) (2016) argue that 'community-based' approaches that have become popular since the 1990s have increased the possibilities for the formation of 'arenas (places for dialogue)'. The BLF has emphasised that the Maasai Olympics is 'community-based', but at the scene of it, with spectacularisation and eventisation, Maasai 'warriors' are more like objects for viewing and shooting as spectacles (cf. Bruner 2004; Roche 2017) rather than persons to dialogue with in the *arena*. In that setting, the basic doctrine of 'community-based' approaches such as participation and dialogue are lost. It is Maasai tradition 'staged' (cf. MacCannell 1973; Roche 2017) by the host of the event that is presented as the spectacle before the eyes of the guest. Meguro (2019) reports that the local Maasai people have materialised their agencies as often as opportunity allows, but here I would like to point out in closing that despite the increased local benefits and popularity, the Maasai Olympics promotes neoliberal capital circulation and the spread of misrepresentation rather than the realisation of local potential and convivial coexistence through dialogue in the *arena*.

Endnotes

[1] When Igoe and Brockington (2007) began the argument about neoliberal conservation, they defined global neoliberalism as something that 'revolves around the restructuring of the world to facilitate the spread of free-markets' (Igoe and Brockington 2007: 433). Thereafter, in their review article on neoliberal conservation, Büscher et al. (2012: 5) define neoliberalism as 'a political ideology that aims to subject political, social, and ecological affairs to capitalist market dynamics'. Or, Holmes and Cavanagh (2016) review a number of previous studies, and argue that neoliberalism is 'an ongoing and dynamic process ... which proceeds in uneven and variegated ways in different empirical contexts', which includes at least one of these five processes: marketisation, commodification, privatisation, financialisation and decentralisation. In this chapter, the term neoliberalism is used according to the definition of these two review articles, that is, the process of change based on a particular ideology.

[2] The issue of neoliberalism and representation is reviewed under the expression of 'representation and spectacle' (Holmes and Cavanagh 2016) and 'appropriation and misrepresentation' (Büscher et al. 2012). On the other hand, Igoe (2010: 7–10) explained that there are 'three facets of separation': 'dissociation', 'control' and 'commodification'.

[3] The author has conducted field research in Amboseli area intermittently since 2005, visiting and observing all Maasai Olympics Games except the first one, and has conducted interviews with stakeholders.

[4] The information in this section is obtained from the official website of the BLF (https://biglife.org/) and of the Maasai Olympics (https://www.maasaiolympics.com/), and also Meguro (2014, 2017, 2019).

[5] BLF's revenues in the fiscal year 2019 were approximately 3.39 billion US dollars, against expenditures of approximately 3.62 million US dollars, with a breakdown of 'contributions & grants' of approximately 95 per cent (around 3.22 million US dollars), 'in-kind contributions' of just over 4 per cent (about 150,000 US dollars) and 'other income' of just under 1 per cent (about 25,000 US dollars) (BLF n.a.). When Brockington (2009) raises the issue of 'the 10 largest conservation NGOs in sub-Saharan Africa,' the financial scale of the BLF is at the same level of the 10th largest NGO in sub-Saharan Africa, namely Dian Fossey Gorilla Fund.

[6] Since 2012, the exchange rate is one US dollar = Ksh. 85–105.

[7] In the official website of the Maasai Olympics, these two organisations are classified as 'gold sponsors' of the fourth Maasai Olympics, who contributed more than 25,000 US dollars.

[8] Although the BLF has developed various activities so far, there is not one that has become an event like the Maasai Olympics. The BLF usually shows appreciation to contributors and supporters just on its website and elsewhere, and has held no event to honour its supporters in front of local people and media outlets in an open manner.

Acknowledgements

This work was supported by JSPS KAKENHI Grant Numbers JP16H06318, JP17H01637 and JP17K13291.

References

Barnes, G. and Child, B. (eds) (2014) *Adaptive Cross-Scalar Governance of Natural Resources*, Oxon: Routledge.

Besnier, N., Brownell, S. and Carter, T. F. (2017) *Anthropology of Sport: Bodies, Borders, Biopolitics*, Berkeley: University of California Press.

Brockington, D. (2009) *Celebrity and the Environment: Fame, Wealth and Power in Conservation*, London: Zed Books.

————— (2014) 'Celebrity spectacle, post-democratic politics, and Nature™ Inc.', in B. Büscher, W. Dressler and R. Fletcher (eds) *Nature Inc.: Environmental Conservation in the Neoliberal Age*, Tucson: The University of Arizona Press, pp. 108–126.

Bruner, E. M. (2004) *Culture on Tour: Ethnographies of Travel*, Chicago: University of Chicago Press.

Bunce, M., Franks, S. and Paterson, C. (eds) (2017a) *Africa's Media Image in the 21st Century: From the 'Heart of Darkness' to 'Africa Rising'*, Oxon: Routledge.

————— (2017b) 'Introduction: A new Africa's media image?', in M. Bunce, S. Franks and C. Paterson (eds) *Africa's Media Image in the 21st Century: From the 'Heart of Darkness' to 'Africa Rising'*, Oxon: Routledge, pp. 1–13.

Büscher, B., Dressler, W. and Fletcher, R. (eds) (2014) *Nature Inc.: Environmental Conservation in the Neoliberal Age*, Tucson: The University of Arizona Press.

Büscher, B., Sullivan, S., Neves, K., Igoe, J. and Brockington, D. (2012) 'Towards a synthesized critique of neoliberal biodiversity conservation', *Capitalism Nature Socialism*, Vol. 23, Issue 2, pp. 4–30.

Child, B. (ed.) (2004) *Parks in Transition: Biodiversity, Rural Development and the Bottom Line*, London: Earthscan.

————— (2019) *Sustainable Governance of Wildlife and Community-Based Natural Resource Management*, Oxon: Routledge.

Debord, G. (1995) *The Society of Spectacle*, New York: Zone Books.

Gallagher, J. (ed.) (2015) *Image of Africa: Creation, Negotiation and Subversion*, Manchester: Manchester University Press.

Holmes, G. and Cavanagh, C. J. (2016) 'A review of the social impacts of neoliberal conservation: Formations, inequalities, contestations', *Geoforum*, Vol. 75, pp. 199–209.

Horne, J. and Whannel, G. (2016) *Understanding the Olympics*, Oxon: Routledge.

Hughes, L. (2006) '"Beautiful beasts" and brave warriors: The longevity of a Maasai stereotype', in L. Romanucci-Ross, G. A. de Vos, and T. Tsuda (eds) *Ethnic Identity: Problems and Prospects for the Twenty-First Century*, Lanham: AltaMira Press, pp. 264–294.

Igoe, J. (2010) *The Nature of Spectacle: On Images, Money, and Conserving Capitalism*, Tucson: The University of Arizona Press.

Igoe, J. and Brockington, D. (2007) 'Neoliberal conservation: A brief introduction', *Conservation and Society*, Vol. 5, No. 4, pp. 432–449.

MacCannell, D. (1973) '"Staged authenticity: Arrangements of social space in tourist settings', *American Journal of Sociology*, Vol. 79, No. 3, pp. 589–603.

Martin, G. (2012) *Game Changer: Animal Rights and the Fate of Africa's Wildlife*, Berkeley: University of California Press.

Meguro, T. (2014) 'Becoming conservationists, concealing victims: Conflict and positionings of Maasai, regarding wildlife conservation in Kenya', *African Study Monographs, Supplementary Issue*, Vol. 50, pp. 155–172.

———— (2017) 'Gaps between the innovativeness of the Maasai Olympics and the positionings of Maasai warriors', *Nilo-Ethiopian Studies*, Vol. 22, pp. 27–39.

———— (2019) 'The unchanged and unrepresented culture of respect in Maasai society', *African Study Monographs*, Vol. 40, No. 2-3, pp. 93–108.

Roche, M. (2000) *Mega-Events and Modernity: Olympics and Expo in the Growth of Global Culture*, London: Routledge.

———— (2017) *Mega-Events and Social Change: Spectacle, Legacy and Public Culture*, Manchester: Manchester University Press.

Suich, H., Child, B. and Spenceley, A. (eds) (2009) *Evolution and Innovation in Wildlife Conservation: Parks and Game Ranches to Transfrontier Conservation Areas*, Oxon: Earthscan.

Yamakoshi, G., Meguro, T. and Sato, T. (eds) (2016) *Who Owns African Nature? African Perspectives on the Future of Community-Based Conservation*, Kyoto: Kyoto University Press (in Japanese).

Chapter 4

Park Scouts/Rangers as Key Persons Connecting Local People and Park Authorities: The Case of Ethiopian Wildlife Protected Areas

Nobuko Nishizaki

1. Community-Based Conservation Approach of Global Neoliberalism

Since the United States President Ulysses S. Grant (1822–1885) signed the Yellowstone Park Act of 1872, which created the world's first national park, the national park system has been emulated by many countries as a model for protecting valuable natural environments. Currently, a vast swathe including about 15 per cent of the world's land area is managed as 'protected areas' (UNEP-WCMC and IUCN 2016). The method of enclosing land to establish such areas, which involved forced displacement and land grabbing, led to fierce resistance from the people living in their vicinity (Keller and Turel 1998).

In Africa, poaching for ivory had become rampant by the 1970s, revealing the failure of the 'fortress conservation approach'; thus, a community-based conservation (CBC) approach is gradually being adopted. In recent years, the neoliberal approach to conservation, which emphasises economics, has begun to be used to encourage the conservation of ecosystems, and, in some cases, it has been combined with forced displacement to 'achieve economic benefits' while emphasising community participation (Nishizaki 2014). Thus, the reality of CBC is difficult to visualise because of the complexity of the conservation approach.

In the first phase of the 'African Potentials' project, I proposed 'negotiation-based conflict resolution' as a way to avoid conflicts between conservation authorities and residents in the management of protected areas (Nishizaki 2014). The purpose of writing this paper was to examine the role of park rangers as communicators in Ethiopia's protected areas. Despite the variety of types of work done by park rangers in Africa, much attention has been paid to criticising the ranger system as a device for violence rather than to creating an *arena* for dialogue, one of the 'African Potentials' created by a CBC approach (see Introduction in this book). This is the reason why it is important to pay attention to the situation of the park rangers. The first part of this chapter reveals the diversity of the types of work done by park rangers in protected areas. The second part is an analysis of their 'African Potentials', namely 'interface function',[1] and includes a discussion about the contradictions inherent in CBC. I examine new efforts to resolve conflicts within communities and create a space for dialogue with conservation authorities, and I consider how to support individual efforts in this arena.[2]

2. Protected Areas and Park Rangers

In the United States, employees who work in protected areas to protect ecosystems are called 'rangers' or 'park rangers', and they have done extensive work in conservation. In Yellowstone National Park, full-time park rangers were not active from the beginning; rather, in the early days, the military patrolled the park (Manns 1980). According to Pennaz, who examined the history of US park rangers, they have assumed a variety of roles, including wildlife conservation work and law enforcement, in addition to being naturalists, hosts and entertainers (Pennaz 2017). The relative importance of the various roles has changed over time; for example, there have been violent incidents in parks and, after the terrorist attacks in New York City in 2001, the need to carry a gun has increased, however, in times of peace, they are strongly encouraged to be unarmed (ibid.).

In Africa, park rangers have often been dedicated to policing poachers since the national park system was introduced during colonial rule and because hunting pressure on African wildlife is still high. As national and state employees, park rangers receive the military training required for their duties, wear a uniform with a camouflage pattern and carry weapons to perform such duties. On the other hand, from the perspective of the local people, their violent behaviour has been criticised (Neumann 1998; Brockington 2002; Masse and Lunstrum 2015). Inhumane acts of violence, such as the 'shoot and kill' policy, have been justified as a 'necessary evil' to carry out conservation work, even in a democratic political context (Mogomotsi and Kefilwe 2017). The military personnel and techniques used to combat poaching are increasingly being enhanced and layered with border security, and have been referred to as 'green militarisation' and 'green violence', especially in the transboundary protected areas of the southern African countries (Lunstrum 2014, 2015; Büscher and Ramutsindela 2015; Shaw and Rademeyer 2016).

In some private/community-protected areas, independently hired rangers are provided with the same training, maintenance, weapons and uniforms as nationally employed ones. In some cases, they are responsible for providing economic benefits to the people living near protected areas, addressing human–wildlife conflicts (HWCs) and conducting wildlife-monitoring activities.

3. Ethiopian Park Scouts

Ethiopia's protected areas are divided into national parks, wildlife reserves, sanctuaries, national forest areas, biosphere reserves and community-protected areas, which cover about 14 per cent of the country. The people responsible for guarding the wildlife in protected areas in Ethiopia are called 'park scouts'.[3] When the new Constitution was enacted in 1995, the government promoted decentralisation, with the administrative divisions being the federal government, regions, zones and *woreda*; the provision related to the management of protected areas was amended to state that the federal government would be responsible for protected areas that straddle regional borders, and the regions would be responsible for the rest. Park scouts are employed by the federal/regional governments responsible for each protected area.

The main duty of the park scouts is to control poachers, and they mainly patrol the protected areas. In addition, in recent years, many tourists have come to Ethiopia (Nishizaki 2019), and some protected areas require visitors to be accompanied on safaris and to tourist sites by rangers to ensure their safety. Rangers are also responsible for ensuring security during work in the park, such as road repairs and other projects. Park scouts wear camouflage uniforms, as in other countries, and can carry guns in protected areas (Figure 1).

Figure 1. Park scouts to watch out livestock grazers (14 February 2014)

Most Ethiopian park scouts are hired from within the local community. This is because they are expected to patrol for poaching using detailed information about local 'poachers'. On the contrary, the risk of poaching being overlooked due to nepotism has been noted, and, in some cases, a balance between local and non-local employment has been reached. The following section includes a look at the specific efforts of the park scouts according to the shifts in Ethiopia's political regime.

Ethiopia's wildlife protection policies were not fully introduced in the country until the socialist era (1974–1991). This happened about half a century later than in the neighbouring colonised countries, where legal systems for wildlife protection (initially game management) were created and effective governance began at the end of the 19th century. During the imperial period of Haile Selassie I (1892–1975), there were only three protected areas in the country. There is little documentation of park management during this period, but there are examples of a park's management recording such details by itself. One of these is the records is that of C. W. Nicol (1940–2020), who was involved in the creation of the Simien Mountains National Park. He was born in 1940 in Wales, UK, and, after working to protect the environment in Canada and other countries, he was appointed by Emperor Selassie in 1967, at the age of 27, as Chief Game Officer of the Ministry of Wildlife Protection of the Imperial Government of Ethiopia, becoming the first warden of the Simien Mountains National Park. He later went to Japan and wrote numerous novels and reflected on his previous activities in Ethiopia. He became the warden at the end of Emperor Selassie's rule and described executing a tough bust, which included tracking down poachers and traders of leopard skins:

> Finally, the local police commissioner warned me not to mess with the local people because I had been so persistent with the smugglers and had made so many arrests. I replied that I was just doing the job I had been assigned to do, which was to arrest poachers, and that I couldn't stop. The man who was the chief of park scouts, a decorated hero of the Korean War, was thrown into jail by the police for messing with poachers. It was not the poachers, but the park scout. In another conservation area, a park scout was targeted and they nearly put a rifle bullet in him. No matter how many poachers, traders, and illegal foresters we hauled in, not once were they convicted (Nicol 2002).

This quote demonstrates that conflicts between conservation authorities and local people have been observed since the initial period of the establishment of protected areas and that the importance of poaching control was not understood then, even by local officials. On the other hand, Nicol (2011), who was assigned to the area after being educated on the importance of Western-style conservation, tried to build a relationship of trust with the local people rather than persisting with a 'fortress conservation' strategy:

> One time, I used my fists and boots to persuade them. I even hired the entire village and spent half of my salary on buying medicines. Moreover, I tried to enclose and protect the spring so that everyone would have access to clean water all year round.

There were many poachers and brigands in the Mt. Simien, and every day was a struggle against them. When they were caught, they would ask me to forgive them and try to kiss my feet. I didn't want them to do that, so I always put my hand under their chins and made them stand up. Then, I pulled out the bolt so they couldn't hit the gun and gave it back to them. That was to protect their dignity. The guns would eventually be confiscated, but it was important not to take away their pride. If I take away their pride, I will create hatred in their hearts. Disposing of them while preserving their dignity is the best way to protect our own lives. At the time, I had a Walther PPK, but I never pointed it at anyone. Sometimes I would shoot it in the air as a threat when arresting someone, but I never pointed it at a person … One day I was in between shootings. I was able to stop the shooting because I was gaining trust from both sides. (Nicol 2011)

The episode above indicates that violence alone could not stop poaching by local people and that the warden perceived how important it was to build trust consistently.

The Derg regime, resulting from the 1974 revolution, was the embodiment of the coercive 'fortress conservation' approach, which was based on the exclusion of local people from protected areas. When I asked local people to relate episodes about the management during this period, I heard complaints and grumbling about the strict policing of park officials:

Wild animals would come out into the crop field and eat the corn, and when I dug a trench in the field to defend against them, the park scouts were angry at me for doing that. (Male, 40s, 10 November 1999)

When I grazed in the park, the park scouts took my livestock away from me. No matter what I said, they wouldn't give it back. (Male, 40s, 7 November 1999)

A scout also said the following:

When I was young, I was complained about a lot by the local people. They asked me what was more important, the wildlife or the livestock.

I hated going back to the village after work as a scout. (Male, 50s, 25 October 1999)

Although some park scouts have been bribed into overlooking such incidents, strict law enforcement during the Derg regime appears to have caused considerable opposition from the local people. During the 1991 revolution, the park scouts and wardens were said to have fled *en masse* in protected areas across the country as residents looted and poached their office equipment (Nishizaki 2004).

The CBC approach was not adopted in Ethiopia until the 1990s, when the EPRDF (Ethiopian People's Revolutionary Democratic Front) government took over, and when the new Constitution was enacted in 1995. As the principles of the CBC approach have become more widespread among conservation authorities, they have begun to create opportunities to discuss park-management issues with local people. Previously, wardens persistently refused to communicate directly with local people, and information on conservation management was only communicated to them in a top-down manner. Residents were also opposed to the strong management of protected areas. This relationship changed when park scouts who had been hired by the local community, acted as a link between the conservation authorities and them. The details of the diversification of the park scout's role and activities since the new administration took over are described below.

4. Various Roles of Park Scouts

Compared to other park management service employees, the job of park scouts is considered a low-status position, as it does not require a high level of education, and the pay for it has remained consistently low. Scouts are sometimes killed in anti-poaching efforts, and the job has a high turnover rate. In the United States, rangers working in national parks are respected by citizens, but, in Africa, they are in the opposite position. Here, I will examine some specific examples.

'B', who is male and in his 40s, has been working as a park scout in one of the protected areas for almost twenty years, and I met him in 2000, twenty years ago. Now he is the most experienced park scout in the conservation area. He came from a small ethnic group living on the periphery of the conservation area and made his living by farming and herding. His father died young, and he drifted alone to a peasant village near his hometown in his early 20s, where he met and married the woman who is his current wife. Influenced by his wife and her family, he converted to Christianity and attended church every day of the week when he was in town. B's wife and children live in the village, while B himself splits his time between the village and his workplace. He has been worked as a park scout since 2000, facing the risk of contracting various diseases, security concerns and the loneliness that comes with working alone and living apart from his family. Table 1 shows a description of his job-related tasks over the course of a week. He works in the conservation area for two weeks in a row and then takes about a week off in the village.

Table 1. Tasks of a park scout (from January 31 to February 6, 2015)

Date	Task
Jan. 31	Patrols the park (overnight)
Feb. 1	Patrols the park
Feb. 2	Acts as a guide for African elephant ecological research
Feb. 3	Patrols the area near the park (day trip)
Feb. 4	Patrols the area near the park (day trip)
Feb. 5	Accompanies a group of tourists to an ethnic minority village
Feb. 6	Accompanies a group of tourists to an ethnic minority village

Source: Created by the author

His main duty is patrolling the area. Depending on the season and the frequency of poaching activities, he and his co-workers go out on patrol almost every day, either on a day trip or overnight. In some cases, they may stay for four days and three nights. They drive to and from the sites and patrol on foot, as gaining access to the areas where poaching is frequent is impossible by vehicle. Poaching takes place early in the morning or before nightfall, but sometimes the poachers wait until after dark to bring in the meat, so the scouts must stay up all night.

The scouts' other duties include assisting with ecological research. They guide national and international ecologists in their research, collecting basic data on wildlife and their habitats. Less frequently, ecologists may stay for long periods of time, and B may act as a research assistant during their stay. His duties also include guarding tourist safaris and camp sites. Cultural tourism is extremely popular in the area, and visitors to the tourist villages must pass through the conservation area. The scouts wait at the gate of the area and ride with the tourists as their cars enter the village. There is no need for a park scout to act as the guide, as there is a tour guide from the town to accompany them; rather, the scouts describe the wildlife in the local language to the tour guide. Normally, the scouts carry guns to keep the tourists safe. Approximately twenty park scouts rotate through the area, so the number of tourists differs greatly between the high and low seasons. On average, the scouts work in this capacity one day every week or two. In addition to doing this work, B sometimes accompanies foreign tourists on trophy-hunting trips to the government's permitted hunting areas.[4] The tips paid by tourists are an important source of extra income outside of his main job.

B was recruited by the park authorities as a scout because he was an outstanding hunter. Good hunters enjoy high social status in the area, and social relationships are fostered in the community through hunting. Even after the government established protected areas and strictly limited hunting by residents, interest in hunting remained high, and half of the park scouts were recruited from neighbouring villages. The park authorities' rationale was that the new recruits would have a lot of information about poachers. It was natural that B, one of the best hunters in the area, was nominated by the local elders for appointment as a park scout. At that time, B himself felt honoured to be employed by the government. However, he never imagined the anguish he would later experience on the conservation side and the residents' side. Only three to four people from the same ethnic group (of approximately 45,000 people) are employed as park scouts, and it is easy to observe that B was a good hunter because many of the people who went hunting with him told stories of his heroics:

> Once upon a time, B and I were on a hunting trip. We heard the grunting of the buffalo. We all crept up on it, and I pulled out my gun. He never misses a shot, and we got him in one. We couldn't go back to the village any time soon because the policing is so tight. We stayed in the forest until it was dark. They hauled him back quietly in the darkness. In the old days, when we returned to the village with meat, they held a festival and danced and drank all the time, and B was so good at finding animals and shooting them that no one could match him. (Male, 30s, 14 June 2004)

When B was officially hired as a park scout by the regional government to control poaching, the members of the community must have been very surprised and concerned because he knows the conservation area and the hunters better than anyone else, not only in his village, but also in his neighbourhood. He knows who in the community is hunting and competent, and he knows where the pathways for poachers are located. Often, in conversations with villagers and B, he was critically referred to in remarks like 'this guy has become the government's side of policing poaching' or 'he's a policeman'. B had mixed feelings about these sentiments. On the surface, he repeated the words of a park scout: 'Poaching is wrong; poaching is bad'. However, the background of poaching lies in the history of deprivation that enveloped the land when protected areas were established without listening to the views of local residents. Because of this background, B expressed complex emotions when explaining the situation in the protected areas. He listened to the critical opinions of the villagers and persisted in talking about the conservation side's views.

4-2. Connecting Conservation Authorities to Local Communities
B engages in farming and cattle herding in a village that borders a conservation area. In addition to hunting, B is an expert in

beekeeping and, during his stay in the village, he gave various consultations about beekeeping (Figure 2). I have already reported on the details of the formation of an anti-poaching team (park militia) that B was involved in, and these are excerpted below.[5]

Figure 2. Villagers who put beehives in the forest (25 August 2004)

During the EPRDF regime, with the end of the Cold War structure, many automatic weapons were allowed into the area. Hunting by residents who had access to these guns became more common, and the population of large mammals declined dramatically. To remedy the situation, park officials stepped up patrolling, which led to frequent conflicts. There were several instances of park scouts and residents killing each other in shootouts, and, in 2002, the local villagers shot and killed the warden.

The warden was about to visit a village with a few park scouts to help in the fight against poaching. Scouts from the same ethnic group had already coordinated the attack, as the people knew that the warden was coming that day. Without listening to the village elders, some hunters from the village had blocked the road with trees to prevent park officials from entering it. However, as the warden and others advanced through the area, the waiting villagers began firing their guns. One of the shots was fatal. The park scouts who were with the warden heard the gunshots and ran away into the bush at once so that no one was injured except him. It was later inferred that park scouts from the same ethnic group did not want to be targeted.

This incident occurred because of the warden's sincere response to robust opposition from some villagers, and many others living around the protected area were deeply grieved. The warden who took over after him belonged to a highland ethnic group but had lived around the protected area for two generations and was familiar with it. He was a well-educated elite who had studied wildlife management at university and was sceptical of the coercive approach of the socialist regime, as evidenced by his willingness to make his own visits to the village, and he wanted to attempt to build a relationship with the community. He and others began to take over the task of the former warden of forming an anti-poaching team. A park scout recruited by the government and members of the group selected from some villagers started patrolling the protected area to control poaching (Figure 3).

Figure 3. Joint patrol of park scouts and park militia (28 August 2004)

There are three neighbourhood watch members in B's village, including his former hunting buddies who hunted with him before he became a park scout. People who are good at hunting are afforded high social status, and their hunting buddies become more visible as well. It is because of B's experience that he can capitalise on these relationships and obtain co-operation from people of high social status in the community. This is something that can only be done by people who understand the web of relationships, or who are themselves part of the web, in such areas. On the other hand, the fact that B was a stranger born in another village was a major reason for ambivalent existence in the area. The members of the anti-poaching team were originally skilled hunters and enjoyed high social status in the village. Their recruitment eased the traditional tensions between the villagers and park authorities. The warden is usually changed after three or four years, but the anti-poaching team is still active, albeit less frequently than before.

4-3. Recent Focus on Employment in the Tourism Industry

Cases such as that of B, who was raised in a local community and became a park scout because of his hunting abilities, are uncommon in other protected areas. Rather, many scouts accept the job for other reasons, work for a while, and then attempt to pursue a different career; the examples of 'P' and 'N' are described below.

P, who was male and in his 40s, retired after fifteen years as a park scout in a conservation area in western Ethiopia. He has been employed as a professional hunting guide by a foreign travel agency in Addis Ababa for three years. He is also preparing to open a guesthouse on the outskirts of the city and start his own tourism business. P was a park scout who was not employed from local community but from other side of the country. However, he had hunting experience in the area where he was born. In addition to his job as a park scout, he frequently guided foreign tourists on trophy-hunting trips. Like P, non-regionally employed park scouts tend to be reluctant to engage in dangerous patrol activities, so he decided early on to give up his job and prepare to start his own business.

N was a park scout in the southwestern conservation area for about eight years. He was born and raised in a neighbouring town and attended school up to grade nine.[6] He can read, write and speak English. He was hired as a park scout, but, with no hunting experience or knowledge of nature, he lost his motivation for the job and decided to switch jobs after eight years. He took his high school diploma exam and began attending a technical school. He said, 'The park scout pay was low, but it was a good job because there were not many jobs in town that offered a monthly salary. However, it is not a job that will continue forever. Everyone thinks about the next opportunity when they have a chance.'

In recent years, many park scouts have been recruited and moved into the tourism industry. In many cases, if they are locally employed, they quit and return to subsistence farming and ranching. The rate of enrolment in primary schools in rural Africa is increasing, and many children are pursuing formal education. Correspondingly, children's opportunities to gain knowledge about their communities and nature are steadily decreasing (Nishizaki 2005). The work of park scouts requires local knowledge, and the reduction in opportunities to acquire this knowledge can be costly for both the conservation authorities and the local community.

Due to the recent development of the tourism industry and a conservation approach that involves the participation of residents, the work of park scouts has diversified to include not only guarding conservation areas but also ensuring the safety of tourists and acting as research assistants. In particular, the park scouts, such as B, who are hired from the local community, play a role as a link between conservation efforts and local communities. On the other hand, the trend in park scouts' seeking to move into the tourism industry shows that there are challenges to the substance and sustainability of the CBC approach.

5. Conclusion

5-1. 'African Potentials' in the Park Scouts

Previous research has described African park scouts as entities willing to commit acts of violence to enforce the wildlife laws. Unlike park rangers in the US and elsewhere, the primary work of African park scouts often includes counter-poaching efforts, and no one can accuse them of behaving strictly as law enforcement agents when they operate in poaching sites that can be compared to war zones. Rather, we must examine the negative sentiments of local people towards the forceful conservation approach that lies behind poaching, policies that promote militarisation in the name of conservation and the expansion of international markets for precious wildlife products.

116

The fact that park scouts, especially locally employed ones, have been engaged in a variety of tasks but have been regarded poorly is an issue to be addressed when considering who should be responsible for CBC. This chapter is focused not on the national park system or anti-poaching measures but on the activities of individual park scouts in the field.

The examination revealed that park scouts play diverse roles. The role of linking local communities to conservation authorities is consistent with the 'interface function'. No attention has ever been paid to the role of park scouts as communicators endowed with bargaining skills acquired while living in the community. In the case of scout B, his ability to negotiate with villagers of different age groups within the community exists because of the region's unique culture of linking hunting ability to social status. Moreover, park scouts can use their communication skills because they are capable of 'relativising the local matter', a skill they acquire while attending to tourists and learning the Western-style wildlife conservation philosophy. All of this leads to the park scouts being 'sympathetic', while conservation authorities 'disseminate' information and attempt to 'persuade' when explaining the importance of conservation to local people. The premise of the park scouts' thinking is based on a desire to manage conflicts between the conservation side and residents as well as a strong sense of investment in their land and nature. Conservation authorities have employed local people to help combat poaching because they recognise the experience-based capabilities of each park scout. However, other bargaining skills have been largely unappreciated. To promote CBC, more emphasis should be placed on the role of linking multiple stakeholders; such people must be recruited from the local community rather than from the outside. The ability of the park scouts to do this will be helpful in the future.

5-2. Incorporation of Park Scouts' Efforts into Conservation Policy

The park scouts' individual efforts alone do not yield due appreciation for their work. It is difficult for them, positioned at the bottom of the bureaucracy, to make proposals to their policy-making superior officers. In the case of minority park scouts, the superior officers tend to come from the northern ethnic group that has historically dominated the others, yielding a dual domination–subject relationship.

Therefore, it is extremely important for a warden to understand what the park scouts do, as it is key to their ability to establish a relationship with local communities. C. W. Nicol and some of the wardens I interviewed worked hard to build a trusting relationship with residents. When a warden with a deep understanding of CBC takes office, he attempts to improve his relationship with the local community, and, if he does not, the conflict continues. Unfortunately, the type of warden who listens to the voices of community members is considered lacking in leadership abilities and is generally less appreciated (personal communication). Therefore, it is incumbent on conservation policymakers to make appropriate assessments of the inherent experience of park scouts and wardens, allocate sufficient resources for them to acquire new knowledge and skills and review pay scales to identify possibilities for increases in economic incentives.

Furthermore, the qualities of bargaining power and tolerance possessed by people working in the field are individual, place-dependent and contingent, and they are difficult to universalise. But reports that, in the case of the Maasai in Kenya, as the number of tourists and the demand for 'wilderness' have increased, the park scouts, who have been tolerant of Maasai grazing, have been cracking down on it more strictly (Butt 2012). Therefore, in the future, it may be necessary to consider what conditions are needed to ensure that individual capabilities are maximised and sustained, and how to support and institutionalise field operations. The decision-making process is complicated by the involvement of multiple actors, including the international community, donor governments and international environmental NGOs. Here, I will examine ways to integrate the lateral connections at the sub-group level, such as between ethnic groups and settlements, that park scouts and wardens have created in the field into vertical connections at the state level.

One is the use of 'associations', such as the anti-poaching team in which park scout B and his colleagues were involved.[7] The team is managed jointly with the community and was created through the 'interface function' of park scouts and wardens, and it draws on existing social relationships to build mutual relationships. The role of associations is to unite people with different attributes from different settlements. The people who participate in these associations are confronted with a variety of problems that arise in the everyday life of their immediate surroundings, and they do not avoid them but rather compromise and negotiate solutions, working with others to gain new perspectives on issues.

The associations in the study area include not only anti-poaching teams but also tourist guide associations, Christian and Muslim religious organisations and various mutual aid financing associations, which maintain loose social relationships at multiple levels and across settlement boundaries. The organisations are familiar to residents, and it is easy to accept that membership in an association is not fixed, with a high degree of freedom of participation and flexibility in joining and leaving. Unfortunately, the voluntary approach to natural resource management has not been successful in Ethiopia. The reason is that natural resources, including land, are owned by the state and there has been a lack of autonomy in resource management. In countries where residents are currently making progress in managing resources autonomously, land ownership is simultaneously being converted to communal and private forms.

In recent years, the Ethiopian government has been facilitating the organisation of associations (Rahmato 2006). Moreover, some of the federal government's authority to manage protected areas has been transferred to regional governments. The expansion of associations and the transfer of authority to local governments can encourage the idea of self-government and provide an opportunity for local people to realise that the issues on the 'public agenda' can be addressed through membership and activities in groups and organisations other than the government.

What is important, at this point, is who sets the agenda for 'public affairs'. Previous CBC projects have been based on a bottom-up ideal, and the issues have been chosen by experts and policymakers. However, based on the discussions to date, the issue of protected areas is only a part of the 'sustainable use of local resources'. Therefore, there is a need to re-organise the ownership and management entities of land and natural resources, including protected areas. In the case of community-protected areas (e.g. a conservancy) in southern (and some eastern) African countries, committees for management have been established and consulted. This approach will be instructive to others. In Ethiopia, community-protected areas are institutionally recognised, but they are few, and the actual situation has not been well-examined. Community-protected areas, where communities or associations take control of affairs, must be realised.

In June 2020, news about the killing of African elephants and the theft of their ivory in a national park in Ethiopia was made public. In an article,[7] the communications director at the EWCA (Ethiopian Wildlife Conservation Association) mentioned that zonal officials were involved in poaching and that park officials had been threatened by them. Ivory cannot be sold without the involvement of international syndicates and politicians. This means that local people cannot carry out such a massive killing on their own. In addition to the lure of poaching syndicates for locally employed personnel in protected areas and the high ethical standards required to resist the temptation to profit from it, the duties of such personnel are extremely dangerous. Furthermore, they are constantly being watched and held to account for their actions by the community. It is my sincere hope that the truth of this incident will be uncovered and that policies for the conservation of the local environment will be considered so that the park scouts and others who risk their safety daily in protected areas can play an active role in conservation without further loss of life.

Endnotes

[1] According to Gebre et al. (2017: 19), 'interface function' means 'the ability to interweave and forge connections within assemblages of values, thoughts and practices that belong to disparate dimensions and different historical phases'.

[2] This chapter is based on field research conducted in a few conservation areas in Ethiopia from 1999 to 2018. I conducted interviews with several

park wardens and scouts at various levels. I additionally engaged in participant observation of park scouts' duties. I have largely withheld interviewees' names and job titles to protect their identities given the often sensitive nature of such discussions.

[3] In Ethiopia, the term 'park scouts' is equivalent to 'park rangers', who are employed by the government.

[4] In Ethiopia, trophy hunting is allowed in accordance with the law.

[5] See Nishizaki (2009) for details.

[6] The Ethiopian school system consists of eight years of elementary school (grades 1–8), two years of junior school (grades 9–10), two years of high school (grades 11–12) and four years of University. Compulsory education is up to the fourth grade.

[7] The various community-based associations found in African societies have been discussed in relation to Western 'civil society' (Kasfir 1998; Comaroff and Comaroff 1999).

Acknowledgements

I wish to thank to all the park rangers and the wardens who took their time to talk with me about their work. This work was supported by JSPS KAKENHI Grant Numbers JP15K00651, JP23221012, JP16H06318 and JP17H01637.

References

Brockington, D. (2002) *Fortress Conservation: The Preservation of the Mkomazi Game Reserve, Tanzania, International African Institute*, Bloomington: Oxford and Indiana University Press.

Büscher, B. and Ramutsindela, M. (2015) 'Green violence: Rhino poaching and the war to save Southern Africa's peace parks', *African Affairs*, Vol. 115, No. 458, pp. 1–22.

Butt, B. (2012) 'Commoditizing the safari and making space for conflict: Place, identity and parks in East Africa', *Political Geography*, Vol. 31, pp. 104–113.

Comaroff, J. L. and Comaroff, J. (1999) *Civil Society and the Political*

Imagination in Africa, Chicago: University of Chicago Press.

Gebre, Y., Ohta, I., and Matsuda, M. (2017) 'Introduction: Achieving peace and coexistence through African Potentials', in Y. Gebre, I. Ohta, and M. Matsuda (eds) *African Virtues in the Pursuit of Conviviality: Exploring Local Solutions in Light of Global Prescriptions*, Bamenda: Langaa RPCIG, pp. 3–37.

Kasfir, N. (1998) 'The conventional notion of civil society: A critique', in N. Kasfir (ed.) *Civil Society and Democracy in Africa: Critical Perspective*, London: Frank Cass, pp. 1–20.

Keller, R. H. and Turel, M. F. (1998) *American Indians and National Parks*, Tucson: University of Arizona.

Lunstrum, E. (2014) 'Green militarization: Anti-Poaching efforts and the spatial contours of Kruger National Park', *Annals of the Association of American Geographers*, Vol. 104, No. 4, pp. 816–832.

————— (2015) 'Conservation meets militarisation in Kruger National Park: Historical encounters and complex legacies', *Conservation and Society*, Vol. 13, No. 4, pp. 356–369.

Manns, T. R. (1980) *History of the Park Ranger in Yellowstone National Park*, National Park Service History Electronic Library (http://npshistory.com/publications/yell/ranger-history.pdf) (accessed: 21 April 2021).

Masse, F., and Lunstrum E. (2015) 'Accumulation by securitization: Commercial poaching, neoliberal conservation, and the creation of new wildlife frontiers', *Geoforum*, Vol. 69, pp. 227–237.

Mogomotsi, G., and Kefilwe, P. (2017) 'Live by the gun, die by the gun: An analysis of botswana's "shoot-to-kill" policy as an anti-poaching strategy', *South African Crime Quarterly*, No. 60, pp. 51–60.

Neumann, R. P. (1998) *Imposing Wilderness: Struggles over Livelihood and Nature Preservation in Africa*, Berkeley: University of California Press.

Nicol, C. W. (2002) *My Natural Life (The World of Nicol C. W.)*, Tokyo: Kawade Syobo Sinsya (in Japanese).

————— (2011) *The Power of Living by C. W. Nicol: The Soloist's Way of Thinking, VolumeII*, Tokyo: Rikuyosha (in Japanese).

Nishizaki, N. (2004) 'Resisting imposed wildlife conservation: Arssi Oromo and the Senkelle Swayne's Hartebeest Sanctuary, Ethiopia',

African Study Monographs, Vol. 25, No. 2, pp. 61–77.

———— (2005) 'Differing local attitudes toward conservation policy: A case study of Mago National Park, Ethiopia', *African Study monographs, Supplementary Issue*, No. 29, pp. 31–40.

———— (2009) 'Community-based "anti-poaching" effort: A case study of the Mago National Park, Ethiopia', T. Megro (ed.) *Re-Conseptualization of Wildlife Conservation: Toward Resonation between Subsistence and Wildlife*, Nairobi: African Centre for Technology Studies (ACTS Press), pp. 57–66.

———— (2014) '"Neoliberal conservation" in Ethiopia: An analysis of current conflicts in and around protected areas and their resolution', *African Study Monographs, Supplementary Issue*, Vol. 50, pp. 96–110.

———— (2019) 'An Ethiopian alternative to "traditional" ethnic tourism', *Global-E*, Vol. 12, Issue 1, (https://www.21global.ucsb.edu/global-e/january-2019/ethiopian-alternative-traditional-ethnic-tourism) (accessed: 19 April 2021).

Pennaz, A. B. K. (2017) 'Is that gun for the bears? The national park service ranger as a historically contradictory figure', *Conservation and Society,* Volume 15, No. 3, pp. 243–254.

Rahmato, D. (2006) 'Civil society organization in Ethiopia', in B. Zewde and S. Pausewang (eds) *Ethiopia: The Challenge of Democracy from Below*, Addis Ababa: Forum for Social Studies, pp. 103–119.

Shaw, M., and Rademeyer, J. (2016) 'A flawed war: Rethinking "green militarisation" in the Kruger National Park', *Politikon,* Volume 43, No. 2, pp. 173–192.

UNEP-WCMC and IUCN (2016) *Protected Planet Report 2016*, Cambridge: UNEP-WCMC and Gland: IUCN.

Chapter 5

Conservation, Power and Politics: Maasai Involvement in Community-Based Conservation in the Amboseli Region of Kenya

Tom G. Ondicho

1. Introduction

Wildlife is one of Kenya's most treasured natural resources and cornerstone of the country's nature-based tourism industry (Puzzolo 2017; Ondicho 2018). However, it is now under constant danger of extinction as burgeoning human, wildlife and livestock populations jostle for a fast-shrinking space (Puzzolo 2017). In the absence of suitable and adequate policies to manage consumptive utilisation of wildlife, poaching, human encroachment and changes in the patterns of land use have contributed considerably to the decline of wildlife populations (Western et al. 2015). Nonetheless, Kenya has had a long history of wildlife conservation spanning from pre-colonial through the colonial to the post-colonial periods. During pre-colonial times indigenous communities accepted the co-existence with wildlife despite human–wildlife conflicts. However, at the advent of colonialism this mutual co-existence was disrupted when both indigenous communities and wildlife were pushed into marginal lands by white settlers (Ondicho 2010). Subsequently, the colonial administration enacted laws which paved the way for the establishment of the first wildlife protected areas (PAs) to conserve and stop depletion of wildlife through poaching and hunting (Pearson and Andrews 2002; Ondicho 2010). The pioneering PAs were modelled on the American National Park System, also known as the Yellowstone model which included forceful evictions and restrictions against people undertaking livelihood and commercial activities in the PAs (Pearson and Andrews 2002; Puzzolo 2017).

The creation of PAs (game reserves and parks) took away more land from indigenous communities thus accelerating settlement in marginal lands prone to overuse and mismanagement (Mburu 2004; Rutten 2004). The PAs that were created during the colonial and post-colonial periods followed a predominantly exclusionary paradigm in which communities were forcefully removed from the designated areas (Norton-Griffiths 2006; Western et al. 2015). Today, state-controlled PAs occupy about 12 per cent of Kenya's total surface area and predominantly lie in the arid and semi-arid lands (ASALs) presently or previously owned by pastoralist communities, especially the Maasai (Ondicho 2018). In addition to these PAs, in 2015 there were 140 private and community conservancies covering 7.5 million acres (30,300 km^2) (King et al. 2015). The dramatic increase in the number of PAs has further deprived indigenous groups access and user rights to land resources which they had for centuries relied upon for their livelihoods (Adams and Hutton 2008; Ondicho 2010; Puzzolo 2017). To make things worse, extremely little of the revenues generated from wildlife tourism are invested in local development or trickle down to the communities that bear the cost of wildlife (Stanonik 2005; Western et al. 2015). It would be safe, to say that the classical top-down paramilitary approach to conservation contributed to the building up of hostility and negative attitudes towards wildlife conservation and tourism by local communities (Pearson and Andrews 2002; Ondicho 2006, 2010). As Talbot and Olindo (1990) report that the affected communities in 'anger and frustration' started to spear wildlife to settle scores with the state .

Despite concerted efforts to conserve biodiversity, wildlife numbers in Kenya have over the past few decades declined at an alarming rate (Ondicho 2010). This led to a realisation that without the goodwill and cooperation of communities living in and around PAs, conservation goals will not be achieved (Norton-Griffiths 2006; King et al. 2015). As a result, Kenya adopted community-based conservation (CBC) as a central pillar to its conservation strategy in the 1990s (KWS 1990). In Kenya, the CBC approach is largely implemented through community conservancies (CCs) (Mburu 2004; Rutten 2004). A 'conservancy' is defined in the Wildlife Conservation and Management Act 2013 as 'an area of land set aside by an individual Land-owner, body corporate, group of owners or a Community for the purpose of wildlife conservation' (King et al. 2015: 9). The terms wildlife sanctuary, community conservancy and community wildlife association are used interchangeably.

Government support for the CBC paradigm hinges on the premise that given the necessary backing, incentives and policy framework, landowners and communities can be stewards of wildlife conservation working collaboratively with other stakeholders to protect biodiversity and benefit from wildlife ecotourism (Mburu 2004; King et al. 2015). While the number of CCs has relatively increased, evidence indicates that they are not a panacea to conservation problems in Kenya. Studies have shown that while a few CCs have generated measurable benefits through wildlife ecotourism in terms of conservation or rural development, many of them have fallen short of expectations (Ondicho 2010; Puzzolo 2017). While the factors that contribute to the failure of community conservancies in Kenya have been extensively studied (Southgate 2006; Ondicho 2012; Rutten 2004), research focusing on the role of community power and political relations is generally rare. This chapter, therefore, analyses the complex and dynamic community power and political interrelationships arising from Maasai involvement in community-based conservation through ecotourism development in the Amboseli region of Kenya.

2. Definition and Origins of Community-Based Conservation

There is no universal definition of the concept 'community-based conservation'. Different actors define and apply the concept differently depending on the context and the person defining it in a way that is beneficial to themselves. This chapter will use Western and Wright's (1994: 7) seminal definition which states that 'community-based conservation includes natural resources or biodiversity protection by, for, and with the local community'. The main goal of the CBC approach is to create potential for the empowerment of people at the grassroots level to benefit from wildlife and, therefore, 'take the initiative in conserving it' (KWS 1996: 37). Basically, the CBC approach seeks not only to grant every community the opportunity to develop a management strategy which meets its own unique and specific needs and conditions but also to ensure that the will and incentive to participate in conservation originates from the community itself (King et al. 2015). The approach is especially popular because it lays emphasis on the use of indigenous knowledge and experiences in natural resource management as well as advocates for active community participation and stewardship in the conservation of biodiversity (Rutten 2004; Drumm and Moore 2005).

The CBC approach emerged in the 1980s when a major paradigm shift occurred in the global conservation movement because of escalating protests and ensuing dialogue with communities that suffered the negative effects of conservation. The CBC paradigm marked a major shift away from the classical fortress, state-controlled and top-down paramilitary 'fence and fines' approach to conservation towards a more people-centered, incentive-based and devolved system of natural resource management (Western et al. 2015; Puzzolo 2017). The CBC approach lays great emphasis on transfer of wildlife rights and responsibilities to local institutions, and active community participation in the sustainable use and management of natural resources as a significant way to preserve nature, to reduce human-wildlife conflicts and alleviate poverty (Puzzolo 2017; Ondicho 2018). The reasoning behind the CBC approach is that once people take charge of biodiversity resources and legitimately draw benefits, they will have stronger stakes in conservation and, thus, be motivated to actively participate in conservation (Mburu 2004; Drumm and Moore 2005). CBC is widely viewed as an effective one-fit-all solution to the problem of protecting biodiversity because communities have a natural proclivity for the conservation of nature due to their adaptation to local ecological conditions and traditional resource use practices which minimise biodiversity loss and damage (Mburu 2004).

In sub-Saharan Africa (SSA), the CBC approach has been implemented in different countries in various forms including Administrative Management Design for Game Management Areas (ADMADE) and Luangwa Integrated Rural Development Program (LIRDP) in Zambia; the Communal Areas Management Program for

Indigenous Resources (CAMPFIRE) in Zimbabwe; Community Conservation Service (CCS) in Tanzania; and Community Conservancies (CCs) in Kenya. Despite variations in the ways these projects have evolved, their main objective is to strike a balance between the long-term goals of conservation and the needs of the local communities living in and around protected areas (Southgate 2006; King et al. 2015). In the literature two distinct but interrelated approaches are often discussed, that is, the partnership approach which grants local landowners limited responsibilities with the government or external partner playing a major role in the overall resource management and the customary community-based natural resource management strategies and practices in which local communities that have through long and adaptive processes of trial and error resulted in sustainable and resilient ecosystems, play a major role in biodiversity protection (Pearson and Andrews 2002; Mburu 2004). Both approaches share some basic principles in the sense that they promote inclusion of long-marginalised indigenous communities in the benefits of conservation and natural resource management including defining user and access rights, obligations and responsibilities (Barrow and Murphree 2001).

3. The Amboseli Region

The Amboseli region, congruent to Loitokitok sub-county, lies in the southern part of Kenya along the northern Tanzania border across the northern slopes of Mt. Kilimanjaro. Apart from private lands from around Kimana town to the foot of Mt. Kilimanjaro, it is divided into six group ranches namely, Kimana Tikondo, Rombo, Olgulului Ololarashi, Imbirikani, Selengei and Kuku, and one wildlife protected area, Amboseli national park (Figure 1). The region is characterised by arid and semi-arid climatic conditions with low and erratic rainfall making lack of adequate amounts of water a major constraint to development (Ondicho 2010). However, the region is dotted with several swamps fed by melting snow from Mt. Kilimanjaro (Reid et al. 1999). These swamps and the Kimana River are the ones that sustain life in an otherwise arid environment. The vegetation is dominated by open grassland and bush savanna, which

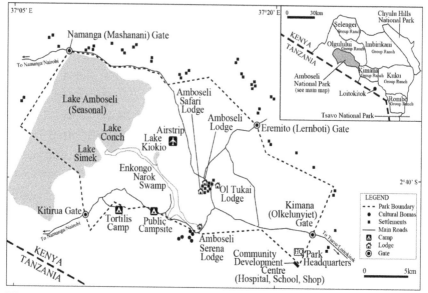

Figure 1. Map showing the Amboseli region

Source: Ondicho 2018

sustain human life and a rich variety of wildlife and bird species and, on account of this, Amboseli National Park was named a Man and Biosphere Reserve by the United Nations Scientific Organization (UNESCO) in 1991 and one of the world's most Important Bird Areas (IBAs) in 2010 (Bulte and Stringer 2006). Due to its beautiful scenery, wide variety of wildlife and allure of the adjacent Mt. Kilimanjaro as well as the magnificent cultural attributes of the indigenous Maasai people, the Amboseli has become a renowned tourism destination in Kenya.

The Amboseli ecosystem is a major source of livelihood for the indigenous Maasai pastoralists who have lived in the area for hundreds of years. Over 95 per cent of the 173,159 people who lived here in 2019 (KNBS 2019) directly or indirectly depend on the natural resources found in the environment for their livelihoods. As a result, competition between agriculturalists, wildlife and livestock herders is common and often results in intense human–wildlife conflicts threatening the well-being and welfare of these user groups and the area's biodiversity. Competition for political control over land, natural resources and tourism benefits make Amboseli one of

130

the highly contested environments and the Maasai one of the most politicised communities in Kenya. The Amboseli region is, therefore, a suitable site to analyse the dynamic power and political relations arising from Maasai involvement in community-based conservation and ecotourism development.

4. Methodology

The data used in this chapter were gathered in two interrelated ethnographic studies in the Amboseli region. The first data set was collected over a twelve-month period, with intermittent breaks, between November 2003 and August 2005 and the second in the months of November and December 2015 as part of two different larger studies. Data were collected through interviews, focus group discussions, personal observations and interactions with key stakeholders in CBC including those in the government, the private sector and local communities in the Amboseli region. Secondary data were also collected from different published and unpublished as well as online sources on CBC and Maasai involvement in tourism and conservation in Kenya, particularly in the Amboseli region.

5. Results

The study determined that Maasai involvement in community-based conservation is a recent development which dates back to 1996 when the Kenya Wildlife Service (KWS) launched the 'parks beyond parks' programme against a backdrop of increased poaching, human–wildlife conflicts and complications caused by changing land-use patterns due to the subdivision and privatization of land ownership in the group ranches surrounding the park (Honey 2008; Ondicho 2010). The aim of this programme was to win space for wildlife by bringing some of the benefits of wildlife tourism to the indigenous Maasai people through involving them in small-scale CBC-oriented ecotourism projects as a form of commercial enterprise (Rutten 2002; Mburu 2004). Under this programme, local communities were encouraged and supported by the KWS to start community-based wildlife conservancies and small-scale ecotourism enterprises in the areas bordering the park. A case study of Kimana Community Wildlife Sanctuary (now renamed Sidai Oleng Wildlife Sanctuary and managed by the Big Life Foundation) was undertaken to analyse the dynamic community power and political relations that produce and are produced by CBC projects in Kenya.

5-1. Case Study Kimana Community Wildlife Sanctuary

Kimana Community Wildlife Sanctuary (KCWS) is situated on the northern foothills of Mt. Kilimanjaro in the Kimana swamps and springs, about 15 km east of Amboseli National Park (ANP), on a very important wildlife migration corridor that links Amboseli National Park to Tsavo and Chyulu Hills National Parks. The sanctuary is jointly owned by 845 Maasai landowners of the Kimana Tikondo Group Ranch who in 1996 set aside a 23 km² piece of land as a community wildlife conservancy. KCWS was widely celebrated not only as one of the first community owned and managed wildlife sanctuary in Kenya but also as a flagship that demonstrates local community involvement in conservation through ecotourism. Ecotourism provides much-needed economic benefits for the Maasai community and is, therefore, regarded as an important incentive for not only protecting wildlife and bird species in the ecosystem but also for preserving them on their land.

5-2. Local Participation and the Negotiation Process

The origin of the idea of establishing KCWS is largely unknown; however, interviews with various community members hinted that the idea was launched in 1992 when the KWS approached the officials of Kimana Tikondo Group Ranch with a proposal to set up a wildlife sanctuary in the Kimana swamp and springs. The proposal was presented to the members in a meeting by the group ranch chairman assisted by the park's Community Warden. The proposal, however, was met with hostility and strong opposition as people could not understand the logic of establishing a wildlife sanctuary in an important dry season livestock grazing and watering refuge. Realising that the proposal was doomed, the KWS targeted a few influential community elders and elites whom it used to sell the idea to other community members. Every landowner was courted in a

132

series of participatory community meetings. Subsequently, community members were divided into two factions (i.e. supporters and opposers).

Although the KWS's participation in meetings was passive, it worked behind the curtains to create awareness and sensitise community members about the potential benefits of sanctuary. It was also instrumental in conducting an environmental impact assessment to ascertain the suitable land use for the area and the potential effects of the proposed sanctuary. In addition, the KWS organised and sponsored a few influential community elders and leaders on a benchmarking tour of successful community projects in Laikipia and Narok Districts, now counties. The findings of the two benchmarking trips were discussed in a consultative community meeting. It is safe to state that these elders and a small clique of elites in the community were instrumental in swaying public opinion and convincing the people of Kimana to accept and support the sanctuary project. Mburu and Birner (2002) state that the project was eventually accepted after the KWS offered the community incentives including the promise to build an electric fence to reduce human–wildlife conflicts and damage to property and crops, that livestock will be allowed in the sanctuary during hard times and an assurance that the sanctuary would not be expanded. However, most of my interviewees stated that the major motivation for accepting the sanctuary project was the promise of economic benefits in the form of an annual dividend, a revolving loan scheme and investments in community projects including a dispensary and secondary school (cf. Rutten 2004; Honey 2008). This depicts a community-based conservation philosophy based on money which not only reinforces uneven power relations projects but also creates room for elite domination in participatory community-based conservation projects.

5-3. Power Struggles for Political Control

The KCWS, which opened its doors for business in February 1996, is registered with the KWS as a community conservancy. In the first year of operation it was managed by the KWS, which employed and paid salaries for a manager and seventeen community game rangers through a revenue-sharing deal with the group ranch (Rutten 2004).

Besides the KWS, a large group of donors including the African Wildlife Foundation (AWF), the Friends of Conservation (FoC) and the Amboseli Community Wildlife Tourism Project (ACWTP) also supported the development of the sanctuary. Despite the initial opposition, the people of Kimana warmly welcomed the sanctuary and started to show positive attitudes towards wildlife and tourism. The sanctuary's success story as the first genuinely community-owned and run CBC project was widely publicised locally and internationally. Subsequently, the sanctuary was conferred on the prestigious 'British Guild of Travel Writers' award for its exemplary work in wildlife conservation in 1996 (Southgate 2006). A British Broadcasting Corporation (BBC) documentary recorded in the sanctuary was used to market it in major tourism-generating countries. A mock traditional Maasai cultural *boma* (village) was constructed at the periphery of the sanctuary to satiate the needs of tourists interested in experiencing Maasai lifestyles. The future looked very promising for people of Kimana as many tourists flocked into the sanctuary because it had its own appeal.

The future also looked bright and promising for the KWS partnership programme. However, problems soon cropped up, and the success stories were replaced with negative reports as the landowners started to voice serious concerns about the KWS's style of management. Knegt (1998 cited in Rutten 2004: 14) opines that from the beginning the KWS 'tried to control the establishment and development of the sanctuary'. It worked closely with a few group ranch officials, leaving the rest of the officials and community members outside the decision-making process and benefit distribution. The twin issues of representation and benefit sharing became controversial and the KWS was forced to relinquish the management role in 1998. The group ranch committee (GRC) subsequently appointed a local management board comprising of a chairman, secretary, treasurer and five members to replace the KWS. However, this board assumed a ceremonial role as the GRC refused to hand over power to it. The board members voiced concern that the GRC was spending colossal amounts of money without consulting them, and for lack of transparency and accountability in decisions and financial matters (Muthiani 2001 cited in Rutten 2004).

The refusal to install the board became a thorny issue that aggravated when the GRC failed to pay the promised dividends to the members and, in protest, the board resigned.

The GRC delayed calling a meeting to elect a new board; instead opting to take up both the management role of the sanctuary and the group ranch. The issue of elections became controversial as members demanded to elect a new board as required by the sanctuary's constitution. Subsequently, a new board was elected but it was also caught up in controversy as the chairman, secretary and treasurer worked closely with the group ranch committee, ignoring the other board members. Southgate (2006), commenting on the wrangles in the sanctuary, points out that leadership has become a means of establishing profitable patron–client relations with those in power appropriating a lion's share of the revenues from conservation and ecotourism activities. The GRC and sanctuary's board enjoy enormous powers to recruit community game scouts, recommend people to be employed in ecotourism, mobilise groups to participate in conservation and ecotourism and to represent the conservancy outside the community, because of their wide range of linkages with political leaders, civil servants, NGOs and tour drivers/guides. Against this backdrop, these elective positions have not only become extremely competitive but also divided the community into factions with the incumbents seeking to maintain a strong grip on power. These power struggles for political control over management decisions and benefits are a major obstacle to local participation in CBC and ecotourism development.

Generally, collaborative decision making and equitable benefits sharing have proven to be painstaking problems which have made it extremely difficult for landowners to undertake joint activities for their mutual benefit. This is partly due to the failure of successful consecutive boards to deliver the much-awaited economic benefits for members. Lack of transparency and accountability as well as non-adherence to laid down regulations for the management of the community sanctuary had let to a situation where a few board members and the GRC appropriated for themselves a lion's share of the benefits. Consequently, positions in the board and the GRC attract a lot of attention during elections because they are perceived as the only avenue to accessing the benefits that accrue from the economic activities in the sanctuary. This, in turn, had engendered social divisions and power contests between various interest groups within the community. The divisions are crystallised during elections for board and GRC positions when contestants appeal to their clan members, age-grade or cronies to vote for them. The competition for political office in order to ensure continued control over the benefits had made it impossible for community members to join hands and pursue common goals for mutual benefit. Thus, inequitable benefit sharing and leadership wrangles were major sources of rivalries between various interest groups which though not easy to notice from outside are a major impediment to the success of the CBC approach in the Amboseli region. As Rutten (2004: 14) aptly states 'the problem of representation and accountability is an issue that is not uncommon in group ranch projects and should have been taken into account by the KWS, all the more so because it also affects operational activities, such as transparency in financial matters and decision-making'.

5-4. Community Power Relations in Partnership Projects

The sanctuary's success stories dried up and many respondents attributed the decline of the sanctuary to mismanagement and lack of transparency and accountability on the part of the officials running the sanctuary on behalf of the members. A decision was taken to revive the previous success story of the sanctuary. Many respondents reported that the new beginning was once again engineered by the KWS which played a leading role in identifying an external partner to operate the ecotourism business in the sanctuary. Some of the companies operating in the area were approached to negotiate a lease agreement. However, only the African Safari Club (ASC) and Abercrombie and Kent (A&K) showed interest. The ASC offered to lease the sanctuary for 6.5 million for a 10-year lease while A&K offered five million over a period of 15 years. The landowners preferred the A&K offer which unlike the one by the ASC allowed trespass and collecting of natural resources in the sanctuary. However, the GRC without proper consultation of all the members signed a contract with the ASC in November 1999 which included an

136

agreement to purchase local produce, to hire locally available and qualified manpower, a Ksh. 200,000 monthly rent and Ksh. 250 bed-night for each client and visitor landing at the Kimana Airstrip. While the members were told that only 6,000 acres could be leased, it later emerged that on paper 14,000 acres had been leased meaning that the size had been extended behind the members' back, a clear manifestation of collusion between local elites and foreign partners to defraud the community. However, the partnership between the ASC and the GRC was not without its own share of problems. Stories about verbal disagreements in meetings and favouritism in the sharing of employment and business opportunities were not uncommon. Several interviewees lamented that over time tensions and uneasy communication between members of different competing factions within the community were becoming palpable. These factional antagonisms within the community threatened to negatively impact the reputation and profitability of this small-scale CBC-oriented tourism enterprise.[1]

6. Discussion

CBC in many developing countries takes place against a backdrop of unequal power and political relations at the local, regional and global levels. Competition for political control over the benefits and decision-making processes constitute the politics of CBC. 'Politics is about power, who get what, where, how, and why' (Hall 1994: 77). Community power and political relations play an important role in deciding who gets involved and how the benefits are distributed within the community and the experiences gained. Community power and political relations are, therefore, important features in community participation in conservation and ecotourism develop-ment in developing countries such as Kenya where participation 'takes place in contexts of great inequality of wealth and power' (Mowforth and Munt 2008: 48). The CBC paradigm is often promoted as a sustainable approach to natural resources management because of its potential to free communities from the hegemonic grip of a few local elites and foreign investors (Scheyvens 2002). Successful local participation in CBC can and does empower indigenous communities to manage resources according to their priorities. However, as the case study of the KCWS found local participation had not contributed to the empowerment of the Maasai to set up their own conservation agenda and priorities as the idea to establish a community sanctuary was initiated by the KWS. This not only runs counter to the ideals of the CBC approach but also renders the local people passive, dependent and powerless victims of external forces. Conservation projects conceived by outsiders and promoted as participatory projects often create unequal power relations in human–environmental interactions (Ondicho 2010). These unequal power relations not only determine who becomes a loser or beneficiary in environmental change but also depict a conservation approach driven by the concerns and interests of the dominant group of actors including the state, non-governmental organisations and tour operators (Campbell 2007). It is, therefore, apparently clear that the efficacy of the CBC approach cannot be understood without taking into consideration the 'politics that produce and are produced by it' (Neumann 2005: 12) or rather the structures and institutions as well as social-economic and political contexts surrounding community participation in conservation projects.

Emerton (2001) aptly points out that community-based approaches to conservation are deemed to be successful, if they not only generate benefits but also ensure that these benefits accrue in appropriate form and are of sufficient value to offset the costs that wildlife imposes on communities and render wildlife an economically viable land use compared with other wildlife-displacing livelihood alternatives. To the contrary, this case study found that with the exception of a few local elites (sanctuary board members and group ranch officials), many community members, cut-off yet from another important part of their natural resource base, had not benefited in any meaningful way from the sanctuary. The elites included people who occupied positions of power and/or were already rich, thus reinforcing the existing power disparities. Such inequalities create asymmetrical power relations in the community. Elite domination, embezzlement and mismanagement were found to be pressing problems that continue to confront local involvement in CBC projects. These issues affect conservation priorities, the modalities of benefit distribution and decision-making patterns. It can be argued that local participation in CBC is one of the ways through which power relations are produced and reproduced at the community level and unless issues relating to equitable benefit sharing, good governance and local political control are addressed, efforts to integrate local communities in sustainable conservation will not succeed. Active local participation in planning, decision making and other control measures would play an important role in achieving sustainable natural resources management and conservation.

The KCWS case study revealed that community leadership struggles for political control over the decisions and benefits of this development process were found to be a major impediment to the smooth operation and cooperative management of CBC projects. While much of the literature on participatory approaches depicts local communities as a homogenous group of people with complementary interests, this case study has demonstrated that communities are heterogenous, dynamic and differentiated internally by gender, age, clan, class, etc. and harbour competing and often conflicting viewpoints about their involvement in conservation and ecotourism development. Leadership wrangles were not only a manifestation of these competing and conflicting interests but also a contributor to the problems of factionalism, social stratification and exploitation. These divisions preclude community members not only from broad-based equitable participation in decision making and benefit sharing but also from working collaboratively to reclaim what is rightfully theirs from the natural resources in their territory. It is argued here that for equitable local participation in benefit distribution and decision making, which will in turn provide incentives for local communities to undertake conservation, these leadership wrangles need to be overcome and efforts put on programmes to assist and guide communities on equitable benefit sharing. Furthermore, the heterogeneity of the local communities and vested interests of different interest groups within and outside the community must be taken into consideration when planning for CBC projects.

The case study of the KCWS has shown that rather than participation in CBC engendering mutually beneficial relationships with political control firmly vested in local hands, it has instead generated a bitter power struggle for political control over the decisions and benefits of this development process. These political and power dynamics have their own repercussions not only on CBC projects in the Amboseli region but also elsewhere. Ondicho (2010) for example, remarks that competition for political control over benefits has made it hard for people to work together. He notes that only a few local elites have benefited in any meaningful way from the community sanctuary. Southgate (2006) notes that these local elites are increasingly influenced by national and local politics. This involves a shift toward a hegemonic control as well as use of political power and influence to determine not only the form the CBC projects in the community take but also the distribution of benefits. These dynamics resonate in many CBC projects in Kenya where the struggle for equitable participation in decisions and benefits has become the order of the day. The KCWS case study clearly demonstrates that the KWS neglected the historically complex power and political relations between people of different age-grades, clans and gender as well as the local political situation. The KWS did not conduct any feasibility study before implementing the project. They started without considering any potential political repercussion of their intervention. The tendency to ignore community power and political relations in CBC has been commented upon and criticised by many writers (Ondicho 2010; West and Brockington 2006). The KCWS case study strongly demonstrates that, without taking into consideration the dynamic and complex community power and political relations, CBC projects are bound to fail. This has often been the case for many CBC projects that are often abstracted from the social context of the respective communities and the local political and power dynamics.

The case study of the KCWS highlights the dangers of partnership in CBC projects between indigenous communities and conservationists, invented outside the community but disguised as a genuine community initiative. This kind of community participation runs counter to the ideals of the CBC paradigm which advocates for active involvement of the local people in all stages of project development including planning, decision making, governance and benefits sharing. While conservation is completely new to the area, political conflicts, and power struggles for the control of group ranch leadership are not. The dynamics of politics conflicts accelerated with flow of revenues from tourism into the sanctuary (Ondicho 2012), as the anticipated dividends failed to materialise, led to increased political conflicts over control of the accrued revenues. Inter- and intra-clan power contests and divisions became common. It was not only clan politics that caused increasing tension and conflicts but also factionalism which made it difficult for members to work together. Corruption and embezzlement of money increasingly became a stormy issue that, sometimes, escalated into physical confrontations. As a result, community relations become highly and increasingly politicised, so that the whole community enmeshed itself in struggles for political control over the decision-making processes and revenues which are now bones of contention and scenes of the clashes. This confirms Fennel's (1999: 217) assertion that 'there is need to be open about expenditures and to share information in an attempt to dispel feelings of mismanagement or corruption or to be transparent in one's approach to management'.

While CBC projects through ecotourism offer enormous opportunities for economic diversification and development, the case study of the KCWS has made it clear that it is questionable whether the Maasai have realised benefits with ASC due (cf. Meguro and Inoue 2011), in part, to mismanagement and power struggles between various interest groups within the community for political control over the benefits and decision-making processes. The case study reflects a community that has not only succumbed to internal conflicts and competing interests of opposing groups but also lacks consensus on the value of collective action and decision making in natural resource management and conservation. Mowforth and Munt (1998: 266), in a brief reference to Kimana, point out that the sanctuary is a best example of an ecotourism project that 'highlights the deep divisions among the Maasai over involvement in community-based conservation projects'. Such divisions suggest that they can generate new and exacerbate existing natural resource management disagreements which are embedded in the historical context of community power and political relations. This confirms the assertion that communities are heterogenous, stratified and characterised by a multiplicity of converging and diverging interests.

While the idea behind CBC is to promote equitable participation and benefit sharing, without due consideration of the interests of all community groups and stakeholders, such projects are bound to fail. This is certainly the case in Kimana where power struggles and competition for political control over benefits have resulted in severe divisions both within and between different interest groups within the group ranch that now threaten to tear the Maasai community part. If, however, the Maasai speak with the same voice and work together to ensure a fair and equitable distribution of benefits, that the conservancies are managed in a professional and transparent manner and cultivate equitable relationships, CBC projects can effectively contribute to sustainable rural development and conservation. It remains only to emphasise once more that for CBC projects, through ecotourism, to succeed a clear understanding of community power and political relations that combine to preclude collective action and consensus must be taken into consideration. Thus, ecological efficacy of participatory approaches to biodiversity protection cannot be understood without consideration of the 'politics that produce and are produced by it' (Neumann 2005: 120) or rather the political and economic structures and institutions within which such approaches are embedded.

7. Conclusion

Using a case study of the KCWS, this chapter contributes to our understanding of how community participation in CBC projects through ecotourism is embedded in a complex web of micro-politics and power struggles linked to the goals and agendas of external forces. While CBC through ecotourism has enormous potential to effectively contribute to the achievement of conservation and development goals for communities, such as the Maasai, living around national parks, elite domination, lack of transparency and accountability and inequitable participation in resource management, ecotourism development, benefit sharing and decision-making have great potential to alter community power and political relations and, ultimately, to become serious impediments to the realisation of the ideals of the CBC paradigm. However, if this praiseworthy approach is implemented without prioritising the needs and aspirations of the local people, power struggles for political control over process will undermine the prospects of the community prospering from CBC through ecotourism. Thus, the understanding of existing and emerging community political and power relations is especially important when considering the prospects and sustainability of CBC projects. Otherwise, if existing community power and political relations are not well understood and addressed, CBC projects are not only likely to produce and reproduce inequalities but also to exacerbate or even stir up new conflicts and, thus, impede the community from achieving sustainable natural resource management and development. In the light of the research results, it can be concluded that, while the philosophy behind CBC is to meet the needs of conservation and development, these benefits have not materialised for the Maasai due to fierce competition and power struggles for political control over this development process. The study suggests that if the Maasai are to support conservation and benefit from their involvement in CBC through ecotourism there is an urgent need for social and political justice issues such as democratic decision-making processes, equitable and active participation in benefit sharing and rights to land resources and livelihoods to be addressed.

Endnotes

[1] Afterwards, the ASC had many troubles with the KGR and withdrew from the management of the sanctuary in 2009 (see Meguro 2014 in detail) and recently the Big Life Foundation became its management body.

Acknowledgements

This work was supported by JSPS KAKENHI Grant Number JP16H06318.

References

Adams, W. M. and Hutton, J. (2008) 'People, parks and poverty: Political ecology and biodiversity conservation', *Conservation and Society*, Vol. 5, No. 2, pp. 147–183.

Barrow, E. and Murphree, M. (2001) 'Community conservation: From concept to practice', in D. Hulme and M. Murphree (eds) *African Wildlife and Livelihoods: The Promise and Performance of Community Conservation*, Oxford: James Currey, pp. 24–37.

Bulte, E. and Stringer, R. (2006) 'Agroecosystem: Benefits in Kenya's Amboseli region', *Roles of Agriculture Project Newsletter*, No. 7, Rome: FAO.

Campbell, L. M. (2007) 'Local conservation practice and global discourse: A political ecology of turtle conservation', *Annals of Association of American Geographers*, Vol. 97, No. 2, pp. 313–334.

Drumm, A. and Moore, A. (2005) *A Manual for Conservation Planners and Managers Volume 1: An Introduction To Ecotourism Planning*, Virginia: Nature Conservancy.

Emerton, L. (2001) 'The nature of benefited and the benefits of nature: Why wildlife conservation has not economically benefitted communities in Africa', in D. Hulme and M. Murphree (eds) *African Wildlife and Livelihoods: The Promise and Performance of Community Conservation*, Oxford: James Currey, pp. 208–226.

Fennel, D. (1999) *Ecotourism: An Introduction*, New York: Routledge.

Hall, C. (1994) *Tourism and Politics: Policy, Power, and Place*, Chichester: Wiley.

Honey, M. (2008) *Ecotourism and Sustainable Development: Who Owns Paradise? (2nd edition)*, Washington, Covelo and London: Island Press.

King, J., Kaelo, D., Buzzard, B. and Warigia, G. (2015) *Establishing a Wildlife Conservancy in Kenya: A Guide for Private Landowners and Communities*, Nairobi: Kenya Wildlife Conservancies Association.

KNBS (Kenya National Bureau of Statistics) (2019) *2019 National Population Census Report*, Nairobi: Government Printer.

Knegt, H. P. (1998) 'Who's (wild) life. Local participation in wildlife-based tourism related activities under the Kenya Wildlife

144

Service's Partnership Programme', MSc Thesis, Catholic University Nijmegen.

KWS (Kenya Wildlife Service) (1990) *A Policy Framework and Development Programme, 1991–1996*, Nairobi: Kenya Wildlife Service.

———— (1996) *National Parks of Kenya 1946–1996: 50 Years of Challenge and Achievement Parks beyond Parks*, Nairobi: Kenya Wildlife Service.

Mburu, J. (2004) 'Wildlife conservation and management in Kenya: Towards a co-management approach', paper presented at the 4th BioEcon Workshop on Economic Analysis of Policies for Biodiversity Conservation, Venice, Italy, 28–29 July 2004.

Mburu, J. and Birner, R. (2002) 'Analysing the efficiency of collaborative wildlife management: The case of two community wildlife sanctuaries in Kenya', *International Journal of Organisational Theory & Behaviour*, Vol. 5, No. 3-4, pp. 259–297.

Meguro, T. (2014) 'Becoming conservationists, concealing victims: Conflict and positionings of Maasai, regarding wildlife conservation in Kenya', *African Study Monograph, Supplementary Issue*, Vol. 50, pp. 155–172.

Meguro, T. and Inoue, M. (2011) 'Conservation goals betrayed by the uses of wildlife benefits in community-based conservation: The case of Kimana Sanctuary in Southern Kenya', *Human Dimensions of Wildlife*, Vol. 16, pp. 30–44.

Mowforth, M. and Munt, I. (1998) *Tourism and Sustainability: Development, Globalisation and New Tourism in the Third World (1st edition)*, New York: Routledge.

———— (2008) *Tourism and Sustainability: Development, Globalisation and New Tourism in the Third World (3rd edition)*, New York: Routledge.

Muthiani, E. N. (2001) *Wildlife Utilization for Community Benefit, An Assessment of Ecological and Socio-Economic Viability of Community Wildlife Utilization Enterprises in Laikipia and Kajiado Districts, KARI/ILRI Internal Technical Report*, Nairobi: Kenya Agricultural Research Institute and International Livestock Research Institute.

Neumann, R. P. (2005) *Making Political Ecology*, London: Hodder Arnold.

Norton-Griffiths, M. (2006) 'The survival of wildlife on Kenya's rangelands - An economic perspective', *1st National Symposium on Wildlife Policy and Legislation Review Process, Nairobi*, p. 21.

Ondicho, T. G. (2006) 'Attitudes of Maasai pastoralists towards Amboseli National Park', *Mila*, Vol. 7, pp. 49–56.

————— (2010) 'Tourism, power and politics: The challenges of Maasai involvement in tourism development', Doctor's thesis, Massey University.

————— (2012) 'Local communities and ecotourism development in Kimana, Kenya', *Journal of Tourism*, Vol. 13, No. 1, pp. 41–60.

————— (2018) 'Indigenous ecotourism as a poverty eradication strategy: A case study of the Maasai people in the Amboseli region of Kenya', *African Study Monographs, Supplementary Issue*, Vol. 56, pp. 87–109.

Pearson, W. and Andrews, R. D. (2002) *Can the US National Park Model Be Applied Successfully to a Unique and Culturally Distinct Society? A Case Study of the Maasai and Amboseli National Park* (http://wwwpersonal.umich.edu/~rdandrew/maasai.html) (accessed: 22 September 2020).

Puzzolo, C. N. (2017) 'The emergence of post-wilderness conservation: Examining the case of Kenya's Maasailand', unpublished MA thesis, The New School.

Reid, D., Sindiga, I., Evans, N. and Ongaro, S. (1999) *Tourism, Biodiversity, and Community Development in Kenya*, Harare: Weaver Press.

Rutten, M. (2004) *Partnerships in Community-Based Ecotourism Projects: Experiences from the Maasai Region, Kenya (ASC working paper 57/2004)*, Leiden: African Studies Centre.

————— (2002) *Parks Beyond Parks: Genuine Community-Based Wildlife Eco-Tourism or Just Another Loss of Land for Maasai Pastoralists in Kenya? IIED Drylands Programme Issues Paper, No. 111*, London: Institute for International Environment and Development.

Scheyvens, R. (2002) *Tourism for Development: Empowering Communities*, London: Prentice Hall.

Southgate, C. R. J. (2006) 'Ecotourism in Kenya: The vulnerability of communities', *Journal of Ecotourism*, Vol. 5, No. 1-2, pp. 80–96.

Stanonik, T. (2005) 'Critical analysis of Maasai manyattas as ecotourism enterprises', *Hohonu*, Vol. 3, pp. 47–48.

Talbot, L. and Olindo, P. (1990) 'Kenya: The Maasai Mara and Amboseli Reserves', in A. Kiss (ed.) *Living with Wildlife: Wildlife Resource Management with Local Participation in Africa*, World Bank Technical Paper 130, Washington DC: World Bank, pp. 67–74.

West, P. and Brockington, D. (2006) 'An anthropological perspective on some unexpected consequences of protected areas', *Conservation Biology*, Vol. 20, Issue 3, pp. 609–616.

Western, D. and Wright, R. M. (1994) 'The background to community-based conservation', in D. Western and R. M. Wright (eds) *Natural Connections: Perspectives in Community-Based Conservation*, Washington DC: Island Press, pp. 1–12.

Western, D., Waithaka, J. and Kamanga, J. (2015) 'Finding space for wildlife beyond national parks and reducing conflict through community-based conservation: The Kenya experience', *Parks*, Vol. 21, No. 1, pp. 51–62.

Chapter 6

On Indigenous Organic Intellectuals: Struggles against Pastoral Land Dispossession in the Maasai Commons in Postcolonial Kenya

Kimaren Ole Riamit and Kariuki Kirigia

1. Introduction

The centrality of land and concerns about land governance in sub-Saharan Africa have continually grown in complexity over time. Kenya is one of the sub-Saharan African countries where land and land governance have remained critical issues from the British colonial period to the present (Okoth-Ogendo 1986, 1991; Manji 2006). Perhaps nowhere in Kenya have these dynamics been more pronounced than in the Maasai rangelands of southern Kenya which have been the site of accelerated shifts in land tenure for the past half a century (Galaty 1992; Rutten 1992; Riamit 2014). After the creation of group ranches (GRs) in the late 1960s, many pastoral Maasai communities embarked on tenure transition, which entailed moving away from collective private title to individual title over land (Mwangi 2006, 2007a). This transition can be understood as a response to pastoral concerns over access to land resources under non-responsive institutional arrangements within the GRs, and changing social-political dynamics in the country (Okoth-Ogendo 1991; Galaty 1992; Rutten 1992; Manji 2006; Riamit 2014). In many studies, it has been found that what was meant to be a process of securing tenure security turned out to be an exercise of accumulation by dis-possession among the powerful and wealthy individuals, inevitably resulting in a growing trend of landlessness among less fortunate pastoralists (Rutten 1992; Mwangi 2007a; Riamit 2014).

This chapter details the process of land subdivision in the former Maji Moto Group Ranch in Narok County, southern Kenya, to highlight the complexities of land subdivision and what has emerged as a unique case of indigenous resistance against local land dispossession using indigenous strategies and state and non-state apparatuses. While many other Maasai communities experienced numerous injustices during land subdivision, the Maji Moto community stands apart in its efforts to challenge and revoke the subdivision process. With the work of Achille Mbembe (2001), *On the Postcolony*, in mind, we discuss the nature of governance in African postcolonial settings, and how state power is appropriated across different political levels to expropriate land and resources from indigenous peoples. We further invoke Antonio Gramsci's concept of organic intellectuals to reflect on how locally informed individuals with strong social networks can be understood as organic intellectuals driving local social movements (Hoare and Nowell-Smith 2005). Gramsci contrasts organic intellectuals from traditional intellectuals, the latter being understood as integral to the mechanics of state institutions of governance who are often disconnected from the masses of society, and reproduce and maintain existing social structures including the state's hegemony. Organic intellectuals on the other hand are located within society and respond to the needs and demands of society which often entail challenging and disrupting existing hegemonic structures (Hoare and Nowell-Smith 2005). The authors build on this understanding to show how organic intellectuals among indigenous peoples can be the fulcrum in the fight against hegemonic structures in postcolonial Africa.

2. Background: Land Subdivision in the Maasai Rangelands

The history of Maasai landownership in Kenya is characterised by land dispossession from the early colonial period to the post-independence period. A primarily nomadic pastoral people, the Maasai occupied vast areas of the Rift Valley in the pre-colonial and colonial period, moving seasonally across the landscape in search for pasture and water. However, the entry of the British colonialists in Kenya set forth a wave of land alienation against the Maasai through the Anglo-Maasai land treaties of 1904 and 1911 (Hughes 2006). In sum, what these treaties accomplished was large-scale alienation of land from the Maasai for settler agriculture and ranching, which subsequently had far-reaching impacts not only by limiting the means of supporting Maasai livelihoods through nomadic pastoralism, but also by eroding the Maasai cultural fabric (Kituyi 1990).

Once Maasai settlement had been confined in the reservation areas, the colonial administration adopted the perspectives of economic productivity and ecological sustainability in governing the Maasai. The reservation area was declared a 'closed district' meaning that the interaction between the Maasai and the outside world by way of trade, for example, was cut off. Various services such as veterinary care and water and dips were provided to the Maasai, which in turn increased livestock numbers significantly. The dearth of offtake of livestock through sales resulted in increased livestock numbers within the limited reservation area. The colonial administration incorrectly perceived this occurrence as pastoral overstocking and, consequently, blamed the Maasai for overgrazing and overall environmental degradation within the reserves (Hughes 2006; Mwangi 2006).

After several attempts to improve the pastoral condition in the country, the Land Adjudication Act of 1968 provided the platform for establishing the GRs, and the Land (Group Representatives) Act contained provisions for governing and administering the GRs as areas held communally under a collective private title. It was anticipated that the GRs would secure pastoral landholdings, accelerate Maasai economic productivity, and curb ecological decline by ensuring the Maasai observed the carrying capacities of the ranches. The Kenyan government received support from the World Bank and the IMF in the implementation of the GRs, a sign of global acceptance of the approach taken by the post-independence state towards governing land in the country (Rutten 1992; Mwangi 2006). According to Mwangi (2006), the GRs were a vital step towards land privatisation in Kenya's Maasailand.

However, rather than following the supposed script for success, the GRs were grossly mismanaged. The GR leadership allowed outsiders into the GRs, and wealthier individuals increased their herds to benefit from the commons at the expense of the rest of the members. As problems mounted within the GRs, subdividing the commons to apportion members individual parcels emerged as the primary solution to the challenges emanating from the GRs. Following research in areas where subdivision took place earliest, it was found that subdivision was marred with extensive corrupt practices as local elites allocated themselves and their comrades the most valuable land parcels, whilst also allocating land to non-GR members (Galaty 1992, 1994; Rutten 1992; Mwangi 2007b). Any dissenting voices were muzzled with threats of being allocated poor quality parcels where it would be nearly impossible to access pasture and water or practise crop cultivation and, in a worse-case scenario, dispossess them of the land they had been allocated (Mwangi 2007a; Riamit 2014). These unequal power dynamics served as mechanisms for cementing land injustices in the former GRs at the hands of powerful local elites such that it has been uncommon for these injustices to be challenged. Maji Moto, therefore, stands as a unique case where local land dispossession during land subdivision has been challenged through a court process.

3. Land Subdivision in Maji Moto Group Ranch

3-1. The Preamble

The former Maji Moto GR is located near the Maasai Mara National Reserve (MMNR). The area serves as one of the dispersal areas for wildlife from the MMNR, constituting one of the areas where pastoralists and wildlife have harmoniously co-existed for a long time. Maji Moto, bearing its name from the hot springs that serve as the main source of water for the community, embodies the co-existence between humans and wildlife with numbers of wildlife such as elephants coming to drink water at the springs. While the main economic activity of the Maji Moto residents has for long been pastoralism, there has been increased uptake of crop cultivation especially among households with plots of land adjacent to water sources.

The Maji Moto GR functioned as pastoral commons where land was owned collectively and livestock individually. In the 1970s, the neighbouring GRs were declared adjudication sections as they embarked on the process of subdividing the commons to apportion individuals with titled parcels of land. On 24 May 1977, Maji Moto was declared an adjudication section, and the next step entailed the registration of all community members who claimed rights and interests in the Maji Moto land in line with the Land Adjudication Act 1968, Cap. 284 of the Laws of Kenya. However, the reality of subdividing the pastoral commons is a more complex process than can be deduced from the laws of the land. On 9 November 1995 during a community general meeting, the majority of the Maji Moto community members finally resolved to dissolve the commons. The consent of the Land Control Board in Narok was then obtained, but subdivision would not start in earnest until 1999, setting forth another long and treacherous journey for the Maasai of Maji Moto (Riamit 2014).

3-2. The Precarious Seat of Group Ranch Leadership

The long duration of subdivision saw many GR committees come and go, and it was mainly due to accusations of corruption which led to their being deposed from leadership positions. It was during this period of land subdivision that the local institutions in Maji Moto would gain increased public attention. With the emergence of subdivision politics, the social conditions of everyday life had changed and local institutions were brought to the centre of attention. The first committee which was constituted in the 1970s, and for which no one appears to remember how it came about, condemned the idea of subdivision. Nonetheless, this leadership carried out the first registration of the GR members where in total, 937 members were registered. However, upon scrutinising the list of the registered members it was revealed that more than half of the members, 593, were absentee members. Many of these absentee members were closely related or had ties with the GR committee members, indicating a collusion by the leadership to corruptly and unfairly allocate the Maji Moto land (Riamit 2014).

A reshuffle of the first committee was conducted in 1987 ushering in the second committee. Maji Moto then became a separate location (an administrative unit headed by a chief) and the GR chairman applied for the chief's position, leading to GR elections. A third GR committee came into office in 1995. While this leadership demonstrated more concerted effort to carry out subdivision, two major concerns emerged that forestalled the process. First, some influential members of the GR pushed for their children to be included in the land register. Second, it occurred that the 593 registered individuals who hailed from outside of Maji Moto could not be easily excluded from the land register. It had been previously agreed that only adults who were the bona fide members of the Maji Moto GR would have their names on the land registry. When the rest of the GR members got wind of the information that there was a plan to register children being hatched under their noses, there was an uproar against the conspiracy. To alleviate this injustice, it was resolved that all male children born to the bona fide members of Maji Moto would be registered as members of the GR with the exception of the children of the 'acceptees'.[1] A seal of approval was attained when the District Land Adjudication Officer approved the proposal to register children (Riamit 2014).

While it appeared that a clear way forward had been found, further unprecedented challenges lay ahead. Being adjacent to the MMNR, Maji Moto became one of the eight GRs earmarked by the Narok County Council to receive a share of the nineteen per cent compensation fee for hosting wildlife as a dispersal area. Under this arrangement, each of the benefiting GRs would receive circa four million Kenya shillings annually, an amount greatly dependent on revenues collected from gate fees to the MMNR. However, the dearth of community projects to showcase these amounts bore discontent within the Maji Moto community, while talks were at advanced stages for an investor to lease land within Maji Moto under an annual leasehold payment arrangement. In the political arena, the 1997 national general elections were around the corner. The eventual outcome was the ousting of the GR committee and the councillor in April 1997, who many felt had served for too long and it was time for new and youthful leadership. The new leadership ran their campaign on the promise of direct dissemination of the nineteen per cent funds to members of the community, registration of all their children, anti-corruption practices and transparency (Riamit 2014).

In keeping with their promise, the new leadership disseminated the first lease revenues collected from the investor in cash to the members. However, rather than cash distribution, the members resolved that the funds be utilised to finance subdivision, for which each member had started to pay an agreed amount of 4,500 Kenyan shillings prior to the arrival of the investor. The committee had to refund a total of 850,000 Kenyan shillings to those who had already made the payment. In addition, the committee oversaw the registration of 1,370 new members: 600 minors and 770 adults. This committee served for the shortest period as it was sent packing in 1998, paving the way for the fifth GR committee which would go on to serve for five years, becoming the longest serving committee in the process. This committee had moved into a position where everything had been put in place, including the hiring of a private surveyor, in readiness for subdivision. A boundary dispute ensued with the former Naikarra GR wherein significant financial resources were used to settle the dispute. After two years, the committee had little tangible output to show to the community, thereby drawing discontent from within the community (Riamit 2014).

A sixth committee was installed in 2005 with the expectation that there would be more public participation in the running of the GR affairs to ensure better public service delivery. In 2010, however, it was discovered that the committee had secretly entered into an agreement with the investor to extend the land lease agreement by twenty-five years effective from 2030, the expected expiry date of the first lease agreement which had begun in 2007, meaning the new leasehold agreement would run until 2055. The GR committee argued that it was critical to raise funds for subdivision since the previous committee had emptied the GR bank accounts. Further, the committee maintained that the community had already given them a mandate to negotiate and carry out such agreements on their behalf by virtue of being elected into the leadership positions. A fifteen-year lease agreement had been scheduled to begin on 1 May 2010, broken into three terms of five years each. Rather than being agitated by the lease agreement for the conservancy project, the GR members were discontented with the continued dearth of involvement in such critical decisions and several provisions of the draft leasehold agreement. The resistance that followed would serve as the final straw for the GR committee, which was consequently removed from office as the negotiations for the conservancy came to a halt (Riamit 2014).

3-3. On Private Indirect Governance in the Maji Moto Group Ranch

The official records of the GR that pertain to land and other resources are maintained as a unit at three different levels. The primary records are generated and kept with the representative committee officials within the GR. The second level is the office of the District Lands Adjudication Officer (DLASO), within the sub-county which oversees the processes of adjudication of communal lands, and the third level is the Office of the Registrar of Group Representatives at the national office. Information regarding any changes to the status of the GR ought to be transmitted from the GR up to the national level to ensure consistency of records across the board. The Land (Group Representatives) and the Land Adjudication Acts provide for free access to GR records by legitimate members of the GR. In the event that information is not accessible at the GR level, the law (the Land (Group Representatives) Act Cap 287)) provides that the same GR information be accessible to the public at the sub-county and/or county and national levels:

The experience of the members of the former Maji Moto GR paints a stark picture of the gap between the provisions of the law and the reality of their engagement with the institutions which are designed to govern land relations within the GR. A look at the number of registered members in January 2005 at the three levels of record keeping showed that there were 2,341, 2,293 and 2,301 members registered in the entries of the GR chairman, District Land Adjudication Officer and the Registrar of Lands Office, respectively. A further discrepancy emerged between the number of registered members and the number of parcels on the area demarcation map, with the latter numbering 2,293, reflecting a difference of 48 parcels short of the number of registered members as per the GR chairman's register, which ought to be the primary adjudication register.

Contrary to the provisions for free access to GR records, the members faced multiple obstacles in their attempts to access information. At the GR level, the representative officials never had any physical address or an office where interested members could visit to get updates and feedback on GR issues. This predicament was exemplified during the struggle to hold the fifth representative committee accountable for funds and activities that members were dissatisfied with during their tenure in office. Challenged to produce authentic account records for funds alleged to have been misappropriated, the then Chairman responded: '*Oyie emikiarierie emodai. Eimina apa irisiiti atii nkishu to Ldoinyio*' (Fellows, do not punish me on account of my ignorance. I lost the receipts while herding cattle in the hills). This reality is heightened when the officials do not cooperate with the members in their attempt to access information, the point at which the members can legitimately seek access of information from the sub-county and/or county and national level offices. Owing to the lack of cooperation, or what may be termed outright sabotage by the Ministry of Lands officials, it took the complainant members of Maji Moto GR not less than four years to collect and extract sufficient information to build a strong case with which to oust the fifth committee from office (Riamit 2014).

In addition to the institutional hindrances on the part of the state and the GR officials, costs associated with the physical distance from the GR in question to the relevant state offices at the county and national levels inhibits ready access to information. For example, a return trip from the Maji Moto GR to Narok town, where the DLASO's office is located, costs about 400 Kenyan shillings (approximately four US dollars) per person. Quite often trips of this nature multiply significantly over time. A trip to the national office in Nairobi about triples the costs. Faced with financial constraints, it does not take long before members seeking redress over certain matters of concern give up and resign themselves to their fate. Even in a hypothetical situation where the above-mentioned barriers were eliminated, questions about the literacy levels abound (Riamit 2014). Of all male adults aged between 21 and 40 years, the average years of schooling completed was reported at 2.9. This figure was far below the average of 4.44 years gathered from the nine GRs in which the survey was administered. The low literacy levels increase with age thereby implying less ability to read and understand GR records, all of which are in English, amongst elderly GR members in reading and the English language, another barrier stood in the way of gaining access to GR information, showing how illiteracy disempowers both individual and collective agency of the citizenry. The nature of these barriers in the postcolony exhibits how institutional hindrance feeds on existing limitations and marginalisation among the citizenry (Riamit 2014).

An important platform in the life of a GR is the annual general meeting (AGM), which is a requirement for GRs by the Land (Group Representatives) Act. During this meeting, the members of the GR collectively review and make decisions pertinent to the GR. In Maji Moto, AGMs were not held consistently and, at one period, there was no AGM held for seven consecutive years: between 1997 and 2005. The rarity of AGMs affected the integrity of data entered and maintained in the GR register, which was only updated thrice since its inception in 1978. Interestingly, questions were raised on each of the three occasions: the first registration saw 593 names entered into the register, but which majority of the members felt were not deserving of entry. On the contrary, several deserving names had been left out and, in total, not less than 30 individuals representing genuine and deserving households were absent from the registry. Had the AGMs been consistently held, many of these anomalies would have been corrected during subsequent registration. In contradistinction, several other individuals had multiple entries into the register and since each entry translates to an equal share of land upon subdivision, it meant that these individuals would be allocated multiple parcels of land at the expense of the rest of the members. A closer look at the names entered multiple times revealed that there was a correlation with individuals from influential households. Further, land expropriation from the members was occasioned through disinheritance. While records indicated no fewer than 26 cases of deceased members, there were no corresponding inheritors (Riamit 2014).

A less direct form of private accumulation at the expense of the collective in Maji Moto is rooted in the lack of oversight and integrity of the GR records, especially following the failure to hold the AGMs. Engagement with the private surveyor became the preserve of a few GR officials, and it was alleged that GR financial resources were to finance subdivision. By the time the GR members passed a resolution to use the leasehold funds from the private developer for land subdivision in 1996, for example, a total of 14 million Kenya shillings (approximately 140,000 US dollars) was purported by a section of GR members to have been either misappropriated or unaccounted for in the period between 1997 and 2005. This situation increases in complexity when it occurs that all local leadership structures (civic leaders, GR and provincial administration) within the community were involved in these dealings. As such, it appears that a tacit agreement exists among leaders across local institutions to evade community oversight and/or effective participation in the management of collective resources, especially land. While these strategies of collusion within private indirect governance facilitate accumulation by expropriation of a few at the expense of the many, a number of informed and concerned Maji Moto residents, termed here as indigenous organic intellectuals, have led the resistance against these injustices that have been perpetrated during subdivision in Maji Moto (Riamit 2014).

3-4. Renewed Hope, Seeking Closure

The latest GR committee came into office in 2010. The committee moved with lightning speed to facilitate complete dissolution of the collective by finalising the area demarcation map, preparing a *land adjudication register* for members (area list with members' names and land parcel numbers), preparing *transfer forms* (forms submitted to the Lands Registrar of titles designating specific land parcels to individual members based on the ranch register endorsed by the ranch officials) and establishing an arrangement for the payment of surveying and title deeds' fees. By 2016 slightly more than 50 per cent of all the Maji Moto GR lands had been privatised through issuance of individual titles (Riamit 2014).

By December 2015 several pertinent issues of concern had emerged from the members questioning the fairness of process and outcomes of the latest privatisation endeavours by the committee in office. In efforts to verify and allay members' fears, an elaborate and intensive appraisal of realities and facts led by a growing pool of Maji Moto GR indigenous organic intellectuals ensued. A host of disturbing realities confronting the GR members were unearthed wherein it was found that several public utilities lands that had been designated for schools, hospitals, an urban centre, access routes and water points had all been grabbed through privatisation. The GR officials had further accumulated through privatisation by illegally allotting themselves multiple land parcels, in some instances 24 times the pre-agreed and approved equivalent fair share of each registered ranch member. To highlight the finite nature of land resources, it occurred that at least 25 bona fide registered GR members had been rendered landless as no land was allocated to them and, to make matters worse, no land remained to be allocated. In what was an appalling twist, several outsiders who were non-members had become beneficiaries of land allocation contrary to the GR constitution and GR members' resolutions, all at the expense of bona fide members. The rot did not stop at land appropriation as the GR resources accruing from existing leasehold arrangements with private investors amounting to about 27,000 US dollars went unaccounted for before members. All this occurred as the GR members were excluded from critical decision-making undertakings related to distribution of land rights, including failure to hold annual general meetings (AGM) as spelled out by law. To keep a lid on these rapacious acts, GR members were intimidated, harassed and even physically assaulted (Riamit 2014).

4. Staking Claims: Exercising Agency and the Place of Indigenous Organic Intellectuals

In asserting their claims and rights over land and other resources, social actors in the GR – ordinary members and those in positions of influence alike – employed a wide array of strategies. As explained in this section, in the endeavour to secure their interests, members laid claim to multiple and overlapping ideas, identities, rights and institutions.

4-1. *Community Level Spaces*

Indigenous means and platforms of engagement and accountability such as *olkiu* and *elatia*, village or neighbourhood, meetings were employed in staking GR members' rights to land. In the quest for customary and traditional legitimacy in the land rights struggle, indigenous social organisations and institutions provided the requisite links to mobilise social actors into action. Individuals and groups, for example, invoked the *olporror*, age-sets' spirit of solidarity and identity, to make peace and amends, and used *olpiron*, fire-stick elders, to bless and curse in the same breath. Largely, these community meetings were very substantive in their deliberation, inclusivity and openness to all GR members, participatory and orderly, yet often full of tension. Community meetings also provided an excellent avenue for broadening an appreciation of the functioning of the land sector state bureaucracy amongst local actors. This means of accountability was the most accessible, familiar and friendly to a greater number of GR members who are mostly illiterate and least informed about the functioning of the modern state bureaucracy.

It soon emerged that the indigenous community-based avenues of accountability were limited and inconclusive in the quest for remedies as decisions made at this level had to be 'legitimised' by agents of the state under the Ministry of Lands who reside outside of the community. GR members, for example, made a unanimous resolution to pass a vote of no confidence on the ranch officials based on the clearly established facts on abuse of office and violation of members' rights to land, and elected a new team. This fundamental right and accountable mechanism were negated through a mysterious court order delivered outside of the county of residence, which invalidated and condemned the GR members' actions as unheard of. In addition, endogenous and exogenous factors, such as geographical dynamics of tough pastoral landscapes characterised by poor infrastructure, low population density and scattered human settlement against a backdrop of human wildlife conflicts, conspired to make community mobilisation an uphill task.

4-2. Rights as Citizens

As citizens, the members of Maji Moto GR reached out to a wide range of relevant state agencies, ministries and administrative institutions, calling on them to rise to the occasion and discharge their legal and administrative duties fairly and expeditiously for the common good. The Ministry of Lands, the provincial administration, local authorities [now County governments] and the national anti-corruption agency were some of the state bureaucratic institutions engaged.[2] In doing so, a number of strategic actions were employed including submission of written petitions, direct actions in the form of peaceful demonstrations, face-to-face dialogue with administrators and policy implementers and public interest litigation. The lobbying and demand for accountability before the relevant organs of the state were premised on legal provisions on the respective mandates for each of the institutions. The demands from the land rights claimers were grounded on GR members' rights to equity and fairness, rights of access to information, effective control in decision making and aspirations to accountability in the management of communal resources through effective communal control over ranch resources. To undertake such highly targeted interventions calls for a certain set of unique skills: ability to read and write; appreciable knowledge and exposure to the functioning of the state; knowledge of constitutionally guaranteed rights as GR members; knowledge on applicable policies, legal and administrative arrangements; exposure to the functioning of the judiciary, among others, skills which only a very limited number of GR members possessed and who, in turn, functioned as the indigenous organic intellectuals.

In response to members' demands for accountability, the implicated GR officials often took advantage of their privileged position – access to information; pre-existing connections with relevant agencies of the state charged with the responsibilities of enforcing the requisite laws and policies; access to technical experts/expertise such as land surveyors, lawyers and judicial systems and land markets – to dispossess and violate the land rights of the underprivileged members. GR officials engaged with the same institutions to maintain the status quo. These ways of co-opting local institutions amount to what Mbembe (2001) terms private indirect governance, whereby individuals employ existing institutions not to serve the public as it is spelled out in theory, but rather to serve individual ends through appropriation of public resources. Where the relevant state agencies were seen not to take action in response to these egregious acts of corruption, GR members made a vote of no confidence on ranch leaders if only to express their lack of faith in them and ultimately impugn their standing in leadership locally. These local actions of resistance underline the unrelenting agency of the GR members in the quest for their land rights.

4-3. Public Interest Litigation: Engaging NSAs and the Media

The history of the country's judicial system in dealing with land-related disputes has not been particularly positive in the general public's reading. Once a matter is lodged in court, GR members feel, their agency is surrendered to the same courts and they lose control of the entire process. Thus, in addition to seeking redress as GR members within customary and national institutions, social actors also appealed to tapping into the emerging vibrant network of non-state actors who shared the same concerns as those of GR members. These networks included non-governmental organisations, research institutions and the media. In some instances, such collaborating non-state actors (NSAs) provided financial resources to defray the rather inhibitive costs of legal fees, supportive strategic exposure trips, enhanced publicity, endorsed joint petitions and supported training and capacity development of GR members on land rights. In addition, the collaborating NSAs often participated in solidarity-building activities such as peaceful demonstration.

The media has remained a central actor in the Maji Moto GR land rights struggle from the onset to the present. The mainstream national print and electronic media have consistently covered the land rights struggle with stories appearing on national TV and in daily newspapers. Maji moto GR land rights claimants have on numerous occasions met with media representatives to ensure issues under contention are clearly understood by the journalists and/or reporters for effective reporting. In addition, social media platforms such as WhatsApp and bulk text-messaging have emerged as powerful and effective avenues for political mobilisation, particularly amongst the literate youth in Maji Moto.

4-4. Indigenous Organic Intellectuals: Their Place and Value

Land rights claimants in Maji Moto GR adopted a multi-pronged approach in their engagement with state agencies. Such a targeted strategy in land rights claims in postcolonial Kenya called for a unique set of skills and competencies, arguably the right mix of repertoire skills, which most of the GR members lacked. Possessing appreciable understanding of the legal and institutional landscape of land management and administration in the country is critical. The ability to both read and write, including technical capacities to draft targeted petitions and letters of demand that speak to both legal entitlements to members and legal mandates of the respective institutions to safeguard the rights is invaluable. Similarly, it is invaluable to be able to isolate critical control points and hierarchy and/or chain of command in decision making within the state bureaucracy.

Further, equally essential is the capacity to meaningfully unpack and communicate back the dynamics of the land rights claims located outside of the traditional reach of a greater majority of the members of the GR. Appreciating, for example, the subtle yet critical link between land management, administration and the quest for justice, with other non-land sector institutions such as state security agencies, human rights institutions, office of the ombudsman and anti-corruption agencies is priceless. In addition, knowledge of citizens' freedoms, rights and responsibility in law in the context of demands for land rights by GR members is fundamental if hope for corrective action is to be kept alive. The ability therefore to mediate and negotiate such a complex labyrinth of legal, political and institutional landscapes, and to communicate all this in a manner legible to the masses who are the GR members, calls for a unique set of skills and competencies such as those embodied by indigenous organic intellectuals. How complex and critical the work of indigenous organic intellectuals is in engaging all GR members can be understood through what Burke (2005[1999]: n. pag.) highlights as the breaking of Gramsci's bond between the rulers and the ruled through counter-hegemony:

> They [the masses] had to see structural change and ideological change as part of the same struggle. The labour process was at the core of the class struggle but it was the ideological struggle that had to be addressed if the mass of the people were to come to a consciousness that allowed them to question their political and economic masters right

to rule. It was a popular consensus in civil society that had to be challenged and in this, we can see a role for informal education.

Following years of relentless engagement by aggrieved members of the Maji Moto GR with all relevant actors and institutions within the land sector, here below is a brief highlight of some of the outcomes. These outcomes of a land rights struggle in postcolonial Kenya speak to the value of indigenous organic intellectuals and the unique qualities, strategies and ultimate outcomes they bring to social movements.

i. All the relevant Government agencies have ascertained and re-affirmed Maji Moto GR land rights claims. The National Land Commission (NLC) chair visited the GR accompanied by several government officials from the Ministry of Lands, criminal investigation officers, political leaders (Area Member of County Assembly and Member of National Assembly). The NLC chair confirmed the allegations and gave direction for remedies in writing;

ii. The Registrar of Group Representatives accompanied by the deputy commissioner, representative of national registrar of titles, sub-county Land Adjudication and Settlement Officer (DLASO), held a consultative meeting with GR members and ascertained the extent of land injustices and dispossession. The Registrar of Group Ranches initially suspended the accused GR officials and thereafter supervised a GR AGM convened for purpose of elections of new ranch officials. This action effectively placed a hurdle before the implicated ranch officials from transacting any business on behalf of the Maji Moto group ranch members;

iii. The Cabinet Secretary in-charge of Lands was convinced to establish an expert (land surveyors, registrar of titles, registrar of GRs, legal) taskforce to look into the claims of Maji Moto GR members and recommend remedies. The taskforce visited the ground and lands offices in Narok County and did a report which entirely agrees with the issues and requests sought for by GR members;

iv.   The Environment and Land Court currently hearing the matter visited the ground and held a court session on the ground to ascertain the realities on the ground of some of the contested land parcels within the GR;

v.   The Registrar of Titles/Land Registrar Narok County and NLC wrote letters of recall of the fraudulently acquired titles that were ignored by the grabbers;

vi.   The entire state department of lands – Ministry and the Commission – came to Court as witness in favour of the community positions. The State Counsel ultimately prepared and submitted a replying affidavit to Maji Moto GR petition in complete agreement with the community claims. This is unprecedented in the recent history of GR land rights claims in the country!

vii. The Environment and Land Court in Narok and other relevant organs of the state department of lands put a hold on all land related transactions on Maji Moto GR, including freezing of GR bank accounts pending full determination of the matter;

viii. The chief officer in the Land Ministry responsible for overseeing effective and legitimate running of GRs – Registrar of Group (Land Representatives) – came to the to the dock and testified as a witness on the side of the community;

ix.   The petitioner's plea has been fully heard with cross-examination done by the defence and the respondents' side of the story has also been heard and cross-examination heard and closed. What remains is the Registrar of Lands, Narok, Attorney General's office, and final submission by both legal sides.

5. Conclusion

Maasai land troubles have persisted since the colonial period to the post-independence period, changing in form and shape, only to find new life every time it seemed that an ostensibly lasting solution had been found. While the forceful expropriation of the fertile

Figure 1. National registrar of group ranches addressing members of the Maji Moto Group Ranch

Maasai lands in northern Kenya by the British colonial administration left an indelible injustice perpetrated by exogenous actors that resonates among the Maasai to date, the land challenges emanating from the group ranches have presented the Maasai with another long-term but endogenous battle that not even the dismantling of these collective areas could alleviate. It is this land-centric reality that this chapter brings into focus with the unique case of the former Maji Moto GR in Narok County, southern Kenya. The processes of dismantling the Maasai GRs were characterised by extensive land injustices, but it is only in Maji Moto that a sustained fight in the quest for indigenous land rights has ensued.

We closely describe and reflect on what such a feat has entailed, especially given the numerous, far-reaching, and complex acts of dispossession involving different regimes of GR leadership and, in extension, non-local actors in the form of state officials, peers of the GR leadership and external investors. Drawing on Mbembe's (2001) work, we detail the art of private indirect governance apparent in Maji Moto and Kenya's postcolony writ large, showing how deposing individuals from positions of power is rendered inadequate as subsequent individuals co-opt and misuse institutions of governance for personal gains. Further, the analysis reveals how the privatisation of communal land, rather than engendering tenure security, opens up opportunities for elite accumulation by expropriation of communal land resources. The Maji Moto experience highlights how institutions installed to organise life in a certain way, such as the creation of the GRs to enhance pastoral life and secure pastoral land, can often take a life of their own to produce reality sometimes so starkly different from that which is anticipated. But, establishing new institutions and installing new individuals at the same time does not guarantee success. What becomes evident, therefore, is that oppressive institutions in the postcolony once co-opted by individuals in positions of power become a complex form of hegemony whose dismantling takes a long time, astronomical resources and immense effort that are often out of the reach of the citizenry and even more so of indigenous peoples with less social and economic capital.

Thus, to fight against what has been a long-term assault on indigenous land rights, the Maji Moto community employed multifaceted and multi-pronged strategies. In particular, several indigenous organic intellectuals with a repertoire of expertise and a thick social network were instrumental in the fight against land injustices. Invoking Gramsci's work, we reflect on how these intellectuals navigated the labyrinthine land governance and administrative system in postcolonial Kenya by employing their skills to penetrate institutional frameworks and collaborate with a host of non-state actors, who together have not only challenged powerful local leadership, but also made often inefficient and unjust judicial system work for the Maji Moto community. That the barriers experienced by the Maji Moto community ranged from the GR leadership, local administrative unit, officials from the land ministry, external investors and even the judicial system clearly illustrate why the rarity of sustained challenges against local land dispossession in the former GRs has been the norm rather than the exception. The unprecedented nature of the achievements attained in Maji Moto in relation to Kenya's Maasailand underline the critical role of indigenous organic intellectuals in social movements agitating for indigenous rights in postcolonial settings such as in Kenya. What is further underscored in this chapter is the significance of collaborative engagement among multiple entities including non-state actors, local media, human rights organisations and, importantly, indigenous organic intellectuals in order to be able to navigate complex governance systems and challenge powerful hegemonic structures at different levels of governance while involving everyone from the bottom up and across board. In conclusion, the role of the indigenous organic intellectuals as the glue that holds together collaborative efforts in the fight against social injustice ought to generate optimism for social movements and civil society in postcolonial Africa, while at the same time underlining the complexity of making such a collaborative undertaking tick.

Endnotes

[1] The notion of 'acceptee' was originally understood to mean someone from another ethnic group who was 'accepted' by the Maasai community to become a member, with rights. This interpretation has in this context been expanded to include members of the Maasai community not resident in Maji Moto GR but who have been granted the same rights. At the point of questioning their inclusion into the register of the ranch, they were 'Absentees', as they weren't settlers nor known to members. They became 'Acceptees' once it became apparent that efforts to exclude them wouldn't be a walk in the park.

[2] District Land adjudication Officer (DLASO); County Commissioner; County Lands Registrar; Ministry of Lands, Housing and Urban Development – Department of Public Complaints and Resolution Committee; Department of Lands Narok County; Governor's Office, Narok County; Directorate of Criminal Investigation Office (DCIO), Narok; Ethics and Anti-Corruption Commission (EACC); National Land Commission (NLC) and the County Land Management Board, Narok; Registrar of Group Land Representatives and Director of Lands and Settlement.

Acknowledgements

This work was supported by JSPS KAKENHI Grant Number JP16H06318.

References

Burke, B. (2005 [1999]) 'Antonio Gramsci, schooling and education', *The Encyclopedia of Pedagogy and Informal Education* (http://www. infed.org/thinkers/et-gram.htm.) (accessed: 29 January 2021).

Galaty, J. G. (1992) '"The land is yours": Social and economic factors in the privatization, sub-division and sale of Maasai ranches', *Nomadic Peoples*, No. 30, pp. 26–40.

———— (1994) 'Ha(l)ving land in common: The subdivision of Maasai group ranches in Kenya', *Nomadic Peoples*, No. 34-35, pp. 109–122.

Hoare, Q. and Nowell-Smith, G. (eds) (2005) *Selections from Prison Notebooks of Antonio Gramsci*, London: Lawrence & Wishart.

Hughes, L. (2006) *Moving the Maasai: A Colonial Misadventure*, New York: Springer.

Kituyi, M. (1990) *Becoming Kenyans: Socio-Economic Transformation of the Pastoral Maasai*, Nairobi: ACTS Press.

Manji, A. S. (2006) *The Politics of Land Reform in Africa: From Communal Tenure to Free Markets*, London: Zed Books.

Mbembe, A. (2001) *On the Postcolony*, Berkeley: University of California Press.

Mwangi, E. (2006) 'The footprints of history: Path dependence in the transformation of property rights in Kenya's Maasailand', *Journal of Institutional Economics*, Vol. 2, Issue 2, pp. 157–180.

———— (2007a) 'The puzzle of group ranch subdivision in Kenya's Maasailand', *Development and Change*, Vol. 38, Issue 5, pp. 889–910.

———— (2007b) 'Subdividing the commons: Distributional conflict in the transition from collective to individual property rights in Kenya's Maasailand', *World Development*, Vol. 35, Issue. 5, pp. 815–834.

Okoth-Ogendo, H. W. O. (1986) 'The perils of land tenure reform:

The case of Kenya', in J. W. Arntzen, L. D. Ngcongco and S. D. Turner (eds) *Land Policy and Agriculture in Eastern and Southern Africa: Selected Papers Presented at a Workshop Held in Gaborone, Botswana, 14-19 February, 1982*, Tokyo: United Nations University, pp. 79–89.

———— (1991) *Tenants of the Crown: Evolution of Agrarian Law and Institutions in Kenya*. Nairobi: ACTS Press.

Riamit, S. (2014) 'Dissolving the pastoral commons, enhancing enclosures: Commercialization, corruption and colonial continuities amongst Maasai pastoralists of Southern Kenya', Master's thesis, McGill University (http://digitool.library.mcgill. ca/thesisfile123174.pdf) (accessed: 29 January 2021).

Rutten, M. (1992) *Selling Wealth to Buy Poverty: The Process of the Individualisation of Land Ownership among the Maasai Pastoralists of Kajiado District, Kenya, 1890–1990*, Saabrucken: Verlag breitenbach Publishers.

Part II

Re-Examination of 'African Potentials' in the Context of Human–Environment Interactions

Chapter 7

African Potentials in Guinean Anthropogenic Landscapes: Land Use, Wildlife Conservation and Environmental Politics

Gen Yamakoshi

1. African Landscapes in Conflict

Conflicts in African wildlife conservation do not exist between humans and nature; rather, they exist between various human actors. Ever since colonialism gave rise to the events that led to the establishment of protected areas in Africa in the early 20th century, authorities have tried rigorously to protect nature from human 'disturbance', with aggressive coercion. This approach is called 'fortress conservation' (Adams and Hulme 2001) and it considers local residents to be enemies or criminals. It has recently caused controversy due to acts of retribution against local populations for their infringement of the environment.

To overcome this nature–culture dichotomy and the conflict over wildlife conservation, it is widely recognised that there is a need to build a cooperative relationship with local populations in and around nature reserves. Instead of regarding local people as negatively interfering with the reserve, the community conservation movement encourages them to participate in conservation activities as collaborators (Barrow and Murphee 2001). A variety of approaches are used to achieve this, including employing local people, who have obtained a rich knowledge of the forest and animals as reserve employees, having local representatives participate in organisations that make decisions regarding problems facing the reserve and distributing tourism income and other profits from the reserve to the local economy (Western and Wright [eds] 1994).

Another approach implemented is 'conservation outside protected areas', which has developed from the understanding that protected areas are not large enough to cover wide-ranging species, such as elephants. This has demonstrated the need to harmonise conservation activities inside and outside protected areas (Western 1989). It also highlights the existence of complex ecosystems in various anthropogenic landscapes and their unique biodiversity. Some wildlife species are known to adapt to landscape changes initiated by various human activities. Crab-eating monkeys and some other macaques, for example, have unique behavioural and ecological characteristics believed to originate from adaptation to recent Asian anthropogenic landscapes (Richard et al. 1989). Some of these animals are given religious and magical significance and are permitted to live in the vicinity of human habitats as sacred animals. Numerous examples of this phenomenon are found all over the world and many of these examples come from Tropical Africa (Fargey 1992; Sugiyama 1978).

The challenges facing research on anthropogenic landscapes include not only examining biodiversity but also looking at cultural diversity and highlighting geography, biology, ethnology, rural developmental potentials and the interrelations among them in the same landscape (Pretty et al. 2009). Additionally, this research should consider practical solutions to environmental, sociological and political problems on the ground. This chapter is aimed at describing land use and landscape-building activities in anthropogenic landscapes and evaluating their potentials for wildlife conservation in West Africa.

2. Guinea's Forest Landscape and Its Origins

Forest areas in the southern part of the Republic of Guinea are part of a unique ecosystem called the 'Upper Guinean Forest Ecosystem', where a large forest 'refuge' remains that was not transformed into savannahs, even during the repeated glacial deforestation period. These ancient forests now boast a diverse array of wildlife and are termed 'hot spots', for which conservation is given a high priority internationally (Myers et al. 2000). However, the

176

region has historically had a relatively dense population engaged in farming activities, such as the growth of rice crops, and the livelihoods of people here have had an effect on the natural environment for a considerable period of time. Therefore, population growth and slash-and-burn agriculture have caused the progressive destruction of the natural environment in the region's modern history following the colonial period. The degradation of the environment has been evaluated and identified as being unilaterally caused by the needs of people.

However, thick empirical research in this area found that the relationship between the locals and environmental vegetation is not one-sided. Rather, the actions people take in their daily lives have created and maintained forests; their symbiosis with the environment is clear. The area surrounding the town of Kissidougou in southern Guinea is within the transitional zone between the forest and savannah. The characteristic landscape of the savannah, dotted with patches of forest 0.5–2 km in diameter, has been noted since the colonial period. Another distinctive feature of this area are the villages that are often found in the centre of these forest patches. Since the colonial period, colonial governments and forestry ecologists have had a strong interest in nature conservation. Therefore, they have explained the origins of the unique form of this forest as being caused by human destruction. According to their explanation, because people destroyed the forests through slash-and-burn agriculture and livestock grazing, the only forest areas remaining were already isolated patches, and the placement of villages within the remaining forest was thought to be an effort to use the remaining forest resources to the fullest.

This simple theory has been proven to be a misconception, similar to the Necker cube illusion, by the research of Fairhead and Leach (1996). They conducted multi-faceted and detailed research on the relationship between forest distribution and human activities in the area surrounding Kissidougou. To investigate the origin of this unique, doughnut-shaped forest distribution (forest islands), they chose eight villages surrounding Kissidougou and compared the results to aerial photography from 1952 and satellite imaging from 1989–1992. The number and area of these forest islands were

177

thought to have decreased over this approximately 40-year period, but the results unexpectedly showed that they had actually increased. The comparison of forest sketches by the French army, drawn between 1902 and 1906, to modern satellite images showed the same trend.

What do these results mean? When interviews were conducted in the villages, many people told traditional stories about the origins of the forest islands, reporting that their ancestors had built villages in the savannah and planted fruitful vegetation around them, which grew into forests. Additionally, statements made by the villagers that they needed to travel farther than before to obtain the savannah plants used for roof construction corroborated the forest growth suggested by image analysis.

Fairhead and Leach identified a variety of mechanisms that have contributed to the conversion of savannahs to forests. This included the selective planting of tree species with economic and military importance in appropriate locations, the fertilisation of the soil through the dispersion of villagers' organic waste products in the forested areas and the wooded areas surrounding the villages, soil improvement resulting from household gardening conducted in the neighbouring areas of the villages, the decreased importance of cattle grazing as a result of changes in crops and farming methods, improved fire prevention monitoring and efficiency due to increased population and increased climate humidity over the course of centuries. They inferred that forest growth had been achieved as a result of the complex interactions of these mechanisms. What is noteworthy about this is that the increasing population, which is generally indicated as a cause of deforestation, is considered to have contributed to forest growth through the above mechanisms.

In this way, the people of Kissidougou, who were thought to be squeezing the last resources out of the wreckage of destroyed forests, may have actually been reclaiming lands that were predominantly savannah and creating patches of forest. By repositioning the local inhabitants at the core of a system of proper management and improvement of natural resources, this study reconsiders the notion that they obstruct conservation of the natural environment.

3. A Village Where People and Chimpanzees Coexist: Bossou

Bossou is located in the south-east of the Republic of Guinea, near the borders with Liberia and Cote d'Ivoire. The village and Kissidougou belong to the same political region, 'la Guinée forestière'. Bossou is roughly 250 km south-east from Kissidougou and has more humidity and forested land. The village had about 2,000 residents (Sugiyama 1978), known as Manon or Mano, who are farmers who speak the Mande languages. Slash-and-burn agriculture is their main occupation, and the main crops grown are upland rice, cassava, maize and bananas (Schwab 1947). The village is known for the chimpanzees that live in groups in the surrounding area. A group of chimpanzees have been continually studied by a Kyoto University research team since 1976, mainly as subjects of biological studies (Matsuzawa et al. 2011).

Although chimpanzees are frequently hunted for meat in the forested areas of southern Guinea, hunting and eating chimpanzees is strictly forbidden in Bossou. Even among the villagers, opinions regarding the reason for this taboo are varied. Although the residents of Bossou now mostly come from four main clans, the clan who founded the village of Zogbila considered the chimpanzee a totem. Therefore, the consumption of chimpanzee meat was taboo. This rule was then passed down to the other clans, leading to the current prohibition in effect throughout the village. Some villagers also believe that the chimpanzees are past villagers in disguise. Since this means they are the villagers' ancestors, they must not be harmed. All of the explanations are steeped in the history and stories of the village's founding, showing the inseparable and intertwined relationship between the village and the chimpanzees present in the villagers' worldview (Yamakoshi and Leblan 2013).

The main habitat of these chimpanzees is the centre of a forest called Gban, which is also treated as the resting place for spirits of the deceased. The habitat extends further to other small patches of forest distributed along hills and streams. Although these patches of forest seem untouched at first glance, facilities such as the resting place for the spirits of the villagers' ancestors, the site where rituals including circumcisions are conducted, as well as other places sacred to the villagers, are located inside them. In places like these, the felling of trees and cultivation of fields are prohibited according to village customs, and the villagers do not enter these forest patches without a special purpose (Yamakoshi 2006).

The first reference to the chimpanzees of Bossou in an academic paper was during the French colonial period in 1942, which noted that '*Les Chimpanzés sont, dans certains villages, protégés par indigènes; à Bossou, par exemple, ils occupent une colline sacrée où s'est maintenu un îlot de belle forêt primitive*' (Lamotte 1942: 115). Additionally, a cultural anthropologist who conducted a survey in the surrounding area in the 1950s noted that, '*Dans le canton voisin (des Manô de Bossou) cependant, la protection de cet animal n'a point besoin d'être assurée par des mesures administratives, parce qu'elle l'est déjà grâce aux croyances religieuses en vigueur*' (Holas 1952: 39–40). Just as these surveys had suggested, the area was never designated a protected area by either the Guinean government or an international organisation until it was added to the 'core area' of the neighbouring UNESCO-designated Mount Nimba Biosphere Reserve in 1991 (Wilson 1992). Still today, many problems related to the forest and chimpanzees are discussed and resolved by discussion among the villagers. In other words, the Bossou chimpanzees have been protected by internal community factors rooted in the village's particular worldview, historical perspectives and the composition of the local landscape, which differ from modern conservation systems.

4. Traditional Buffer Zone System

Chimpanzees are the closest relative extant species of humans. They have a long life cycle, which puts them at risk of extinction. Normally, a chimpanzee group requires several hundred square kilometres of forest for their habitat. However, the Bossou chimpanzees are living in just a 10 km^2 habitat. In addition, aside from tiny patches of sacred forest, the area surrounding Bossou village, where they live, is entirely composed of secondary forest growth on fallow land following slash-and-burn agriculture, and the landscape shows extensive human influence. Scientifically, this kind of landscape cannot be considered an ideal habitat for chimpanzees.

What biological mechanism creates this coexistence between humans and chimpanzees? Although the Bossou sacred forest is rich in fruit trees, which produce food for chimpanzees, its area is small, and the availability of the fruit varies wildly from season to season. In fact, the Bossou sacred forest can only be used as a principal food source for about four months out of the year, and the chimpanzees are strongly dependent on the fallow bush and orchards in the surrounding area for the remaining months (Yamakoshi 1998). In other words, this holy forest alone is insufficient to support the lives of the chimpanzees, and their dietary needs throughout the year are dependent on extensive use of the surrounding secondary forest growth, thickets, slash-and-burn agriculture fallow lands, among others.

During the time of year when fruit from the forest is unavailable, the oil palms that grow here play an important role for the chimpanzees. The Bossou chimpanzees use these oil palms for a variety of purposes. The items they eat include the fruit pulp, nuts, pith and dead tree fibres. The fruit pulp is eaten as is, whereas the nuts have hard outer husks, so the chimpanzees use two stones as tools to break them open, with one functioning as a hammer and the other as an anvil, to eat the inside. To eat the pith of young leaves, the chimpanzees begin by first extracting the leaf stalks from the crown and chewing their roots. Furthermore, in many cases, they then insert the leaf stalks into the hole created by extracting them, using the stalks like a pestle to pound and deepen the hole. They then remove the mashed pith with their hands and eat it. The tool-use repertoire of wild chimpanzees differs widely depending on the survey area. Since environmental differences insufficiently explain this, the actions are considered to have similar roots to human culture (Whiten et al. 1999). Through their tool-use culture, Bossou chimpanzees can easily eat foods that are normally difficult for chimpanzees to consume without tools; they have adapted to the difficult environment (Yamakoshi 1998, 2001). The people of Bossou leave the useful oil palm trees uncut during their slash-and-burn agriculture operations. High-density concentrations of oil palm trees seen in the fallow lands is clearly a product of human culture. The coexistence of humans and chimpanzees that is being preserved in Bossou is the result of chimpanzees adapting to the environment created by human culture by using their own tool-use 'culture'.

The distribution of vegetation in Bossou can be modelled as concentric circles with the sacred forest surrounded by fallow lands from slash-and-burn agriculture, fruit orchards, and villages extending outward based on the gradation of human involvement. UNESCO's 'Man and the Biosphere (MAB) Programme' proposed a biosphere reserve zoning model (Batisse 1982) considered effective for promoting both environmental preservation and sustainable development for local people. This system recommends a 'core area', where strict preservation rules are in effect, surrounded by a 'buffer zone' where sustainable livelihood activities of the local residents are partially permitted. The coexistence of humans and chimpanzees in Bossou is based on spatial distribution, which can be considered a traditional form of the buffer zone system. Aside from its small scale, this area achieves the goals for which modern conservation ecology is heading.

5. Eco-History of Oil Palm-Based Agro-Landscapes in Tropical West Africa

As demonstrated thus far, the survival of chimpanzees appears to depend heavily on the usefulness and overabundance of oil palm trees in the anthropogenic landscape at Bossou. This oil-palm based agricultural landscape spreads rather widely in Tropical West Africa. Interestingly, the oil palm has a several-thousand-year historical origin in the region. During these years, the palm, with its fire-resistant trunk and high oil productivity, seems to have established a symbiotic relationship with people who have invaded and changed the tropical forest environment using fire, tools and agriculture.

The oil palm is native to Tropical West Africa. According to archaeologists, the oil palm has historically spread across the so-called 'palm belt', along the coastline of the Gulf of Guinea, for approximately 8,000 years until now. Until around 4,000 years ago, the distribution was limited to the western Dahomey Gap. However, thereafter, these palms rapidly increased their density and expanded their distribution further east through the Congo Basin to Lake

Tanganyika (Andah 1993; Sowunmi 1999). Researchers have linked the increase and expansion with human population growth, suggesting a close interdependence of this species of trees with indigenous swidden-fallow cultivation systems that we can still observe in contemporary rural land-use systems in Tropical West Africa.

Countless numbers of oil palms grow around villages in the forested region of the Republic of Guinea. The oil palm is so instrumental that people leave trees uncut even during the slashing phase of their traditional swidden cultivation. The oil palm is resistant to fire (Swaine 1992) and grows well under conditions of intense cultivation (Andah 1993). They survive after burning and cropping phases and are dominantly composed of a canopy stratum growing in fallow bush (Madelaine et al. 2008). Notably, the trees are left almost uncared for during such cycles, and no selective breeding occurs at this time. In this way, the palm grows like a weed within various generations of bush fallow and constitutes a basic component of the Tropical West African rural landscape.

The plant provides cooking oil, construction materials and various other products for local villagers. The oil is sold at markets for cash income (Sugiyama 1978). The villagers still actively practise the small-scale production of palm oil in the village, which constantly earns a good amount of income in a relatively short time (Ito 2010). In the local market for palm oil domestic consumption, locally-produced oil competes with the oil from recently-developed plantations using domesticated, hybrid palms. Interestingly, village oil is currently more preferred and is competitive with plantation oil because of its quality and taste, according to the locals.

As for the ownership of the palm trees, it is commonly held that 'Palms are a gift from the God, they are for everyone, and you are free to harvest them'. It is tempting to ask why such an economically important natural resource is so freely accessible. Harvesting oil palm bunches takes hard work even at plantations with short trees; naturally growing Guinean oil palms often reach a height of 20–30 m. The bottleneck of producing palm oil appears to lie in the hard and dangerous labour of climbing the tree, which is often life threatening. Even though the palms are freely accessible, there are a limited number of specialists who have been well trained and can climb them (Ito 2010). This bottleneck appears to function as a preventative measure, protecting this resource from overexploitation.

As seen above, the fallow bush with plenty of oil palm trees constitutes an important part of the chimpanzee habitat. Local people are very tolerant of chimpanzees using oil palms in the fallow bush (Figure 1). This tolerance may be due to the fact that the tree is over-abundant. Moreover, the villagers believe oil palm trees should be accessible for everyone and they may extend this rule to the chimpanzees (Yamakoshi 2011).

Figure 1. A Bossou chimpanzee feeding on an oil-palm shoot

Recent rural development projects often try to combine forest conservation and wetland paddy introduction, foregoing indigenous slush-and-burn methods and shifting cultivation. However, as suggested above, it is this indigenous shifting cultivation system on which oil palms depend. The income and other various benefits from oil palms are obtained with few overall negative consequences. Giving up their shifting cultivation system means the locals have to give up these relatively easily obtained benefits altogether. As a result, the locals have been rather reluctant to move toward advancing wetland paddy projects. Although it needs further quantitative research, it would likely be remiss to judge the observed reluctance of local people as laziness and/or neophobia. It is more likely that this would be a decision by the locals after careful calculation of costs (loss of non-labour demanding crops and palm products) and benefits (productive but labour-demanding and single-cropping rice).

6. Historical Changes and Struggles for Forest Cover in the Gban Forest

Compared to the oil-palm-based agricultural landscape, the vegetation composition of the sacred forest in Bossou appears eternal and unchanging. This is due to its preservation, which comes as a result of the customs of the village wherein the forest is deemed to be a resting place for spirits of the deceased. However, the Gban sacred forest is also a critical habitat for the Bossou chimpanzees and has also been subject to change under the influence of the environmental politics of the time. Examining information on available resources shows that the village's forest coverage has undergone a variety of changes up to the present day. Looking at aerial photographs taken by the French colonial government in 1954 and 1955, the foot of Gban Hill, which is completely covered by forest at the present, was cultivated farmland partway up, and the forest at that time was limited to the section extending from the upper-middle to the peak of the hill.

This change was brought about by the work of the Kyoto University research project. The research indicated that the habitat size and population of the Bossou chimpanzees were found to be smaller compared to other chimpanzee groups. Foreign researchers felt a sense of impending crisis in relation to maintaining the population and requested that the Gban Forest area be broadened and its use of slash-and-burn agriculture be terminated. As part of this request, the usage rights of applicable lands were suspended in exchange for a lump sum payment and construction fees for a bridge and school (Yamakoshi and Leblan 2013). By 2002, the forest covered the entirety of the Gban Hill (Figure 2).

Figure 2. Current forest cover of Gban Hill, Bossou

In other words, the growth of the secondary forest in Gban was a 20-year process, and many of the older villagers have clear memories of the time when part of the hill was cultivated farmland. One villager expressed this as follows: 'Forest only covered the top half of the Gban hill, sitting atop it like a beret.' Materials collected in the 1960s by the Amsterdam University research team also confirm the existence of this type of landscape in the past. In addition, the oldest photos from the Kyoto University research team clarify this change as well. However, Kortlandt, who visited Bossou twice in 1960 and 1965, states that three-quarters of the total area of the lower half of the Gban Forest was converted to farmland over this five-year period (Kortlandt 1986). Since the beret-shaped Gban forest is plain to see in the 1956 aerial photographs taken by the French colonial government, what Kortlandt saw in 1960 was most likely fallow land, which had been used for slash-and-burn agriculture roughly five years prior. Even earlier, local people recall the first half of the 20th century under French occupation as an era of severe hardship. Therefore, it is still debatable whether the beret-shaped forest is its original formation or the result of hardships caused by colonisation.

The environmental struggles continue today around the Gban Forest. When the Institut de Recherche Environnementale de

Bossou (IREB) was established and started studying chimpanzees as part of the Guinean national research facility in 2001, the following year, the villagers used this as an opportunity to carry out the clearing of the forest that made up the chimpanzees' habitat as an act of resistance, implicitly saying, 'If you take our chimpanzees, you will lose the forest.' Thereafter, some families continued to clear the land until 2005. At the time of these activities, most of the deforestation took place in secondary forests, which developed in response to requests from foreign researchers, and the original trees in the sacred forest of the upper portion of the Gban Hill were preserved. These tree-felling activities arose from the conflict between forest expansion for research and the village's rights to autonomy. These efforts can be considered an attempt to re-establish farmland at the base of the Gban Forest and to return the landscape to its previous 'beret' appearance (Yamakoshi and Leblan 2013).

7. Potentials in Anthropogenic West African Landscapes

The case studies of management systems in anthropogenic landscapes and wildlife conservation in Guinea, as we have seen above, show us the complexity of interrelations between history, environmental policies, indigenous ecological knowledge, forest and animal ecology, and so forth. These cases show the positive engagements of local people in landscape formation and conservation, which is in sharp contrast to the colonial labelling of them as destructive and uncontrolled resource consumers. In each case, it is not an easy task for short-term visitors to understand the landscape adequately in local contexts, even if they have specific scientific knowledge in this area.

From a mainstream viewpoint of conservation policies that value the ideal of 'untouched nature', these anthropogenic landscapes look fragile and endangered. However, in reality, Guinea is richer in wildlife species diversity than its neighbouring countries (Barnett and Prangley 1997). Although protected areas have been very poorly established, Guinea is estimated to harbour the largest number of remaining chimpanzee populations among West African countries, with 95 per cent of them living outside protected areas (Kormos et al. 2003).

This reality resonates with the provocative discussion by Nyamnjoh (2017), who also highlighted the complexity of West African anthropogenic landscapes depicted in Nigerian novelist, A. Tutuola's masterpiece, *The Palm-Wine Drinkard*. According to Nyamnjoh, in Tutuola's West African landscape, 'Everyone and everything is malleable and flexible, from humans and their anatomies, to animals and plants, gods, ghosts and spirits' and, '… the supernatural is quite simply natural,' with a hero 'to collapse the boundaries between nature and culture, village and town, home and bushes, human and supernatural, plausible and implausible, rational and superstitious, primitive and civilised, Africa and the West, etc.'

To trust the chaotic complexity of anthropogenic landscapes and to discover their potentials for conservation are difficult tasks for conservationists today. However, the cases in Guinea suggest that these are not unrealistic. We should at least keep in mind that in the anthropogenic landscape in West Africa, actors in conservation such as local populations, wildlife, livestock, crops, forests, soil, rain, streams, spiritual practices, epidemics, and so on, are all intertwined and difficult to separate from each other. In this regard, conservation approaches to try to isolate or eliminate particular actor(s), as in fortress conservation, would damage this balance and would have less support from local communities.

Acknowledgements

This work was supported by JSPS KAKENHI Grant Numbers JP21H03688, JP20H05806, JP19H05591, JP16H06318, JP25300012, JP22651088, JP18681036, JP15710182 and SPIRITS 2018 of Kyoto University and Collaborative Research Project 'Studies on the Social History of Environmental Problems' of Institute for Research in Humanities, Kyoto University. I thank la Direction Nationale de la Recherche Scientifique et Technologique, l'Institut de Recherche Environnementale de Bossou, Republic of Guinea, and the Japanese Embassy in Republic of Guinea for their permissions and support. I am grateful to the people of Bossou village and the colleagues of Bossou chimpanzee research project.

References

Adams, W. M. and Hulme, D. (2001) 'If community conservation is the answer in Africa, what is the question?', *Oryx*, Vol. 35, Issue 3, pp. 193–200.

Andah, B. W. (1993) 'Identifying early farming traditions of west Africa', in T. Shaw, P. Sinclair, B. W. Andah and A. Okpoko (eds) *The Archaeology of Africa: Foods, Metals and Towns*, London/New York: Routledge, pp. 240–254.

Barnett, A. A. and Prangley, M. L. (1997) 'Mammalogy in the Republic of Guinea: An overview of research from 1946 to 1996, a preliminary check-list and a summary of research recommendations for the future', *Mammal Review*, Vol. 27, Issue 3, pp. 115–164.

Barrow, E. and Murphree, M. (2001) 'Community conservation: From concept to practice', in D. Hulme and M. Murphree (eds) *African Wildlife & Livelihoods: The Promise and Performance of Community Conservation*, Oxford: James Currey, pp. 24–37.

Batisse, M. (1982) 'The biosphere reserve: A tool for environmental conservation and management', *Environmental Conservation*, Vol. 9, Issue 2, pp. 101–111.

Fairhead, J. and Leach, M. (1996) *Misreading the African Landscape: Society and Ecology in a Forest-Savanna Mosaic*, Cambridge: Cambridge University Press.

Fargey, P. J. (1992) 'Boabeng–Fiema Monkey Sanctuary; An example of traditional conservation in Ghana', *Oryx*, Vol. 26, Issue 3, pp. 151–156.

Holas, B. (1952) 'Echantillon du folklore Kono (Haute-Guinee Francaise)', *Etudes Guineennes*, Vol. 9, pp. 3–90.

Ito, M. (2010) 'Living with palm wine: Utilization of Raphia palm in tropical forest region of the Republic of Guinea', in D. Kimura and K. Kitanishi (eds) *Ecological History of Forest Dwellers: Peoples,*

Nature and History in African Tropical Forest, Kyoto: Kyoto University Press, pp. 243–261 (in Japanese).

Kormos, R., Humle, T., Brugière, D., Fleury-Brugière, M.-C., Matsuzawa, T., Sugiyama, Y., Carter, J., Diallo, M. S., Sagno, C. and Tounkara, E. O. (2003) 'The Republic of Guinea', in R. Kormos, C. Boesch, M. Bakkar and T. M. Butynski (eds) *West African Chimpanzees: Status Survey and Conservation Action Plan*, Gland: IUCN (International Union for Conservation of Nature), pp. 63–76.

Kortlandt, A. (1986) 'The use of stone tools by wild-living chimpanzees and earliest hominids', *Journal of Human Evolution*, Vol. 15, Issue 2, pp. 77–132.

Lamotte, M. (1942) 'La faune mammalogique du Mont Nimba (Haute Guinée)', *Mammalia*, Vol. 6, pp. 114–119.

Madelaine, C., Malezieux, E., Sibelet, N. and Manlay, R. J. (2008) 'Semi-wild palm groves reveal agricultural change in the forest region of Guinea', *Agroforestry Systems*, Vol. 73, pp. 189–204.

Matsuzawa, T., Humle, T. and Sugiyama, Y. (eds) (2011) *The Chimpanzees of Bossou and Nimba*, Tokyo: Springer.

Myers, N., Mittermeier, R. A., Mittermeier, C. G., Da Fonseca, G. A. B. and Kent, J. (2000) 'Biodiversity hotspots for conservation priorities', *Nature*, Vol. 403, pp. 853–858.

Nyamnjoh, F. B. (2017) 'Incompleteness: Frontier Africa and the currency of conviviality', *Journal of Asian and African Studies*, Vol. 52, Issue 3, pp. 253–270.

Pretty, J., Adams, B., Berkes, F., De Athayde, S. F., Dudley, N., Hunn, E., Maffi, L., Milton, K., Rapport, D., Robbins, P., Sterling, E., Stolton, S., Tsing, A., Vintinner, E. and Pilgrim, S. (2009) 'The intersections of biological diversity and cultural diversity: Towards integration', *Conservation and Society*, Vol. 7, No. 2, pp. 100–112.

Richard, A. F., Goldstein, S. J. and Dewar, R. E. (1989) 'Weed macaques: The evolutionary implications of macaque feeding ecology', *International Journal of Primatology*, Vol. 10, Issue 6, pp. 569–594.

Schwab, G. (1947) *Tribes of the Liberian Hinterland*, Cambridge Massachusetts: Peabody Museum.

Sowunmi, M. A. (1999) 'The significance of the oil palm (*Elaeis guineensis* Jacq.) in the late Holocene environments of west and west central Africa: A further consideration', *Vegetation History and Archaeobotany*, Vol. 8, pp. 199–210.

Sugiyama, Y. (1978) *The People and Chimpanzees at the Bossou Village: Ecology in Rural West Africa*, Tokyo: Kinokuniya Shoten (in Japanese).

Swaine, M. D. (1992) 'Characteristics of dry forest in West Africa and the influence of fire', *Journal of Vegetation Science*, Vol. 3, Issue 3, pp. 365–374.

Western, D. (1989) 'Conservation without parks: Wildlife in the rural landscape', in D. Western and M. C. Pearl (eds) *Conservation for the Twenty-first Century*, New York: Oxford University Press, pp. 158–165.

Western, D. and Wright, R. M. (eds) (1994) *Natural Connections: Perspectives in Community-based Conservation*, Washington DC: Island Press.

Whiten, A., Goodall, J., McGrew, W. C., Nishida, T., Reynolds, V., Sugiyama, Y., Tutin, C. E. G., Wrangham, R. W. and Boesch, C. (1999) 'Cultures in chimpanzees', *Nature*, Vol. 399, pp. 682–685.

Wilson, R. (1992) 'Guinea', in J. A. Sayer, C. S. Harcourt, N. M. Collins, C. Billington and M. Adam (eds) *The Conservation Atlas of Tropical Forests: Africa*, London: Macmillan, pp. 193–199.

Yamakoshi, G. (1998) 'Dietary responses to fruit scarcity of wild chimpanzees at Bossou, Guinea: Possible implications for ecological importance of tool use', *American Journal of Physical Anthropology*, Vol. 106, Issue 3, pp. 283–295.

———— (2001) 'Ecology of tool use in wild chimpanzees: Toward reconstruction of early hominid evolution', in T. Matsuzawa (ed.) *Primate Origin of Human Cognition and Behavior*, Tokyo: Springer-Verlag Tokyo, pp. 537–556.

———— (2006) 'An indigenous concept of landscape management for chimpanzee conservation at Bossou, Guinea', in J. Maruyama, L. Wang, T. Fujikura and M. Ito (eds) *Proceedings of Kyoto Symposium 2006, "Crossing Disciplinary Boundaries and Re-visioning Area Studies: Perspectives from Asia and Africa"*, Kyoto: Kyoto University, pp. 3–10.

———— (2011) 'Pestle-pounding behavior: The key to the coexistence of humans and chimpanzees', in T. Matsuzawa, T. Humle and Y. Sugiyama (eds) *The Chimpanzees of Bossou and Nimba,* Tokyo: Springer, pp. 107–115.

Yamakoshi, G. and Leblan, V. (2013) 'Conflicts between indigenous and scientific concepts of landscape management for wildlife conservation: Human-Chimpanzee politics of coexistence at Bossou, Guinea', *Revue de primatologie (on line)*, Vol. 5, document 6 (https://doi.org/10.4000/primatologie.1762) (accessed: 8 July 2021).

Chapter 8

African Potentials for Biodiversity Conservation: Tamarind, Lemurs and the Tandroy People in the Gallery Forests of Southern Madagascar

Shinichiro Ichino

1. Introduction

1-1. Biodiversity Conservation in Fragmented Forests

The conservation of biodiversity in African tropical forests is a significant global environmental issue. Madagascar is known for its unique flora and fauna and its high rates of endemism. Despite its uniqueness, it is estimated that more than 90 per cent of natural forests in Madagascar have disappeared, and most plant and animal species are at risk of extinction (Myers et al. 2000). As such, Madagascar is considered to be among the biodiversity hotspots where conservation efforts are most urgently required.

In the 2003 Durban Vision, the Malagasy government committed to a tripling of protected areas in Madagascar (Mittermeier et al. 2005); however, despite the ongoing expansion of protected forest areas in the country, most forests have already been fragmented. Forests in southern Madagascar are severely fragmented and effectively constitute islands in a sea of agriculture (Tengö et al. 2007); it is impractical to establish new protected forest areas in the context of this severe fragmentation.

In such areas, it is necessary to conserve as many of the small, remnant forest patches as possible to maintain diversity across a region. In Africa, some of these small forest patches have historically been protected by local people (e.g. Fairhead and Leach 1996). In southern Madagascar, local taboos provide strong, well-enforced protection for remaining forest patches (Tengö et al. 2007). In addition, African tropical forests are not pristine, as previously thought, but may have been substantially shaped by human activities (Bhagwat et al. 2008; Willis et al. 2004). Thus, biodiversity conservation in this region requires an understanding of the relationships between people and the forests.

1-2. Objectives

I explored the relationship between local people, forest animals and gallery forests in southern Madagascar to highlight the positive aspects of local knowledge and cultural practices as 'African Potentials' for biodiversity conservation. Specifically, I explored these relationships through the lens of 'African Potentials', which is the notion that Africans have developed their own knowledge and institutions that can be used to solve the problems they face (Matsuda 2014; Ohta 2016).

In many African studies, Africa is treated as being in a state of *deficiency* (Gebre et al. 2017: 5). In this study, I take the opposite view; that is, I consider the activities and knowledge of local peoples as potential resources for biodiversity conservation in a region characterised by highly fragmented remnant forests.

2. Study Area

2-1. Berenty Reserve

The focus of this study is Berenty Reserve and surrounding villages in southern Madagascar (Figure 1). Mean annual rainfall in the study area for the period 1989–1998 was 580.6 mm (Koyama et al. 2001). Berenty Reserve is a private reserve established in 1936 by the de Heaulme family in consultation with the local Tandroy people, beginning when the de Heaulme founded a sisal plantation beside the Mandrare River (Jolly 2004, 2012). The Mandrare River is the largest river in the region, and the forests of Berenty Reserve represent the largest relict patches of the richest forest type in southern Madagascar (Rambeloarivony and Jolly 2012).

The gallery forest of Berenty Reserve is characterised by a closed canopy and trees greater than 20 m in height. Forest type varies with increasing distance from the river according to the following sequence: closed-canopy gallery forest, open forest, scrub forest and

194

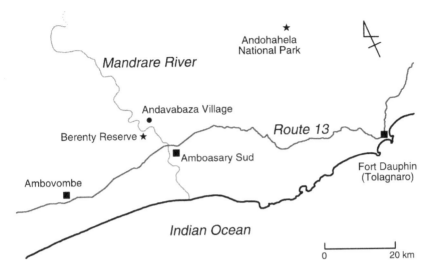

Figure 1. Map of south eastern Madagascar

spiny forest (Budnitz and Dainis 1975). The forest is important for biodiversity in southern Madagascar, and particularly for lemurs (Lemuroidea), a group primates endemic to Madagascar. Most lemur species are endangered (Mittermeier et al. 2010).

2-2. The People of Berenty Reserve

Most villagers in the region are of Tandroy origin, although immigrants, who came to work in the sisal plantation and factory, also live in Berenty Village. Most immigrants are Tanosy, a neighbouring ethnic group from Fort Dauphin, or Tandroy people from Ambovombe (Figure 1).

The Tandroy are one of twenty major ethnic groups in Madagascar, and have traditionally inhabited the Androy region in southern Madagascar, between the Menarandra and Mandrare Rivers. The Tandroy number approximately 600,000, the majority of whom live in the region (The Diagram Group 2013; Olson 1996). According to Heurtebize (1986), the Tandroy are a composite ethnic group comprising several clans of diverse origin, including the Sakalava, Bara, Mahafaly and Tanosy, who arrived in the Androy region several centuries ago. They are a primarily pastoral people who herd zebu cattle, but they also cultivate cassava, millet, maize and rice. The

195

Tandroy population has more than doubled in the last 30 years, and the combined effect of a growing population and a reluctance to change traditional lifestyles and production systems has led to increased ecological pressure on the dry forest (Andrés-Domenech et al. 2014).

3. Gallery Forest in Southern Madagascar

3-1. Gallery Forests

Southern Madagascar is semi-arid and characterised by dry, spiny forests with an abundance of Didiereaceae (e.g. *Alluaudia procera*) and arborescent Euphorbiaceae species. Tamarind (*Tamarindus indica*)-dominated gallery forests occur along river margins in southern and southwestern Madagascar, including the Mangoky, Sakamena, Linta, Menarandra, Onilahy, Fiherenana, Manambovo and Mandrare Rivers (Sussman et al. 2003). While its origin is unclear, tamarind is a major food source for numerous lemur species (Labat and Moat 2003). Canopy trees provide substantial shade in gallery forests and, unlike the dry spiny forest, the gallery forest remains semi-evergreen year-round. Trees in the gallery forest rarely drop all their leaves, thus providing protection for light-sensitive understorey plants (Goodman et al. 1997).

Despite their significance for biodiversity, the gallery forests of southern Madagascar are among the most threatened forest types in Madagascar, and most are highly fragmented. The forests of the Androy region have been decreasing at a rate of 3.9 per cent per year, which is higher than all but one other region in Madagascar (Rambeloarivony and Jolly 2012).

3-2. Protection of Gallery Forests by Local Communities

The original tamarind trees of Berenty Reserve have persisted as local people have not cut them down (Jolly et al. 2006). Four patches of gallery forest remain along the Mandrare River; two of these occur in private reserves owned by de Heaulme family (200 ha Berenty Reserve and 100 ha Bealoka Reserve), whereas the other two, smaller patches are sacred forests near Ifotaka (Rambeloarivony and Jolly 2012). All four patches have been protected by local communities.

3-3. Deforestation in Gallery Forests

Although many small forests in southern Madagascar are socially and culturally protected by local communities (Tengö et al. 2007), some forests remain at risk of deforestation. In March 2016, I observed that the forest in the 150 ha Akesson-Kaleta Reserve had completely disappeared. This forest was part of another private reserve which was connected to a part of Berenty Reserve, but was under different ownership. Local people indicate that the forest was harvested for firewood and charcoal production after the reserve closed. Aerial photographs from the region indicate that the forest was present in 2011, but had disappeared by 2016 (Figure 2, 3). Repeated droughts and economic problems following the 2009 political crisis in Madagascar may have led to the deforestation.

Figure 2. Deforestation in the Akesson-Kaleta Reserve (photo taken by the author on 3 March 2016)

Similarly, Raymond Decary, the local administrator of the Androy region during the colonial era, reported deforestation in Ifotaka near Berenty during times of heavy drought (Decary 1930). Thus, while the Tandroy have many taboo forests (*ala faly* or *ala fady*) where tree removal is prohibited, deforestation of gallery forests is not always taboo.

197

Figure 3. Aerial photographs around Berenty Reserve (2011 and 2016)
Source: Google Maps 2011 and Google Maps 2016

4. Tamarind and Local People

4-1. Tamarind in Southern Madagascar

Tamarind is a slow-growing, long-lived tree. Some tamarind trees in Berenty Reserve have diameters at breast height in excess of 130 cm and are believed to be at least 200 years old (Koyama et al. 2006). It is unclear whether tamarind is native to Madagascar or not; however, if tamarind was introduced from the African continent (Kull et al. 2012), introduction was likely to have occurred well before the 17th century. Étienne de Flacourt (Flacourt 1661) made reference to the village of Montefeno, south of the town of Ambondro. The name means 'full of tamarind' (Pearson and Godden 1999), suggesting the presence of a village with tamarind trees in the 17th century. In addition, there are records of tamarind trees being exported from Madagascar during the 17th century; in particular, the *Saint-Laurent* returned to France in 1650 carrying tamarind (Pearson 1997). Large tamarind trees were also described by Drury (1729); many details in this book are considered authentic, and the story itself is one of the oldest written historical accounts of life in southern Madagascar during the 18th century (Pearson 1996). Finally, the most common word for tamarind in southern Madagascar is *kily* (or *kile*); *monty* (or *monte*) and *madiro* (or *madilo*) are also used elsewhere in Madagascar. The names of many villages and towns in southern and southwestern Madagascar include *kily* (e.g. Bekily, Ankilizato, etc.), suggesting a long history of tamarind in these regions.

4-2. Cultural Uses of Tamarind

There are several possible reasons why tamarind trees are protected by local communities. One is that tamarind is a useful, multipurpose tree (El-Siddig et al. 2006). For example, tamarind trees provide abundant shade for people and herds owing to their wide, dense crowns; this is especially valued in semi-arid regions such as southern Madagascar. In the Berenty area, tamarind fruits (Figure 4) are mixed with sugar cane and used as a starter for a local variety of rum (*toake* or *toaka gasy*). Rum production is the most important means of earning cash in the region. The fruit is also eaten raw and used for juice. In addition, tamarind wood is used as a fuel and for charcoal production. Charcoal production, however, has frequently resulted in deforestation and is therefore prohibited by local communities. To avoid deforestation, only dead tamarind trees are used as a firewood in the Berenty area.

Tamarind bark and leaves are also used as medicines; Yuasa et al. (2000) report on the use of a tamarind decoction for eye problems, toothaches and bloody stool. Similar medicinal usage has been reported from other regions of Madagascar. For example, tamarind is used by the Mahafaly people of southwestern Madagascar to treat eye problems (Andriamparany et al. 2014), and the plant is used for oral care in Mahajanga, in northwestern Madagascar (Ranjarisoa et al. 2016).

Figure 4. Tamarind (*Tamarindus indica*) fruit pods at Berenty Reserve (Photo by Ai Kuribayashi)

Other medicinal uses have also been reported from other regions of Madagascar. The bark is used to treat headaches, and the fruit is used as a mild laxative (Labat and Moat 2003). In the Sakalava dialect, tamarind is known as *voamatory*, meaning 'fruit that makes you sleep', because small amounts of fruit pulp are given to small children who suffer from constipation; this light laxative calms them and facilitates sleep (Boiteau and Allorge-Boiteau 1993). Usage for hypotension (leaves, infusion), inflammation (bark, rubbing on skin) and fever or abdominal pain (fruits, beverage) have been reported from Kirindy forest in western Madagascar (Norscia and Borgognini-Tarli 2006). Thus, tamarind has various medicinal uses throughout southern and western Madagascar.

4-3. Tamarind as Famine Food

Tamarind pulp is the most common famine food in southern Madagascar (Jolly 2015). Tamarind fruits are likely to be important as famine food due to the semi-arid climate of the region, which is prone to repeated drought and famine (Jolly 2004). Local people report soaking pods in water, and mixing them with ash to reduce

200

acidity. The same procedure is used in southern Mozambique (Berger 2003) and in the Bahamas (Morton 1987).

Numerous other famine foods are eaten in southern Madagascar, including prickly pears (*Opuntia* spp.) and wild yam roots (*Dioscorea* spp.). Some authors have emphasised prickly pears as an important famine food in southern Madagascar (Kaufmann 2004; Swingle 1929); however, tamarind fruits are also important because they are produced during the dry season, whereas prickly pears fruit in the rainy season. In addition, prickly pears were first introduced to Madagascar in the late 18th century, suggesting that tamarind has a longer history as famine food.

4-4. Sacred Significance of Tamarind

Tamarind is culturally and socially important in southern and western Madagascar, and both tamarind and the baobab (*Adansonia* spp.) have sacred significance in this region (e.g. Sibree 1880). In Berenty, village assemblies traditionally comprised circles of adult men meeting under tamarind or baobab trees (Jolly 2004), and a tamarind tree located in the centre of Ifotaka village, near Berenty, is sacred (Jackson 2013). Historical narratives of the Karembola, a neighbouring ethnic group related to the Tandroy, suggest that people performed sacrifices beneath tamarind trees (Middleton 2001). Linton (1928) also documented sacrifices made under tamarind trees in southern and western Madagascar. There are many taboo forests (*Ala fady* or *Ala faly*) in southern Madagascar where tamarind trees are planted. Many stories of taboo forests involve the planting of *Alluaudia procera* or tamarind as a symbol of a friendship (Tengö and Von Heland 2014; Von Heland 2011).

In western Madagascar, tamarind is protected as a sacred tree (*hazo faly*). People in the region believe that ancestral spirits (*koko* or *komba*) live in the trees (Stiles 1998), and certain important social events, including judgements, communal meetings, political decisions and blessings, are conducted beneath tamarind trees (Fritz-Vietta et al. 2017). It is taboo to urinate or defecate near a tamarind tree (Iida 2005). The *ala be*, in the Sakalava region of western Madagascar, is thought to be inhabited by diverse spirits who are wary of humans and can only be found deep in the forest. They are strongly associated with large, old trees such as tamarind and baobab. These trees are often the focal points for *zomba*, or sacred places for traditional practices (Scales 2012). The 18th century Sakalava kings of Menabe held court daily underneath a large tamarind tree (Hooper 2010).

The seeds of tamarind are used for *sikily* (or *sikidy*), a system of geomancy practised in Madagascar; the name of this practice may be derived from *kily*. Geomancy is practised by *ombiasa* (or *ambiasa*), the traditional healers or witch doctors of Madagascar, and is likely to be related to the sacred character of the tamarind tree.

5. Forest Animals and Local People

5-1. Animals in Gallery Forests

The remaining gallery forests in southern Madagascar provide critical habitat for forest animals, and at least 27 mammals, 106 birds, 46 reptiles, and six amphibians inhabit Berenty Reserve (Ichino et al. 2018). Among these animals are three critically endangered species, including one lemur (the Verreaux's sifaka, *Propithecus verreauxi*) and two tortoises (Madagascar radiated tortoise, *Astrochelys radiata*, and the spider tortoise, *Pyxis arachnoides*), as well as two endangered lemurs, including the ring-tailed lemur (*Lemur catta*) and the white-footed sportive lemur (*Lepilemur leucopus*). While the two tortoise species are rarely observed in the forest, population densities of the three endangered lemur species are higher than elsewhere, suggesting that Berenty Reserve provides high quality habitat (Hladik and Charles-Dominique 1974; Jolly et al. 2002; Koyama et al. 2002).

5-2. Protection of Forest Animals by Local People

With the exception of three tenrec species, the Tandroy do not use mammals for bush meat in Berenty (Ichino et al. 2018). The three species that are used include *Tenrec ecaudatus*, *Setifer setosus* and *Echinops telfairi*. All three are relatively secure at present, with a status of 'Least concern' according to the International Union for Conservation of Nature.

The three endangered lemurs and two endangered tortoises are culturally protected in Berenty by Tandroy food taboos (*fady* or *faly*). Consumption of certain animals is rigorously controlled by food taboos. According to an informant, it is believed that unintentional consumption of taboo species causes something akin to an allergic reaction. Dogs are the strongest taboo animal, and a person who eats dog will be socially excluded and cannot be placed in the family tomb. The Tandroy also have a strict taboo against killing and eating lemurs. Tandroy folklore, which states that the ring-tailed lemur and the Verreaux's sifaka were initially humans who escaped from their stepmother into the forest (Ichino et al. 2018), may underlie the taboo. This folklore is shared by the Mahafaly people, a neighbouring ethnic group of south western Madagascar, who have the same taboo against eating lemurs (Loudon et al. 2006). By contrast, eating lemurs is not taboo for the Tanosy people, an ethnic group in southeastern Madagascar. The Tandroy in Berenty often refer to the Tanosy as lemur eaters, probably to emphasise that they themselves do not eat lemurs. Thus, the food taboo seems to be partly linked to ethnic identities.

The Madagascan flying fox (*Pteropus rufus*) is also a taboo food for the Tandroy (Ichino et al. 2018; Racey et al. 2010). The physical appearance of animals appears to play a role in Tandroy food taboos. For example, a local informant explained that the Madagascan flying fox is taboo because of its similarity to lemurs. The nocturnal mouse lemur is also considered inedible because of its similarity to both diurnal lemurs and mice.

In contrast to mammal species, birds are typically regarded as food species by the Tandroy. Most bird species constitute hunting targets, although at least 11 birds are considered inedible (Ichino et al. 2018). However, hunting pressures may be lower than elsewhere because hunting is mostly practised opportunistically. As a result, most mammals, including endangered species, are protected by local cultural norms in the gallery forests of southern Madagascar, whereas most bird species are at risk of poaching.

5-3. Tandroy Identity as Cattle Herders

Hunting is not central to Tandroy culture, and they do not consider most mammals to be edible (Ichino et al. 2018). This food culture is likely to be linked to the semi-arid climate and the traditional reliance of the Tandroy on zebu herding. The Tandroy people of the region identify as cattle herders, whereas hunting and gathering are considered supplemental activities. Heurtebize (1986: 28) described the situation as such: 'The Tandroy is a herdsman before he is a farmer, he is a zebu herder and not a labourer'. Zebu have symbolic value in Tandroy culture: they represent prosperity, personal and social success and, by extension, individual and family prestige (Guérin 1977). This might reflect the influence of the East African Cattle Complex (Herskovits 1926). According to Frère (1958), zebu are the primary sign of wealth and personal success among the Tandroy.

In contrast to the positive cultural associations of zebu herding, the Tandroy have a negative view of forest-based activities. Some young Tandroy men sometimes stay in the forest, but these men are referred to as *hako*, which translates as 'person hiding in the forest', or *vazimba*, which is a mythical forest-dweller. An informant explained that choosing to live in the forest is *votro*, which means 'weak, needy or cowardly' in the Tandroy dialect (Rajaonarimanana and Fee 2011).

6. Ecological Interactions in Gallery Forests

6-1. Ecological Functions of Tamarind

Tamarind is a key tree species in gallery forests, providing forest animals with food, shade, resting places, shelter from potential predators or storms and sleeping places. Owing to their wide, dense crowns, tamarind trees provide high-quality shelter, resting and sleeping sites for animals. Tamarind trees also appear to have better wind resistance than other large trees: when a violent windstorm hit Berenty in 1999, tamarind trees suffered less damage than *Acasia rovumae*, another large tree species (Rasamimanana et al. 2000).

Six lemur species inhabit Berenty Reserve, all of which use tamarind trees for food (Hladik and Charles-Dominique 1974; Simmen et al. 2003), nesting (Génin 2010) or sleeping (Mertl-Millhollen et al. 2003). Tamarind trees also provide protection from the Madagascan harrier-hawk (*Polyboroides radiatus*), a large raptor that preys on lemurs (Goodman et al. 1993).

Among lemur species, the ring-tailed lemur (Figure 5) relies most heavily on tamarind, spending approximately half of its feeding time on tamarind fruit pulp or leaves throughout the year. Population density patterns largely mirror the availability of tamarind trees, and in seasons where there is a dearth in the usual range, animals may make long excursions to find fruiting trees (Blumenfeld-Jones et al. 2006; Koyama et al. 2006; Mertl-Millhollen et al. 2003, 2004, 2006; Rasamimanana and Rafidinarivo 1993; Soma 2006).

Figure 5. The ring-tailed lemur (*Lemur catta*) at Berenty Reserve
(photo taken by the author)

Tamarind also provides food and roosting sites for the Madagascan flying fox (*Pteropus rufus*). Tamarind fruits are an important food item for this species (Long and Racey 2007), and the flying fox colony in Berenty roosts in large tamarind trees at the centre of the forest. This population ranges in size from 500–600 individuals during the wet season (January–February) to 1,800–2,000 individuals at the end of the dry season (August–September), and is relatively large compared to populations elsewhere in Madagascar (Bollen and Van Elsacker 2002; MacKinnon et al. 2003).

At least 14 bird species have been documented using tamarind trees in Berenty (Goodman et al. 1997). Five species have been observed using the species for food, including the greater vasa parrot (*Coracopsis vasa*), the lesser vasa parrot (*Coracopsis nigra*), the souimanga sunbird (*Cinnyris sovimanga*), the Madagascar white-eye (*Zosterops maderaspatanus*) and the white-headed vanga (*Artamella viridis*). Two species, the black kite (*Milvus migrans*) and the Madagascar paradise flycatcher (*Terpsiphone mutata*), use the tree as perches, and seven species nest in tamarind trees, including the Madagascar sparrow-hawk (*Accipiter madagascariensis*), the Madagascar buzzard (*Buteo brachypterus*), the gray-headed lovebird (*Agapornis cana*), the giant coua (*Coua gigas*), the broad-billed roller (*Eurystomus glaucurus*) and the crested drongo (*Dicrurus forficatus*).

Owing to a lack of intensive research on reptiles, amphibians, small mammals and invertebrates, it is unclear whether, or to what degree, these taxa rely on tamarind trees (Ichino et al. 2018). However, tamarind trees may have some value to these groups, because tamarinds form tall, closed canopy forests, providing strongly contrasting environmental conditions to those of dry spiny forests.

6-2. Tamarind Seed Dispersal

Tamarind is shade intolerant, and regeneration under parent trees is often poor. Large, frugivorous animals, which are capable of swallowing tamarind seeds, are thus important seed dispersers, facilitating regeneration by moving seeds away from the parent tree.

The most important disperser is the ring-tailed lemur; this species feeds on large amounts of tamarind fruits, and intact seeds have been found in their faeces (Mertl-Millhollen et al. 2011). The red-fronted brown lemur (*Eulemur rufifrons*), which hybridises with the red-collared brown lemur (*E. collaris*), also feeds on large amounts of tamarind fruits, but is not considered a key disperser because it was introduced from western Madagascar in 1975 and does not occur naturally in the gallery forests of southern Madagascar. The Verreaux's sifaka also feeds on tamarind fruits, but is primarily a seed predator (Rasamimanana et al. 2012). The only other potential seed disperser in this region is the Madagascan flying fox (Bollen et al. 2004) but, to date, no tamarind seeds have been observed in its faeces at Berenty (Raheriarisena 2005). Thus, interactions between the tamarind and the ring-tailed lemur comprise a key ecological relationship in the gallery forests of southern Madagascar.

6-3. Mutualistic Relationships among Tamarind, Lemur and Humans

The relationship between tamarind, ring-tailed lemurs and humans (the local Tandroy people) in the gallery forests of southern Madagascar is a mutually beneficial one (Figure 6). First, protection of tamarind trees by the local people benefits forest animals, particularly the ring-tailed lemur, because tamarind is the most important food source for this species. Second, the Tandroy have strict taboos against killing and eating lemurs, which indirectly benefit the tamarind because the ring-tailed lemur is a key seed disperser for the species, playing a substantial role in tamarind recruitment. Furthermore, the tamarind–lemur relationship may indirectly benefit local people by increasing tamarind regeneration, thus potentially increasing famine food supplies (Figure 6). Although it may seem that there should be competition between the Tandroy and the lemurs for tamarind fruits, local people tolerate lemurs as tamarinds produce large food crops. This high fruit production is sustained even in drought years, and a local Tandroy proverb states that, 'The tamarinds take care of us during famine' (Jolly et al. 2006).

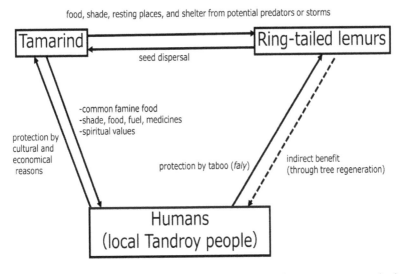

Figure 6. Mutually beneficial relationships between tamarind, humans and ring-tailed lemurs

207

7. Conclusions

In this chapter, I described relationships between tamarind, forest animals and the Tandroy people in the gallery forests of southern Madagascar. This relationship fits the definition of African Potentials with respect to biodiversity conservation. First, the cultural taboos (*faly*) of the Tandroy may protect forests and animals, including endangered species. As reported in other studies, taboos relating to place and natural resources are deeply rooted in Tandroy life, and may serve as a strong deterrent against deforestation and lemur poaching (Ichino et al. 2018; Tengö et al. 2007), although in some cases the Tandroy have destroyed gallery forests for charcoal production.

Second, the semi-arid climate of the region is critical to the relationship between the forest and the local people. The relationship between people, tamarind and ring-tailed lemurs is closely linked to drought and famine (Figure 6). The region experiences major droughts approximately every ten years, with the worst droughts resulting in significant loss of human life; such events occurred in 1932, 1943, 1984, and 1991–1992 (Jolly 2004). Cultural and/or social constraints on the use of forest resources may be important in semi-arid regions, where plant productivity is relatively low. Thus, it is important to understand and account for the ecological conditions experienced by local peoples, and the practices they have developed to cope with these conditions.

Finally, there is a mutualistic relationship between the Tandroy, the tamarind and the ring-tailed lemur. The relationship is a blend of ecological, social and cultural relationships and must be understood holistically. Previous studies on African Potentials for resource conservation issues have based arguments on 'indigenous knowledge' or 'local manners to avoid conflict' (Shigeta and Itani [eds] 2016). But as I have demonstrated here, key ecological interactions in African tropical forests can involve three or more species, and the relationships cannot be simplified as an assembly of independent interactions. Thus, to apply the idea of African Potentials to biodiversity conservation, it is critical to understand not only the activities and rationale of local people but also the comprehensive relationships among key species, including ecological interactions and their cultural significance.

Acknowledgments

I am grateful to Ms Claire Foulon, Ms Benedict de Heaulme and their family members for their kind permission to carry out my studies and their hospitality at Berenty Reserve. I also thank Dr Hajanirina Rakotomanana and Dr Felix Rakotondraparany for supporting my fieldworks in Madagascar, and the Government of the Republic of Madagascar for kindly providing permission to conduct research. This work was supported by JSPS KAKENHI Grant Numbers JP23221012, JP16H06318, and JP19K12501, JSPS Program for Advancing Strategic International Networks to Accelerate the Circulation of Talented Researchers 'Network formation for reconstructing the paradigm of African Area Studies in a globalizing world (PI: Jun Ikeno)' and the Toyota Foundation (D14-R-0527).

References

Andrés-Domenech, P., Saint-Pierre, P., Fanokoa, P. S. and Zaccour, G. (2014) 'Sustainability of the dry forest in Androy: A viability analysis', *Ecological Economics*, Vol. 104, pp. 33–49.

Andriamparany, J. N., Brinkmann, K., Jeannoda, V. and Buerkert, A. (2014) 'Effects of socio-economic household characteristics on traditional knowledge and usage of wild yams and medicinal plants in the Mahafaly region of south-western Madagascar', *Journal of Ethnobiology and Ethnomedicine*, Vol. 10, No. 82 (https://doi.org/10.1186/1746-4269-10-82) (accessed: 1 October 2020).

Berger, A. (2003) 'Food resources at Chibuene and Manyikeni, two archaeological sites in Southern Mozambique', International Symposium on Urban Landscape Dynamics, Session 4 Socio-Environmental Interactions: Resource Utilization Strategies, Uppsala, 28–30 August 2003.

Bhagwat, S. A., Willis, K. J., Birks, H. J. B. and Whittaker, R. J. (2008) 'Agroforestry: A refuge for tropical biodiversity?', *Trends in Ecology and Evolution*, Vol. 23, Issue 5, pp. 261–267.

Blumenfeld-Jones, K., Randriamboavonjy, T. M., Williams, G., Mertl-Millhollen, A. S., Pinkus, S. and Rasamimanana, H. (2006) 'Tamarind recruitment and long-term stability in the gallery forest at Berenty, Madagascar', in A. Jolly, R. W. Sussman, N. Koyama and H. Rasamimanana (eds) *Ringtailed Lemur Biology: Lemur Catta in Madagascar*, New York: Springer, pp. 69–85.

Boiteau P. and Allorge-Boiteau, L. (1993) *Plantes médicinales de Madagascar: Cinquante-huit plantes médicinales utilisées sur le marché de Tananarive (Zoma) à Madagascar*, Paris: Karthala.

Bollen, A. and Van Elsacker, L. (2002) 'Feeding ecology of *Pteropus rufus* (Pteropodidae) in the littoral forest of Sainte Luce, SE Madagascar', *Acta Chiropterologica*, Vol. 4, No. 1, pp. 33–47.

Bollen, A., Van Elsacker, L. and Ganzhorn, J. U. (2004) 'Relations between fruits and disperser assemblages in a Malagasy littoral forest: A community-level approach', *Journal of Tropical Ecology*, Vol. 20, Issue 6, pp. 599–612.

Budnitz, N. and Dainis, K. (1975) '*Lemur catta*: Ecology and behavior', in I. Tattersall and R. W. Sussman (eds) *Lemur Biology*, New York: Plenum Press, pp. 219–235.

Decary, R. (1930) *L'Androy, extrême sud de Madagascar: Essai de monographie régionale*, Paris: Société d'éditions géographiques, maritimes et colonials.

Drury, R. (1729) *Madagascar: Or Robert Drury's Journal during Fifteen Years Captivity on That Island*, London: Meadows.

El-Siddig, K., Gunasena, H. P. M., Prasad, B. A., Pushpakumara, D. K. N. G., Ramana, K. V. R., Vijayanand, P. and Williams, J. T. (2006) *Tamarind: Tamarindus indica*, Southampton: Southampton Centre for Underutilised Crops.

Fairhead, J. and Leach, M. (1996) *Misreading the African Landscape: Society and Ecology in a Forest-Savanna Mosaic*, Cambridge: Cambridge University Press.

Flacourt, É. (1661) *Histoire de la grande isle Madagascar*, Paris: Chez Nicolas Oudot.

Frère, S. (1958) *Madagascar: Panorama de l'Androy*, Paris: Éditions Aframpe.

Fritz-Vietta, N. V., Tahirindraza, H. S. and Stoll-Kleemann, S. (2017) 'Local people's knowledge with regard to land use activities in southwest Madagascar–Conceptual insights for sustainable land management', *Journal of Environmental Management*, Vol. 199, pp. 126–138.

Gebre, Y., Ohta, I. and Matsuda, M. (2017) 'Introduction: Achieving peace and coexistence through African Potentials', in Y. Gebre, I. Ohta and M. Matsuda (eds) *African Virtues in the Pursuit of Conviviality: Exploring Local Solutions in Light of Global Prescriptions*, Bamenda: Langaa RPCIG, pp. 3–37.

Génin, F. (2010) 'Who sleeps with whom? Sleeping association and socio-territoriality in *Microcebus griseorufus*', *Journal of Mammalogy*, Vol. 91, Issue 4, pp. 942–951.

Goodman, S. M., O'Connor, S. and Langrand, O. (1993) 'A review of predation on lemurs: Implications for the evolution of social behavior in small, nocturnal primates', in P. M. Kappeler and J. U. Ganzhorn (eds) *Lemur Social Systems and Their Ecological Basis*, New York: Plenum Press, pp. 51–66.

Goodman, S. M., Pidgeon, M., Hawkins, A. F. A. and Schulenberg, T. S. (1997) 'The birds of southeastern Madagascar', *Fieldiana Zoology*, Vol. 87, pp. 1–132.

Guérin, M. (1977) *Le défi: L'Androy et l'appel à la vie*, Fianarantsoa: Librairie Ambozontany.

Herskovits, M. J. (1926) 'The cattle complex in East Africa', *American Anthropologist*, Vol. 28, Issue 1, pp. 230–272.

Heurtebize, G. (1986) *Histoire des Afomarolahy: Clan Tandroy, extrême-sud de Madagascar*, Paris: Editions du Centre National de la recherche scientifique.

Hladik, C. M. and Charles-Dominique, P. (1974) 'The behaviour and ecology of the sportive lemur (*Lepilemur mustelinus*) in relation to its dietary peculiarities', in R. D. Martin, G. A. Doyle and A. C. Walker (eds) *Prosimian Biology: Proceedings of a Meeting of the Research Seminar in Archaeology and Related Subjects Held at the Institute of Archaeology, London University*, London: Duckworth.

Hooper, J. L. (2010) 'An Empire in the Indian Ocean: The Sakalava Empire of Madagascar', unpublished Ph.D. thesis, Emory University.

Ichino, S., Maehata, T., Rakotomanana, H. and Rakotondraparany, F. (2018) 'Forest vertebrate fauna and local knowledges among the Tandroy people in Berenty Researve, Southern Madagascar: A preliminary study', *African Study Monographs, Supplementary Issue*, Vol. 54, pp. 115–135.

Iida, T. (2005) 'The past and present of the coral reef fishing economy in Madagascar: Implications for self-determination in resource use', *Senri Ethnological Studies*, Vol. 67, pp. 237–258.

Jackson, H. (2013) 'Traditional healing in Madagascar: A study of a Tandroy ombiasa and his methods of healing', *Independent Study Project (ISP) Collection*, No. 1506 (https://digitalcollections.sit.edu/isp_collection/1506) (accessed: 30 June 2020).

Jolly, A. (2004) *Lords and Lemurs: Mad Scientists, Kings with Spears, and the Survival of Diversity in Madagascar*, Boston: Houghton Mifflin Harcourt.

———— (2012) 'Berenty Reserve, Madagascar: A long time in a small space', in P. M. Kappeler and D. P. Watts (eds) *Long-Term Field Studies of Primates*, Berlin: Springer, pp. 21–44.

———— (2015) *Thank You, Madagascar: The Conservation Diaries of Alison Jolly*, London: Zed Books.

Jolly, A., Dobson, A., Rasamimanana, H. M., Walker, J., O'connor, S., Solberg, M. and Perel, V. (2002) 'Demography of *Lemur catta* at Berenty Reserve, Madagascar: Effects of troop size, habitat and rainfall', *International Journal of Primatology*, Vol. 23, Issue 2, pp. 327–353.

Jolly, A., Koyama, N. Rasamimanana, H. Crowley, H. and Williams, G. (2006). 'Berenty Reserve: A research site in Southern Madagascar', in A. Jolly, R. W. Sussman, N. Koyama and H. Rasamimanana (eds) *Ringtailed Lemur Biology:* Lemur Catta *in Madagascar*, New York: Springer, pp. 32–42.

Kaufmann, J. C. (2004) 'Prickly pear cactus and pastoralism in southwest Madagascar', *Ethnology*, Vol. 43, No. 4, pp. 345–361.

Koyama, N., Nakamichi, M., Ichino, S. and Takahata, Y. (2002) 'Population and social dynamics changes in ring-tailed lemur troops at Berenty, Madagascar between 1989–1999', *Primates*, Vol. 43, Issue 4, pp. 291–314.

Koyama, N., Nakamichi, M., Oda, R., Miyamoto, N., Ichino, S. and Takahata, Y. (2001) 'A ten-year summary of reproductive parameters for ring-tailed lemurs at Berenty, Madagascar', *Primates*, Vol. 42, Issue 1, pp. 1–14.

Koyama, N., Soma, T., Ichino, S. and Takahata, Y. (2006) 'Home ranges of ringtailed lemur troops', in A. Jolly, R. W. Sussman, N. Koyama and H. Rasamimanana (eds) *Ringtailed Lemur Biology: Lemur Catta in Madagascar*, New York: Springer, pp. 86–101.

Kull, C. A., Tassin, J., Moreau, S., Ramiarantsoa, H. R., Blanc-Pamard, C. and Carrière, S. M. (2012) 'The introduced flora of Madagascar', *Biological Invasions*, Vol. 14, Issue 4, pp. 875–888.

Labat, J.-N. and Moat, J. (2003) 'Leguminosae (Fabaceae)', in S. M. Goodman and J. P. Benstead (eds) *The Natural History of Madagascar*, Chicago: University of Chicago Press, pp. 346–373.

Linton, R. (1928) 'Culture areas in Madagascar', *American Anthropologist*, Vol. 30, Issue 3, pp. 363–390.

Long, E. and Racey, P. A. (2007) 'An exotic plantation crop as a keystone resource for an endemic megachiropteran, *Pteropus rufus*, in Madagascar', *Journal of Tropical Ecology*, Vol. 23, pp. 397–407.

Loudon, J. E., Sauther, M. L., Fish, K. D., Hunter-Ishikawa, M. and Ibrahim, Y. J. (2006) 'One reserve, three primates: Applying a holistic approach to understand the interconnections among ring-tailed lemurs (*Lemur catta*), Verreaux's sifaka (*Propithecus verreauxi*), and humans (*Homo sapiens*) at Beza Mahafaly Special Reserve, Madagascar', *Ecological and Environmental Anthropology (University of Georgia)*, Vol. 2, No. 2, pp. 54–74.

MacKinnon, J. L., Hawkins, C. E. and Racey, P. A. (2003) 'Pteropodidae, fruit bats, fanihy, angavo', in S. M. Goodman and J. P. Benstead (eds) *The Natural History of Madagascar*, Chicago: The University of Chicago Press, pp. 1299–1302.

Matsuda, M. (2014) 'Learning from African Potentials', in M. Matsuda (ed.) *For Those Studying African Societies*, Kyoto: Sekaishisosha, pp. 1–5 (in Japanese).

Mertl-Millhollen, A. S., Blumenfeld-Jones, K., Raharison, S. M., Tsaramanana, D. R. and Rasamimanana, H. (2011) 'Tamarind tree seed dispersal by ring-tailed lemurs', *Primates*, Vol. 52, Issue 4, pp. 391–396.

Mertl-Millhollen, A. S., Moret, E. S., Felantsoa, D., Rasamimanana, H., Blumenfeld-Jones, K. C. and Jolly, A. (2003) 'Ring-tailed lemur home ranges correlate with food abundance and nutritional content at a time of environmental stress', *International Journal of Primatology*, Vol. 24, Issue 5, pp. 969–985.

Mertl-Millhollen, A. S., Rambeloarivony, H., Miles, W., Kaiser, V. A., Gray, L., Dorn, L.T., Williams, G. and Rasamimanana, H. (2006) 'The influence of tamarind tree quality and quantity on *Lemur catta* behavior', in A. Jolly, R. W. Sussman, N. Koyama and H. Rasamimanana (eds) *Ringtailed Lemur Biology: Lemur Catta in Madagascar*, New York: Springer, pp. 102–118.

Mertl-Millhollen, A. S., Rambeloarivony, H., Miles, W. and Rasamimanana, H. (2004) 'Tamarind leaf quality and *Lemur catta* population density and behaviour', *Folia Primatologica*, Vol. 75, pp. 157–158.

Middleton, K. (2001) 'Power and meaning on the periphery of a Malagasy Kingdom', *Ethnohistory*, Vol. 48, No. 1-2, pp. 171–204.

Mittermeier, R. A., Hawkins, F., Rajaobelina, S. and Langrand, O. (2005) 'Wilderness conservation in a biodiversity hotspot', *International Journal of Wilderness*, Vol. 11, Issue 3, pp. 42–45.

Mittermeier, R. A., Louis Jr, E. E., Richardson, M., Schwitzer, C., Langrand, O., Rylands, A. B., Hawkins, F., Rajaobelina, S., Ratsimbazafy, J., Rasoloarison, R., Roos, C., Kappeler, P. M. and Mackinnon, J. (2010) *Lemurs of Madagascar (Third Edition)*, Arlington: Conservation International.

Morton, J. (1987) *Fruits of Warm Climates*, Miami: J. F. Morton.

Myers, N., Mittermeier, R. A., Mittermeier, C. G., Da Fonseca, G. A. and Kent, J. (2000) 'Biodiversity hotspots for conservation priorities', *Nature*, Vol. 403, Issue 6772, pp. 853–858.

Norscia, I. and Borgognini-Tarli, S.M. (2006) 'Ethnobotanical reputation of plant species from two forests of Madagascar: A preliminary investigation', *South African Journal of Botany*, Vol. 72, Issue 4, pp. 656–660.

Ohta, I. (2016) 'Series introduction: Exploring "Africa Potentials" – Toward dispute resolution and realization of coexistence', in M.

Matsuda and M. Hirano-Nomoto (eds) *Culture Coping with Conflict: Incompleteness and Practice of Bricolage*, Kyoto: Kyoto University Press, pp. i–xxxi (in Japanese).

Olson, J. S. (1996) *The Peoples of Africa: An Ethnohistorical Dictionary*, Westport: Greenwood Publishing Group.

Pearson, M. P. (1996) 'Reassessing *Robert Drury's Journal* as a historical source for southern Madagascar', *History in Africa*, Vol. 23, pp. 233–256.

———— (1997) 'Close encounters of the worst kind: Malagasy resistance and colonial disasters in southern Madagascar', *World Archaeology*, Vol. 28, Issue 3, pp. 393–417.

Pearson, M. P. and Godden, K. (1999) 'Lost kingdoms: Oral histories, travellers' tales and archaeology in southern Madagascar', in P. P. A. Funari, M. Hall and S. Jones (eds) *Historical Archaeology: Back from the Edge*, London: Routledge, pp. 233–254.

Racey, P. A., Goodman, S. M. and Jenkins, R. K. (2010) 'The ecology and conservation of Malagasy bats' in T. H. Fleming and P. A. Racey (eds) *Islands Bats: Evolution, Ecology, and Conservation*, Chicago: University of Chicago Press, pp. 369–404.

Raheriarisena, M. (2005) 'Régime alimentaire de *Pteropus rufus* (*Chiroptera: Pteropodidae*) dans la région sub-aride du sud de Madagascar', *Revue d'ecologie (La Terre et la Vie)*, Vol. 60, pp. 255–264.

Rajaonarimanana, N. and Fee, S. (2011) *Dictionnaire Malgache Dialectal-Francais Dialecte Tandroy*, Paris: Langues & Mondes.

Rambeloarivony, H. and Jolly, A. (2012) 'Berenty Reserve: Past, present, and future', in J. Masters, M. Gamba and F. Génin (eds) *Leaping Ahead: Advances in Prosimian Biology*, New York: Springer, pp. 353–359.

Ranjarisoa, L. N., Razanamihaja, N. and Rafatro, H. (2016) 'Use of plants in oral health care by the population of Mahajanga, Madagascar', *Journal of Ethnopharmacology*, Vol. 193, pp. 179–194.

Rasamimanana, H. R. and Rafidinarivo, E. (1993) 'Feeding behavior of *Lemur catta* females in relation to their physiological state', in P. M. Kappeler and J. U. Ganzhorn (eds) *Lemur Social Systems and Their Ecological Basis*, New York: Plenum Press, pp. 123–133.

Rasamimanana, H., Ratovonirina, J. A., Jolly, A. and Pride, E. (2000) 'Storm damage at Berenty Reserve', *Lemur News* No. 5, pp. 7–8.

Rasamimanana, H., Razafindramanana, J., Mertl-Millhollen, A. S., Blumenfeld-Jones, K., Raharison, S. M., Tsaramanana, D. R., Voahirana, Razoliharisoa, V. and Tarnaud, L. (2012) 'Berenty Reserve: Interactions among the diurnal lemur species and the gallery forest', in J. Masters, M. Gamba and F. Génin (eds) *Leaping Ahead: Advances in Prosimian Biology*, New York: Springer, pp. 361–368.

Scales, I. R. (2012) 'Lost in translation: Conflicting views of deforestation, land use and identity in western Madagascar', *The Geographical Journal*, Vol. 178, Issue 1, pp. 67–79.

Shigeta, M. and Itani, J. (eds) (2016) *How People Can Achieve Coexistence through the Sound Use of Ecological Resources*, Kyoto: Kyoto University Press (in Japanese).

Sibree, J. (1880) *The Great African Island: Chapters on Madagascar: A Popular Account of Recent Researches in The Physical Geography, Geology, and Exploration of The Country, and Its Natural History and Botany; and in The Origin and Divisions, Customs and Language, Superstitions, Folk-Lore, and Religious Beliefs and Practices of The Different Tribes*, London: Trübner.

Simmen, B., Hladik, A. and Ramasiarisoa, P. (2003) 'Food intake and dietary overlap in native *Lemur catta* and *Propithecus verreauxi* and introduced *Eulemur fulvus* at Berenty, Southern Madagascar', *International Journal of Primatology*, Vol. 24, Issue 5, pp. 949–968.

Soma, T. (2006) 'Tradition and novelty: *Lemur catta* feeding strategy on introduced tree species at Berenty Reserve', in A. Jolly, R. W. Sussman, N. Koyama and H. Rasamimanana (eds) *Ringtailed Lemur Biology: Lemur Catta in Madagascar*, New York: Springer, pp. 141–159.

Stiles, D. (1998) 'The Mikea hunter-gatherers of southwest Madagascar: Ecology and socioeconomics', *African Study Monographs*, Vol.19, No. 3, pp.127–148.

Sussman, R.W., Green, G. M., Porton, I., Andrianasolondraibe, O. L. and Ratsirarson, J. (2003) 'A survey of the habitat of *Lemur catta* in southwestern and southern Madagascar', *Primate Conservation*, No. 19, pp. 32–57.

Swingle, C. F. (1929) 'Biological control of the prickly pear in Madagascar', *Science*, Vol. 70, Issue 1802, p. 37.

Tengö, M., Johansson, K., Rakotondrasoa, F., Lundberg, J., Andriamaherilala, J. A., Rakotoarisoa, J. A. and Elmqvist, T. (2007) 'Taboos and forest governance: Informal protection of hot spot dry forest in southern Madagascar', *AMBIO: A Journal of the Human Environment*, Vol. 36, Issue 8, pp. 683–691.

Tengö, M. and Von Heland, J. (2014) 'Trees and tree-planting in southern Madagascar: Sacredness and remembrance', in K. G. Tidball and M. E. Krasny (eds) *Greening in the Red Zone: Disaster, Resilience and Community Greening*, Dordrecht: Springer, pp. 333–337.

The Diagram Group (2013) *Encyclopedia of African Peoples*, London: Routledge.

Von Heland, J. (2011) 'Rowing social-ecological systems: Morals, culture and resilience', Doctoral dissertation, Department of Systems Ecology, Stockholm University.

Willis, K. J., Gillson, L. and Brncic, T. M. (2004) 'How "virgin" is virgin rainforest?', *Science*, Vol. 304, Issue 5669, pp. 402–403.

Yuasa, H., Abe, K., Rakotozafy, A. and Andriamahery R. R. (2000) 'Antandroy medicinal plants in Madagascar', *Science Report of the Research Institute of Evolutionary Biology*, Vol. 9, pp. 219–246 (in Japanese with English abstract).

Chapter 9

Rethinking the Potential for the Commodification of Africa's Natural Resources: A Case Study of Marula Use in Phalaborwa, South Africa

Yuichiro Fujioka

1. Introduction

The human activities of using natural resources work as disturbance factors in an area of the ecosystem, and these activities have formed various types of anthropogenic biomes (anthromes) in many areas of the world. Foley et al. (2005) summarised the schematic changes in land cover in the world. The results showed that global croplands, pastures, plantations and urban areas have expanded in recent decades, and are accompanied by large increases in energy, water and fertiliser consumption along with considerable losses of biodiversity. One study, conducted by Ellis et al. (2010), calculated that nearly half of the terrestrial biosphere was wild, without human settlements or substantial land use in 1700. Furthermore, most of the remainder was in a seminatural state (45 per cent) with only minor sections being used for agriculture and settlements. Then, by 2000, the opposite was true, with much of the biosphere in agricultural and settled anthromes, with less than 20 per cent of it is seminatural and only a quarter left wild (Ellis et al. 2010).

The sense of values about economic development has transformed from development strategies to consume inexhaustible natural resources into one of focused sustainability of the use of limited resources regarding the preservation of our planet. The limitations of resources and environmental capacity of Earth with its planetary boundaries (Rockström et al. 2009), were exceeded; thus, our society needs to transform its development based on underground resources to become a sustainable society based on the ecosystem resources. Desirable social values and the well-being of humans should be examined, and we should change our perception of values and our daily lives. In various projects for the development of African rural areas, achieving sustainable development is one of the main focal points. The concept of 'African Potentials' is also expected to involve the sustainability stabilisation of people's daily lives.

Secondary vegetation, which includes artificial or semi-artificial vegetation, is an expression of typical anthropogenic biomes. This type of vegetation specifically involves the destructive aspects of natural ecosystems in developed countries by human activities such as deforestation for gathering timber and fuel wood along with slash-and-burn shifting cultivation. In the context of ecosystem and biodiversity conservation, decreasing forest cover and deforestation – mostly tropical rainforests – are the serious causes of biodiversity reduction. Therefore, the expansion of secondary vegetation is considered as a kind of symbolic indicator of the destruction of the natural environment. Especially in developed countries, the local people's daily lives and activities in the forests have been considered as part of a process of deforestation or biodiversity loss since the 1980s.

In contrast, the functions of secondary vegetation have been reexamined from the point of a unique ecosystem that formed high biodiversity by living organisms adapted to the human environment. Long-term processes between humans and the environment have formed seminatural (semi-artificial) vegetation. This includes agro-ecosystems, agroforests and Satoyama ecosystems in Japan, where some species allow for the adaptation of those ecosystems and a moderate disturbance has increased living species. Thus, secondary vegetation with moderate human disturbances is reevaluated from the viewpoint of maintaining the unique ecosystem and biodiversity.

Anthromes also provide many ecosystem services for human societies and strongly relate to human well-being. The ecosystem and land use changes have enabled humans to appropriately increase natural resources, enabling the sustenance of food production and forest resources, regulation of climate and air quality, etc. However, we also confront the issues of balancing immediate human needs and maintaining the capacity of the ecosystem to provide resources and services in the long term. The functions of anthromes varied in the area by indigenous environmental and sociocultural factors, mainly in relation to human society. Therefore, scientists need to clarify the mutual relationships between an anthrome and human society in each area to examine the potential of anthromes.

There are several cases of commodification of natural resources and their products by local communities and entrepreneurs in the domestic and global markets in recent rural African communities. In particular, commodities made of/from non-timber forest products (NTFPs) have focused on the sustainable use of natural resources and promote the economic development of local communities – especially in developed countries. In other words, ecosystem services are expected to enhance the income level of low-income groups and empower households and local communities. Some African rural communities and entrepreneurs are connected to the global market through sales of products made of/from NTFPs; for example, the sale of shea nuts and its butter in Ghana (e.g. Chalfin 2004) and baobab oil in Tanzania. The company emphasised the benefits and beautiful stories relating to the products, such as economic contributions to local communities and the maintenance of local ecosystems. Then, how we can evaluate those activities of commodification processes of NTFPs from a viewpoint of African Potentials?

African Potentials is a concept which was presented by an international collaborative research project of the Japan Society for the Promotion of Sciences (JSPS) from 2011 to 2016 (Gebre et al. [eds] 2017a; Matsuda and Hirano-Nomoto [eds] 2016). As mentioned in the Introduction in this book, African Potentials were defined as 'philosophies, knowledge, institutions, values and practices that African societies have developed, modified and utilised in handling conflicts and achieving peaceful coexistence' (Gebre et al. 2017b: 3). This concept challenges the problematic stereotypical view of Africa based on Western ideas such as liberal democracy and the modern judicial system, while neglecting the manner of coexistence widely seen in African societies. This is based on dialogue and reconciliation rather than judgement and punishment (Introduction in this book). One of the aims of this book is to expand the target range of our analysis, and we expect that overlooked and hidden characteristics concerning African Potentials will be discovered. Accordingly, this chapter examines the case of marula use as one activity to modify NTFPs in South Africa.

How should we appraise the potential for commodification of rural Africa's natural resources? Drawing on intensive empirical research around Phalaborwa in South Africa, this chapter focuses on the use of marula fruit and its commodification as a case to examine the features of NTFP use in Africa. Marula (*Sclerocarya birrea*; subspecies *caffra*) is an indigenous tree species found in the semi-arid areas of sub-Saharan Africa; hence, *caffra* can be found south of the equator, spanning the continent from the Atlantic to the Indian Oceans (Nghitoolwa et al. 2003). Marula juice, which is derived from marula fruit, is used to make drinks, including fermented marula brew (sometimes called marula beer), in some societies of Southern Africa (Shackleton and Shackleton 2002; Hall et al. 2002; Shackleton et al. 2002). Many people in various countries sell the brew, particularly in some South African societies (Shackleton 2002, 2004).

First, I will present basic information about the research area, and then introduce the custom of marula use before commodification; notably, this is accomplished through an ethnographic survey in the Phalaborwa area from 2012 to 2018. Next, I will explain the process of commodification of marula products and their diversification with several related actors, such as established cooperatives and emerging entrepreneurs. However, the number of people who harvest the fruit also rapidly increased, which then led to conflict in a saturating market – a fact rarely aired in public. I especially focus on the functions of traditional leaders in dealing with this conflict. Finally, I examine the African Potentials of this case study of commodification from the viewpoint of an adjustment system that furnishes a provision for several factors such as the ecological environment, social systems, and market economies.

2. Marula Use with the Formation of Unique Vegetation in the Phalaborwa Area

2-1. The Livelihood of the People around the Phalaborwa Area

Phalaborwa is a local town in the Limpopo Province on the northeast side of South Africa. In 2010, the population of this town

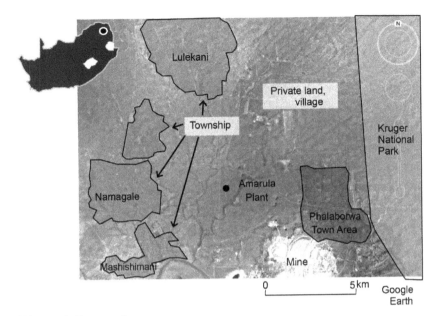

Figure 1. Research area

was 13,108. Although the size of its population is not very large, many tourists visit Phalaborwa because this is one of the gate towns of Kruger National Park. Its features include hilly terrain covered by savanna vegetation; wild animals primarily live inside the park. The climate in the area is semi-arid with an average annual rainfall of approximately 500 mm, falling mostly from November to April. Precipitation fluctuates considerably year by year, ranging from 237 mm (1961/1962) to 998 mm (2010/2011).

Several ethnic groups live in suburban Phalaborwa, including some Bantu ethnic groups such as Sotho, Shangani and Pedi. White people also reside there. The land ownerships around Phalaborwa are divided into two types: Phalaborwa town, townships, private lands, villages in communal lands and then national parks (Figure 1). By the 1990s, in the era of apartheid, the land ownership was strictly related to ethnicity. For example, white people could live inside the town, and workers of indigenous groups lived in the townships. Most of the private lands were farms or residential places of white people, and indigenous farmers mainly lived in communal lands. After abolishing the apartheid regime, the legacy structure of land ownership remains in this area.

223

The basic social unit in townships and villages is the nuclear or extended family residing in the same household. The mainstay of the rural livelihood of Sotho and Shangani is farming and livestock husbandry. The principal crops are maize, sorghum, cowpeas, and squashes. Maize is the main ingredient of their staple food, which is a hard porridge made of maize flour. They raise cattle and small stocks (goats and sheep) around the village. Apart from farming and grazing, they are also engaged in fishing, hunting, and gathering of wild plants and insects. For example, people gather wild edible plants grown in farmlands, wild birds, and edible caterpillars on mopane trees (e.g. *Gonimbrasia belina*, familiarly known as the mopane worm). Villagers also often utilise indigenous trees such as palm and marula in multifaceted ways such as construction materials, fuel, fodder, and materials for making alcohol. The people who live in town have permanent jobs with high salaries or manage farmland, accommodations, and mines as well as engage in the tourism sector. Many people who live in townships and villages are engaged in temporary or wage jobs in towns, mines, private farms, and tourism sectors. There is a considerable economic gap between wage earners and others, and economic disparity among households has recently grown wider.

2-2. Fruit Use of the Marula Tree

The marula tree is deciduous, and its leaves sprout from October to November; its fruit ripens in a sex-separate manner on different trees from February to March (Palgrave 2002: 539–540). This tree bears a plethora of juice-rich fruit and the diameter of each one is approximately 4 cm. In South Africa, one tree was reported to have produced over 17,000 pieces of fruit, and another produced 120,000 (Shackleton et al. 2002). The average fresh weight of one fruit is 31.5 g, of which 17 per cent (5.5 g) is juice.[1] Therefore, approximately 93.5 kg of marula juice can be produced from 17,000 pieces of fruit.

The ripening season of marula fruit is a long-awaited festive time for the local people in this area. Most of the adults like to drink marula beer (*vukani* in the Sotho language). It is a fermented drink brewed from the juice of marula fruit, and is considered to be the tastiest alcohol among the local people (Figure 2). From February to

224

Figure 2. Marula brew making: (left) squeezing marula juice, (right) marula brew

March, when marula fruit is available, women are busy squeezing it and making the beer. Because of the custom of sexual division of labour, only women engage in gathering and squeezing the fruit and making the brew. People enjoy making and drinking marula brew together, and they gift it to each other during this season. People eat raw marula fruit, but they mainly use the juice of the fruit to make the brew. In addition, they also make juice (*zowa*), which is made of water and seeds with a remnant of fresh fruit that is left after squeezing the juice. People are told *zowa* is a drink for children because it is not fermented. Moreover, the seed in the marula nut is used to make cooking oil and also used for raw eating. Marula brew is a special brew compared to others, such as sorghum brew and palm liquor, because marula brew was once used as a tribute to the traditional leaders.

2-3. The Formation of Unique Seminatural Vegetation

The vegetation around the area has been continuously affected by human activities. The natural vegetation type is classified as mopane woodland. Mopane vegetation is a unique vegetation type found in Southern Africa, and is dominated by the mopane tree (*Colophospermum mopane* Kirk ex Benth), which is a member of the Caesalpinioideae. Many ecological and physiological studies on mopane vegetation have indicated a homogeneity of species

225

composition, which can account for more than 90 per cent of the total phytomass (Werger and Coetzee 1978: 352–363) and few other species present. Actually, the closing area in Kruger National Park from Phalaborwa consists of widely distributed mopane-dominated woodland. In contrast, the vegetation which is around the human settlements is composed of a different vegetation, even near the park itself.

The natural landscape around this area is composed of small mountains, rivers and flat plateaus. Most of the residential area is located on a flat plateau, and mopane woodlands primarily cover the flat plateaus. Mopane wood is hard and resistant to termites. People use mopane wood for timber, which is then used to build residential huts and make charcoal materials. Therefore, residents tend to favour the mopane trunk and cut down the tall trees of this species relatively more than other species. Nevertheless, people tend not to cut down the tree species that produce edible fruits; accordingly, the local chiefs prohibit the cutting of specific fruit trees such as marula. Even inside crop fields, people retain the indigenous fruit trees. So, these tree species are protected when compared with other species and their presence may relatively increase the number of trees (Figure 3).

Figure 3. Landscape around village (white arrows show marula trees)

Local people living in rural areas rarely plant seedlings and seeds of indigenous tree species such as marula. Although town or township residents sometimes plant seeds or seedlings of indigenous tree species inside a new residential plot, people do not tend to intentionally plant them in crop fields and communal land in rural areas. However, they throw away seeds after eating the fruit, and as a result, the seeds are unintentionally distributed. Thus, the tree seeds gathered from other areas tend to be dispersed at a relatively high density around human residential areas. This is another factor which influences the growth of a vegetation that is composed of a high ratio of edible fruit-bearing tree species. This is a kind of seminatural vegetation formed through not highly disturbed human activities.

3. Commodification of Marula Products and Creating Stories

3-1. The Development History of the Amarula Brand

In 1983, Distell Group Limited (Distell) built a plant for liquor development in the suburban area of Phalaborwa. The company developed distilled liquor made from marula juice and gave it the brand name 'Amarula'. Although both the local marula brew and this Amarula brand are made using marula fruit, their taste and production processes are totally different.

This is a brief explanation about the making of Amarula. First, a company gathers a lot of raw marula fruit and crushes the fruit pulp after removing the big seeds. The fruit pulp contains a significant amount of fruit juice which is naturally fermented; next, it is distilled and aged in French oak barrels for two years. It is then blended with cream to create the smooth taste associated with Amarula. One of the important points is that Amarula can be preserved for a long duration because of the distilling process.

Distell sells the Amarula in the domestic and international markets. In the domestic market, they sell it not only in the local liquor shops as they also have a strategy to make this liquor an 'African' souvenir for foreigners. They promote the sale of this liquor in souvenir shops and international airport shops, and provide advertisements in tourism magazines. Foreign visitors to South Africa can easily find this liquor through the posters in the airport and the many shops.

Besides, since 1994, after the abolishing of apartheid and economic sanctions, Distell began selling Amarula to the international market. Subsequently, they have expanded the distribution network and have reached more than 100 countries.

To market this brand as an African souvenir, Distell added a special value to its African image by advertising it with some stories. The label of the bottle is a figure of an elephant and a marula fruit because elephants like to eat marula fruit. This label may contribute to emphasising the image of Africa to visitors. Even so, Distell emphasises their contribution to job creation by buying the fruit from local people (see section 4). These images and stories are strongly involved in the process to establish this brand as an indigenous African liquor.

3-2. Development and Diversification of the Commodification Process of Marula Products

After the democratisation of South Africa, economic activities have been developed and diversified by several actors. According to local farmers, men were mainly engaged in wage labour, such as in mines and as commercial farmers, and women were rarely employed as wage labourers. Since the 1990s, the employment environment has drastically changed, and some people have secured permanent jobs regardless of their ethnicity, and the number of employed women has increased. Besides, some entrepreneurs and groups voluntarily set up economic organisations, companies, cooperatives and non-governmental organisations (NGOs), and are supported by the affiliated organisations of the government.

Regarding the commodification of marula products, several actors participated or were involved in this process. Table 1 shows the main actors relating to the commodification of marula products. The pioneering company that sells the marula product is Distell, which developed the Amarula brand; in contrast, local women voluntarily sell the local marula brew in the independent sector. For example, some women sell the marula brew from the roadsides of Phalaborwa town or from houses in the villages or townships.

Table 1. Actors involved in commodification of marula products

Unit	The details	Price	Limitation
Company	Company developed distilled liquor, and buy fruit from local people since 1994	Purchase price (fruit) 12R/10kg	No limitation
Cooperative	Five cooperatives were established around Phalaborwa since 2009	(brew) 18R/2L	Limitation to members of cooperative (Enrolment fee is R100)
Individual	Some women sell homemade marula brew	(brew) 15R/2L	No limitation
	Some women collect marula fruits and sell to company	(fruit) 12R/10kg	No limitation
Municipality	Municipality buy 900 liters of marula brew for an event 'Marula Festival' from appointed cooperatives	Purchase price (brew) 18R/2L	Only from appointed cooperatives

At the end of the 2000s, some women tried to set up five cooperatives in different areas to sell marula brew (Table 2). These cooperatives were strongly related to the development activities of local administrations. For example, the local administration buys an adequate amount of marula brew for preparation for the annual Marula Festival of which they were one of the sponsors. The Marula Festival is a new annual event in this area related to development activities and tourism policy. The first one was held in March 2008, and it has been occurring every year since that time. Around 30,000

Table 2. Cooperatives for marula brew production

No	Cooperative name	Members (2012)
1	Moruwameetse Marula Cooperative Ltd	10
2	Mashishimale Phalaborwa Marula Primary	11
3	Makhushane Marula Primary Cooperative	10
4	Kgodung ya lapa la Setso Primary Cooperative	10
5	Possani Cooperative	10
-	Ba-Phalaborwa Marula Secondary Cooperative	plan

people from inside/outside of South Africa participate in the event, and several activities such as marathons, contests and football games are held during the festival. A lot of marula brew is sold or distributed to the participants in the event; therefore, the administration needs to prepare plenty of this brew. They buy 900 L of marula brew from one appointed cooperative for around R16,200 (rand: approximately ten rand equals one US dollar). One of the main activities of these five cooperatives is to make 900 L of marula brew to sell on behalf of the administration.

Each cooperative is based on a geographical area approved by the traditional leader of each location. Only women are members of the cooperatives, and around 10 of them participate in each cooperative (Table 2). Each cooperative utilises a portion of land and a building to squeeze marula brew. Most of the members live around the cooperative area, and they gather marula fruit around their area from February to March. The activities to make the brew are limited to this particular season, so they also undertake the challenge of selling marula nuts and nut products such as oil during other seasons. Since 2009, these five cooperatives have tried to establish new cooperatives to sell nuts and nut products to the market. In the process of establishing these cooperatives, the local affiliated organisation, Limpopo Business Support Agency (LIBSA), supported the procedures and consulting. In addition, some companies tentatively invest their money in cooperatives.

In summarising this subsection, people use unique natural resources in the area for sale and the context of rural development. Regarding this commodification process, several actors, such as companies, administrations, local residents and involved cooperatives have proceeded in this area.

4. The Involvement of Women in the Commodification of Marula Products and Its Impact

4-1. The Use of Opportunities to Earn Money from Marula

A plant manager of Distell stated, 'around 60,000 people depend on marula for their income'. Actually, many women engage in some activities relating to marula sales. According to an interview survey, women engaged in several types of activities such as gathering fruit, squeezing juice, selling nuts, developing new products and helping in cooperative activities.

To understand the women's marula-related activities, three women's activities are presented as case studies. The first is the case of 'Malia' (her pseudonym), who gathers fruit along the roadside. She lives in a township with five family members, and she does not have any other jobs. She picks fruit in the forest of the communal land along the roadside as well as private land after submitting a payment. She picks around ten bags a day (approximately 200 kg). Every year, she collects marula fruit from the middle of February to March and then sells it to Distell. The purchase price is around 10 kg/R12; a rough income estimate is around R240 per day. She and two other women hire a car with a male driver to help carry the fruit. They pay him R50 for three days of work. This is a typical case in which marula fruit is sold to a company.

The second case is a woman named 'Linda' (her pseudonym) who sells marula brew from an informal temporary tent shop along the roadside. For two months, from the beginning of February to March, she collects fruit in the early morning from 4:00 a.m. to 9:00 a.m., and then after 10:00 p.m. in the town. She usually collects around two bags of fruit (approximately 40 kg) per hour, coming to approximately ten bags per day for 30 L of marula brew. She squeezes the juice, makes the brew by herself and then sells it. The price is R15

231

per 2 L, with daily sales coming to about R225. She does not sell her fruit to Distell because it offers a low price.

The third example is a unique case of setting up a fruit-collecting camp in Phalaborwa. During a visit in February 2016, around 60 women set up a temporary camp in a public park in Phalaborwa. They slept and ate there while collecting fruit every day. Notably, one woman began this type of camp, which started around 1997. Every Wednesday, the company truck arrives to pick up the fruit at the camp; subsequently, the company pays cash on Mondays. They return to the house once a week. About this situation, one woman said, 'It's something like being a migrant worker. Most of the women are widows and we do not have any jobs'. She also said that the price of a standard marula sale was R28 per bag (50 L content), and she sold around 40 bags in one week, thus receiving R895. This meant that one person received R700 to R1,000 per week on average. At the time (2016), the average wage of a temporary job was R700 to R900 per month; therefore, some women were paid more money for those types of jobs. However, they can gather fruit only in February and March, so the money from the fruit is just temporary income.

4-2. The Structure of the Economic Gaps Regarding the Sale of Marula

In previous studies using NTFPs, the existence of economic structure and gender issues were pointed out by some case studies. One paper specifically emphasised that low-income women engaged in this type of labour and intensified the work of a specific low layer of income level and women.

As shown in the third case study, some people implied or directly spoke about the existence of economic structure related to these economic activities. One woman said, 'only poor women or no income women engage in these economic activities such as fruit gatherings and its sales'. Actually, most of the women who made temporary camps were unemployed women and widows. Some women who took part in the interview also mentioned the structure of the economy, especially this 'labourious work' for low-income people. In addition, some women complained of the low price offered by the company for the fruit.

Although marula fruit provides opportunities to obtain additional income for unemployed or low-income women, we have to focus on the negative aspects, such as intensifying the labour force for some economic and social groups. From the perspective of annual income sources, this economic activity consists of only a few months of the rainy season. This point is also important when evaluating these activities from an economic perspective.

On the other hand, this activity is not only a form of an income source, but people also experience the cultural meanings of this activity and engage in self-consumption. People enjoy drinking this tasty alcohol and partake in a custom to gift this brew to other households and traditional leaders. Some women said, 'making marula brew is our traditional custom. Squeezing the fruits with other women is our enjoyable time'. Thus, social connection through gathering fruit and making brew is important for the residents. In recent years, although the value of economic meaning or income has been added to the activities of marula, it is not only evaluated as a method of economic worth.

Summarising the movement around Phalaborwa, the commodification of marula products has been moving forward. Specifically, the progress is from launching the Amarula factory and connecting the global market through sales of marula-based liquor involving indigenous livelihood, local economy, plant use culture and social systems.

5. Experiencing Tradition: Regulating Function by Traditional Authority

In general, the increasing demand for natural resources would sometimes result in the privatisation of resources and lands. In the case of marula use in Phalaborwa, however, serious competition or privatisation did not occur after the commodification, as shown by the results of the interview survey and group discussion. Regarding the question about the situation of fruit gathering, some women reported that the number of marula fruit gatherers has in fact increased compared with the time before the 1990s. Presently, there is still a similar situation regarding individual competitive gathering.

One of the factors that maintain orderly gathering situations is the existence of traditional leaders. The position and role of a 'traditional leader' in South Africa has drastically changed with the sociopolitical conditions in the country. This is especially the case of the apartheid regime ending in the 1990s and then the establishment of democratic laws after it was abolished. One of the most significant aspects of the apartheid regime was the establishment of segregation between cities and rural areas and the different mechanisms of rules based on these land types (Mamdani 1996). The government in the apartheid regime segregated the rights of citizens. Although the people who lived in cities had citizenship, people in the rural areas were ruled by customary laws along with traditional leaders such as kings, chiefs and headmen. From a historical perspective, these traditional leaders were indigenous leaders of each ethnic group and local area. However, the colonial regime had been established by whites, and traditional leaders had been involved in the colonial regime. So, given this, they were forced to cooperate in the whites' regime, thus playing the function of absorbing complaints of the people living in the homelands.

After the abolishment of apartheid and the transformation into a democracy, the new government discussed these roles and the dealings with traditional leaders. The significant discussion point was the possibility of coexistence of the regime ruled by traditional leaders and democratic national law. Some people criticised the customary laws and the traditional leaders' regime because it was not a democratic rule; for example, women's rights were not established and there was inequality. Even with those critical opinions, the new Constitution of the Republic of South Africa was published in 1996 and it officially approved the positions of traditional leaders based on customary law. This meant that the role of traditional leaders in dealing with local issues relating to a community was recognised by national law. In addition, a new representative institute of traditional national and regional leaders was established as an advisory board to the national and regional governments.

6. Concluding Remarks

Summarising the changes in marula use in the area, the commodification of marula products has existed since the 1980s. Furthermore, Distell has expanded the market of its Amarula product to the global market after the abolishing of the economic sanctions on South Africa. Consequently, the indigenous custom of marula use has changed, the number of people involved in the commercial use of marula resources has increased and the varieties of marula products and actors have diversified. Although several benefits from the process of marula commodification have been given to local people, some disadvantages have also been reported. One of these factors is the income derived from sales of marula brew. This is not necessarily stable in the context of the whole year for most local people because the ripening season of marula fruit is limited to only two months, given the nature of the marula tree. Sales of nuts have the potential to be an economic activity for the whole year, which is on its way to being developed as an industry. Some people claim that the sales price of marula fruit is not equivalent to the labour load. One of the critical points of these activities is the labour exploitation which takes place at the bottom of the economic structure. On the other hand, these economic activities play a role in providing an economic opportunity for people who face many difficulties in obtaining jobs and labour work in the company. In fact, some people said that money from marula products is an essential income source for their household. Some people start their own business through entrepreneurship; for example, they form cooperatives to sell marula brew, sell it on the roadside and they create new products from marula fruit. In addition, the names 'marula' and 'Phalaborwa' are advertised through the sale of products to domestic people and international tourists. Furthermore, this awareness has also been activated through a big annual event (Marula Festival) and a visiting tour of the marula factory as a tourism site.

How can we consider or evaluate those activities from the perspective of African potentials? I will discuss this point in three aspects in the final part of this chapter.

First, the ecological environment characteristics in this area that provide natural resources as one of the economic services are pointed out as the essential background of these cultural and substantial activities of marula use. Notably, local vegetation is not an artificial afforestation or natural vegetation, but a seminatural vegetation in which the number of some specific and useful plants has increased relative to other species in long historical relations between local residents and plants. This type of seminatural vegetation is also formed in other areas of Africa, such as the marula distributed area in Namibia (Fujioka 2016); also, shea trees are distributed in rural areas in Ghana (Chalfin 2004). These areas of seminatural vegetation have three potential functions for local people. The first one is that local people can obtain more natural resources from specific plants because the number of specific plants is relatively high as a result of being protected from logging and by local rules for using the plant. Moreover, there is the accumulation of local knowledge about the nature of the plant and the proper way of using it. This feature set is a potential situation to mitigate the risk of annual fluctuations of production and the stable use of natural resources by many local people. Second, one of the features of this vegetation is that it is mainly composed of indigenous species. A case of artificial vegetation introduced by alien or improved species sometimes causes risks in sustainability due to its unfitness in an indigenous environment. Finally, this type of vegetation is formed by a long historical process; therefore, local people usually develop local rules to use natural resources to adjust their natural resources among community members and implement the proper utilisation methods of specific plants. Although this works to prevent unsustainable or exclusive utilisation of natural resources, it also works to limit free economic activities.

The second point of potential is that the commodification of NTFPs has the potential to develop local economic environments and improve the economy of households. The commodification of marula products is also a case that contributes to developing the local economy. One of the features of this commodification process in South Africa is that many local people are involved in the global market. A similar case is the commodification of shea butter (using shea nuts) in Ghana (Chalfin 2004). Although the size of the market is different, the commodification process in South Africa also involves various actors and proceeds with various levels of economic activities undertaken by local entrepreneurship. As also pointed out by previous studies, on the other hand, the issues of NTFPs commodification have occurred in the area, existing economic structure and gender inequality regarding works on marula products. In addition, there is an issue of failing economic management of cooperatives, which is a typical problem in the cases of rural development in Africa. For example, sales of marula nuts (not juice) have not proceeded, and have not succeeded in mechanisation and management strategies. NTFPs have the potential to contribute to local economic development, but local people have to overcome several issues to access those activities for sustainable activity.

Third, establishing social ties through the process of using marula is also an important potential aspect to sustain and develop the area. People use marula not only for food or economic resources, but they also use marula products in various social and cultural contexts. One of the important social aspects is connecting marula brew to traditional authority, which is a fundamental indigenous political structure. Wynberg and Laird (2007) examined the role of customary law in the use of the marula tree in South Africa and Namibia. The traditional authorities set some rules about accessibility and utilisation of tree resources, and ruled on the obligation for households concerning tribute marula brew. In addition, the traditional authority has developed a social and cultural manner to use marula resources, such as the ritual tasting of the first seasonal marula brew and holding a festive marula ceremony. People generally maintain these social and cultural manners and rules after the commodification of marula products and thus make a connection to the global market.

Some scholars have pointed out that traditional rules and customary laws sometimes prevent rational economic activities in the market economy. In South Africa, some issues relating to customary laws are also criticised – in particular, gender inequality. For example, women's rights and positions are treated as being relatively lower than men in customary laws. These points were discussed at the national level of the legal dimensions in the transition process of democratisation in South Africa, especially regarding the political position of the traditional leaders and the legal setting of customary laws. After the results, although customary laws and traditional leaders were maintained in national law, several issues still existed. However, critics claim that the radical procedure of commodification for natural resources and transforming the rural economy into a market economy would destroy social connections, livelihoods and daily lives in rural areas. Traditional leaders and customary laws have the function of adjusting and maintaining indigenous manners of daily lives and sociocultural aspects in the area. In this case of marula commodification, local people frequently mentioned traditional leaders and customary laws regarding marula fruit use. Even the economic activities of global companies also proceeded with negotiations by traditional leaders. From the perspective of sustainability of the commodification of natural resources in this area, traditional leaders and customary laws are important factors to adjust to new economic mechanisms with local sociocultural practices, which are also key factors considering the potential of NTFPs and their sustainability.

In general, the commodification process of natural resources that is connected with the global economy and tourism sectors is considered one of the African Potentials. Accordingly, these proper processes might lead to a bottom-up local economy and household income. On the other hand, these activities are strongly affected by the demand of the global market, the price of buying by company and the number of tourists, and so there is a high risk of fluctuation and a temporary trend of economic activity. The local people continuously live in political situations and establish social connections in local areas with regard to the future, so people tend to consider the stability of their lives as well as their increases in income. Therefore, innovation harmonised with local politics and social connections is more important for local people than the rational transformation of social and economic systems in the context of rural economic development. From this standpoint, the ability to adjust and balance challenging new economic activities and indigenous social and cultural systems is a kind of African Potentials that we found in this case study. Even so, we should not discuss African Potentials without a solution for gender inequality in economic and social structures in the area and existing economic structures relating to the apartheid structure. The challenging issue for African Potentials is the potential ability to improve these different levels of problematic issues in the future.

This case study shows some actors involved in the commodification of marula resources which can be expressed as African Potentials, such as local women, entrepreneurs, cooperatives, companies, traditional authorities and anthropogenic biomes. The African Potentials for commodification are embedded in an adjustment system that furnishes provisions for several factors, and subjects of African Potentials are not only human society, also supported by basal ecosystem in the area.

Endnotes

[1] The weight was measured using 100 pieces of fruit produced by one tree. The ratio of juice was calculated from squeezing out juice by hand, which is the normal method the local people use for squeezing juice.

Acknowledgements

This work was supported by JSPS KAKENHI Grant Number JP16H06318.

References

Chalfin, B. (2004) *Shea Butter Republic: State Power, Global Markets, and the Making of an Indigenous Commodity*, New York and London: Routledge.

Ellis, E. C., Goldewijk, K. K., Siebert, S., Lightman, D. and Ramankutty, N. (2010) 'Anthropogenic transformation of the biomes, 1700 to 2000', *Global Ecology and Biogeography*, Vol. 19, pp.

589–606.

Foley, J. A., Defries, R., Asner, G. P., Barford, C., Bonan, G., Carpenter, S. R., Chapin, F. S., Coe, M. T., Daily, G. C., Gibbs, H. K., Helkowski, J. H., Holloway, T., Howard, E. A., Kucharik, C. J., Monfreda, C., Patz, J. A., Prentice, I. C., Ramankutty, N. and Snyder, P. (2005) 'Global consequences of land use', *Science*, Vol. 22, pp. 570–574.

Fujioka, Y. (2016) *Socio-Ecosystem of Agroforest in Savanna: Social Transition and Natural Resource Uses in Namibia*, Kyoto: Showado (in Japanese).

Gebre, Y., Ohta, I. and Matsuda, M. (eds) (2017a) *African Virtues in the Pursuit of Conviviality: Exploring Local Solutions in Light of Global Prescriptions*, Bamenda: Langaa RPCIG.

Gebre, Y., Ohta, I. and Matsuda, M. (2017b) 'Introduction: Achieving peace and coexistence through African Potentials', in Y. Gebre, I. Ohta and M. Matsuda (eds) *African Virtues in the Pursuit of Conviviality: Exploring Local Solutions in Light of Global Prescriptions*, Bamenda: Langaa RPCIG, pp. 3–37.

Hall, J. B., O'Brien, M. O. and Sinclair, F. L. (2002) *Sclerocarya birrea: A Monograph, School of Agricultural and Forest Sciences Publication Number 19*, Bangor: University of Wales.

Mamdani, M. (1996) *Citizen and Subject: Contemporary Africa and Legacy of Late Colonialism*, Princeton: Princeton University Press.

Matsuda, M. and Hirano-Nomoto, M. (eds) (2016) *Cultural Creativity for Conflict Resolution and Coexistence: African Potentials as Practice of Incompleteness and Bricolage*, Kyoto: Kyoto University Press (in Japanese).

Nghitoolwa, E., Hall, J. B. and Sinclair, F. L. (2003) 'Population status and gender imbalance of the marula tree, *Sclerocarya birrea* subsp. *caffra* in northern Namibia', *Agroforestry Systems*, Vol. 59, pp. 289–294.

Palgrave, M. C. (2002) *Trees of Southern Africa (third edition)*, Cape Town: Struik Publishers.

Rockström, J., Steffen, W., Noone, K., Persson, Å., Chapin III, F. Stuart, Lambin, E., Lenton, T. M., Scheffer, M., Folke, C., Schellnhuber, H. J., Nykvist, B., de Wit, C. A., Hughes, T., Van der Leeuw, S., Rodhe, H., Sörlin, S., Snyder, P. K., Costanza, R., Svedin,

U., Falkenmark, M., Karlberg, L., Corell, R. W., Fabry, V. J., Hansen, J., Walker, B., Liverman, D., Richardson, K., Crutzen, P. and Foley, J. (2009) 'Planetary boundaries: Exploring the safe operating space for humanity', *Ecology and Society*, Vol. 14, Issue 2, Article 32.

Shackleton, S. (2002) *The Informal Marula Beer Traders of Bushbuckridge, Limpopo Province, South Africa*, Grahamstown: Department of Environmental Science, Rhodes University.

———— (2004) 'Livelihood benefits from the local level commercialization of savanna resources: A case study of the new and expanding trade in marula (*Sclerocarya birrea*) beer in Bushbuckridge, South Africa', *South African Journal of Science*, Vol. 100, pp. 651–657.

Shackleton, C. M., Botha, J., Emanuel, P. L. and Ndlovu, S. (2002) *Inventory of Marula (*Sclerocarya birrea *subsp. caffra) Stocks and Fruit Yields in Communal and Protected Areas of The Bushbuckridge Lowveld, Limpopo Province, South Africa, Report to UK DFID Forestry Research Programme (Project No. R7795)*, Grahamstown: Department for International Development, Rhodes University.

Shackleton, S. and Shackleton, C. (2002) *Use of Marula Products for Domestic and Commercial Purposes by Households in the Bushbuckridge District, Limpopo Province, South Africa*, Grahamstown: Department of Environmental Science, Rhodes University.

Werger, M. J. A. and Coetzee, B. J. (1978) 'The Sudano-Zambezian Region', in M. J. A. Werger (ed.) *Biogeography and Ecology of Southern Africa (Monographiae Biologicae 31)*, The Hague: Dr. W. Junk, pp. 301–462.

Wynberg, R. P. and Laird, S. A. (2007) 'Less is often more: Governance of a non-timber forest product, marula (*Sclerocarya birrea* subsp. *caffra*) in Southern Africa', *International Forestry Review*, Vol. 9, No. 1, pp. 475–490.

Chapter 10

The Political Ecology of the Kapenta Fishery in Lake Kariba, Zambia

Chihiro Ito

1. Introduction

Inland fisheries are an essential component of African fisheries, providing one-third of the total catch (FAO 2014). It has been estimated that the fisheries and aquaculture sector in Africa employs approximately 12.3 million people including both fishers and processors, of whom 40.4 per cent are employed in inland fisheries (De Graaf and Garibaldi 2014). However, the socio-economic potential of inland fishing has often been undervalued and overlooked (Cooke et al. 2016; Welcomme 2011). Therefore, it is important to shed light on the dynamics of inland fisheries in African countries.

Zambia is a landlocked country, but it has abundant areas of water that cover approximately 19 per cent of the national territory, including rivers, lakes and wetlands. Artisanal and commercial fisheries provide important economic activities for residents living along the rivers and lakes. With the development of technology and transportation networks, fish caught in rivers and lakes have been increasingly transported, either fresh or frozen, to large cities such as Lusaka and cities in the Copperbelt, which are major consumers. Fish, which is generally cheaper than meat, is widely distributed in rural areas and regional small towns in the form of dried, smoked and salted fish, and is an important protein source for residents in both urban and rural areas.

Kapenta (*Limnothrissa miodon*) are small clupeids and are consumed in significant numbers as a side dish in Zambia. Kapenta (also referred to as Tanganyika sardines) were introduced from Lake

Tanganyika into Lake Kariba. Although frozen kapenta are available in supermarkets in major urban areas, kapenta are mainly distributed as dried fish. They can be stored for a long time, which facilitates distribution more widely within urban and rural areas throughout the country.

In recent years, environmental issues regarding kapenta fishing have been reported. Using data obtained from both Zambia and Zimbabwe, Magadza (2011) observed a decrease in the long-term catch trend. The kapenta catch peaked at 37,000 tons in 1990, after which both the catch trend and the catch per unit effort (CPUE) steadily declined. Another study concluded that the kapenta catch declined by 50 per cent between 1974 and 2003 (Ndebele-Murisa et al. 2011). These environmental studies claimed that the decreases in kapenta catch and CPUE are attributable to climate change.

However, few empirical studies have examined the social aspects of this fishing industry even though various social factors exist that may have contributed to the declines in catch and CPUE. Therefore, this chapter investigates the kapenta fishing industry in Lake Kariba from the viewpoint of political ecology.

Political ecology combines 'the concerns of ecology and a broadly defined political economy' (Blaikie and Brookfield 1987a: 17). It attempts to understand 'the political sources, conditions, and ramifications of environmental change' (Bryant 1992: 13) and has been conceptualised primarily through the study of environmental changes in developing countries (Blaikie and Brookfield 1987b; Bryant 1992).

A key premise of political ecology is that ecological change cannot be understood without considering the political and economic structures and institutions within which it is embedded (Neumann 2009). For example, in their pioneering work, Blaikie and Brookfield (1987a: 2) claimed that 'land degradation has social causes as well as consequences' and that a complex interaction of factors occurs over time. Therefore, to understand the complexity of human–environment interactions, investigation required 'an approach which can encompass interactive effects, the contribution of different geographical scales and hierarchies of socioeconomic organisations (e.g. person, household, village, region, state, world) and the contradictions between social and environmental changes through time' (Blaikie and Brookfield 1987a: 17). Thus, exploration of multi-level connections between global and local phenomena in terms of environment, decision-making and hierarchies of power is essential (Adger et al. 2001: 682).

Political ecology has become established as a dominant field of human–environmental geographical research (Walker 2005). By using a political ecological perspective, this chapter aims to describe the dynamics of the kapenta fisheries in Lake Kariba in Zambia based on the results of a field survey, with a focus on the historical context and interactions among various actors, and to situate the relevant dynamics within the wider political-economic context.

2. Overview of Kapenta Fishing and the Research Field

Kapenta fishing is conducted in both Zambia and Zimbabwe. Operators must have a commercial fishing permit for kapenta fishing in both countries. In the case of Zambia, the Department of Fisheries (DoF) within the Ministry of Fisheries and Livestock is the authorising body responsible for issuing fishing permits.

Kapenta fishing in Lake Kariba can be characterised as capital-intensive and industrialised. Fishing involves the use of catamaran vessels, called 'rigs', with diesel engines and steel pontoons, equipped with fishing lights and nets. Fishing occurs from midnight until dawn by companies or private groups consisting of operators, fishers and other staff. The operators hold the commercial fishing permits, own the fishing vessels and gear and are responsible for the overall operation. The fishers and other staff are those employed for fishing and drying/packing kapenta (Ito 2021).

Lake Kariba forms part of the Zambezi River system, which has the largest catchment area in Zambia,[1] and is located on the border of Zambia and Zimbabwe (Figure 1). It is an artificial lake created through construction of the Kariba Dam in the late 1950s.[2] The Zambian side of the lake is divided into four strata. There were 151 operators with 631 vessels overall in 2011 (DoF 2011), with 15 operators running 90 vessels in stratum I, 74 operators running 349

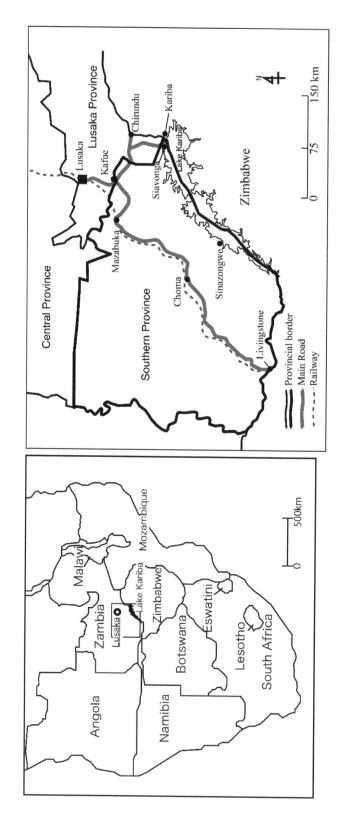

Figure 1. The location of Lake Kariba and the research sites

vessels in stratum II, 16 operators running 26 vessels in stratum III and 45 operators running 166 vessels in stratum IV.

The author conducted a field survey at two key kapenta fishing locations, namely, Siavonga in stratum IV and Sinazongwe in stratum II, in 2013 and 2015, respectively. Siavonga is located approximately 200 km south of the capital city, Lusaka, and easily accessed through paved roads. It has been the capital of Siavonga District in Southern Province since 1993, with a population of about 16,000 (CSO 2012). Kapenta fishing, aquaculture and tourism provide the main employment opportunities in this town. Sinazongwe is located approximately 330 km south-west of Lusaka. The road network is not in good condition, and it takes six to seven hours to travel there from Lusaka. It is within the Sinazongwe District in Southern Province, but the main town of this district is Sinazeze, which is located 15 km north of Sinazongwe. Sinazongwe is in a more rural setting than Siavonga, and most of the kapenta operators there are based in surrounding rural areas.

In undertaking fieldwork, the author interviewed 40 key informants, including kapenta operators (15 in Siavonga, 20 in Sinazongwe) and local engineers engaged in rig building (4 in Siavonga). The interviews were semi-structured, in-depth and open-ended. The author also interviewed to officials from the DoF in both the Siavonga and Sinazongwe branches about fishing regulations.

3. Historical Context of the Kapenta Fishing Industry

3-1. The Beginning of Commercial Fisheries

In 1963, surveys began to assess introducing clupeids into Lake Kariba. Of two clupeids available from Lake Tanganyika (*Stolothrissa tanganicae* and *L. miodon*), *L. miodon* was selected as more suitable for Lake Kariba, transferred in 1967 and 1968 and released at Sinazongwe. *L. miodon* appeared established throughout the lake by 1970 (Marshall and Langerman 1979).

The fishing industry started on the Zimbabwean side, and experimental commercial fishing began in 1973 (Cheater 1985; Langerman 1979). Kapenta fishing on the Zambian side did not start until the 1980s due to previous political issues that prevented commercial fishing. During the Zimbabwean war of liberation, the Rhodesian army attacked bordering Zambian areas and the road network along the lake was damaged by land mines set by the Rhodesian army. Therefore, fishing activities on the Zambian side could not be conducted. After Zimbabwe gained independence in 1980, commercial fisheries in Zambia opened in 1981 (Overa 2003).

The rig and fishing method now popular throughout the lake was developed in Zimbabwe and adopted by early Zambian operators (Ito 2021). Given the large initial investment needed to equip fishing rigs and gear, it would have been difficult for the local 'black'[3] residents to enter the kapenta fishing industry in the 1980s. As a result, kapenta fishing began with the entry of 'white' entrepreneurs from within Zambia and from outside countries such as Zimbabwe and South Africa (Overa 2003).

Of the 35 kapenta operators interviewed, five were white operators who had started fishing in the 1980s (two in Siavonga, three in Sinazongwe). Of those interviewed, the average number of rigs for white operators was 21.3, much higher than the average number of rigs for the black operators (5.6). Both run by white operators, Company A, based in Siavonga, and company B, based in Sinazongwe, typified operations that started in the 1980s. Company A was founded in 1981 and still owns the most fishing rigs in Siavonga. At the time of the 2012 survey, it owned 28 rigs and had 160 employees. The owner of Company B had heard about kapenta fishing from the founder of Company A and started operations in Sinazongwe. These white operators have consistently owned more rigs than the black operators. White operators generally own land in the coastal areas comprising a vast space for drying fish, a refrigeration vehicle and a workshop for repairing fishing rigs and gear. Their businesses are larger in scale than their black competitors' and have significant weight within the industry.

3-2. A Rapid Increase in New Entrants

With the assistance of Norway and Denmark, the governments of Zambia and Zimbabwe conducted a 'Zambia/Zimbabwe SADC Fisheries Project (ZZSFP)' from 1990 to 2000 (Hesthagen et al. 1994). This project was carried out to ensure that kapenta reproduction was kept at ecologically sustainable and economically viable levels within an equitable framework (Nyikahadzoi and Raakjær 2009).

In 1997, based on the results of ecological and economic studies conducted as part of ZZSFP, the Zambian and Zimbabwean governments set 500 fishing rigs as the appropriate scale for maintaining adequate levels of kapenta reproduction. Since Zambia controls 45 per cent of Lake Kariba and Zimbabwe 55 per cent, it was agreed that the two countries could operate 230 and 270 rigs, respectively (DoF 2011).

However, a gradual reduction in surveys and monitoring after the project and related assistance ended led to the issuance of new fishing permits, with a noticeable increase on the Zambian side. Figure 2 shows the changes in the number of operators and fishing rigs. It can be seen that, until 1998, the number of fishing vessels was kept below the appropriate level of 230 as set by the project but, by 2005, the number of rigs had increased to nearly 300. Beginning in 2010, the number of rigs increased sharply and prior research had claimed that the number may have exceeded 1,000 in 2014 (Paulet 2014).

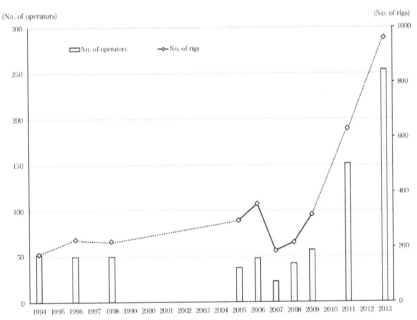

Figure 2. Changes in the number of operators and fishing rigs by year

Source: Data until 2011 from the DoF (2011), data for 2013 from Paulet (2014)

249

As of 2011, the number of rigs controlled by enterprises having operated fewer than five years comprised approximately 65 per cent of the total. In other words, the increase in the number of fishing rigs was not led by long-established companies but rather by a rapid increase in new entrants. The same study found that 66.1 per cent of these companies were owned by individuals, with only 32.3 per cent registered to private companies and 1.6 per cent owned by co-operative groups (DoF 2011).

4. The Diversity of Current Operators: Who Are They and Why Did They Start?

This section describes the characteristics of current operators based on interviews with 29 black operators who started kapenta fishing after 2000 and also includes an analysis of the relevant socio-economic context affecting their entry into this industry.

The 29 operators were all male, with 12 operating in Siavonga and 17 in Sinazongwe. Fifteen operators had started their businesses between 2003 and 2009, and 14 had started after 2010. In terms of origin, two operators in Siavonga were born in and had grown up within the Siavonga District; three operators came from other districts in Southern Province; six operators came from other provinces.[4] Those who moved to Siavonga had arrived at various times between the 1980s and the 2000s. In the case of Sinazongwe, only one fisher had come from another district in Southern Province, whereas all others were from rural areas in Sinazongwe District.

Three social categories, namely, 'urban elites' (eight people in Siavonga), 'rural residents' (three people in Siavonga; seventeen people in Sinazongwe), and 'retiree' (one person in Siavonga) were identified based on their involvement in the kapenta fishery. Table 1 shows the number of rigs and workers in terms of each category.

First, those belonging to urban elites were found only in Siavonga. They lived in Siavonga or in other urban areas and had entered the kapenta fishing industry as a side business while holding relatively stable formal sector employment in the city. For example, several worked as public servants and workers at parastatal companies, private companies or international NGOs. The interviewees explain-

Table 1. Characteristics of the recent operators divided into three categories

Operator	No. of operators	Average no. of rigs	Maximum no. of rigs	Average no. of workers	Year of start fishing	
					2003-2009	after 2010
Urban elites	8	2.1	5	11.4	4	4
Rural residents	20	7.2	30	22.3	10	10
Retiree	1	1	1	5	1	0
Total	29	5.6	30	19.0	15	14

ed that they had chosen to supplement their income because 'the current salary is not enough for my life plan for myself and my children', 'it is better to invest in something so that you can increase your assets rather than spending all of it', and 'no money comes in when I retire'.

Two operators in this category lived in Lusaka and Kitwe, though those living in Siavonga comprised the majority. For example, G had permanent formal sector employment related to the mining industry in Kitwe, Copperbelt Province. He also ran a commercial farm and a shop in Siavonga. He lived in Kitwe but had a house in Siavonga and travelled as needed.

These members of urban elites, with relatively stable formal sector employment, had become engaged in kapenta fishing due to economic changes in Zambia after 2000. In Zambia, economic liberalisation and privatisation policies have been implemented since the 1990s as part of structural adjustment programmes (SAPs). However, the annual GDP growth rate in the 1990s remained at 0.2 per cent, and economic growth was extremely limited (Wobst and Thurlow 2005). Subsequently, however, the Zambian economy improved beginning around 1999. The annual average GDP growth rate was 6.8 per cent between 2000 and 2009 and 5.3 per cent between 2010 and 2018. From 2003 to 2013, the average GDP growth rate maintained a high level of 5 per cent or more.[5] This economic growth in recent years has been driven by expansion of the mining, construction, transportation and communications sectors (UNDP 2011).

During the period of economic expansion, the number of urban elites participating in kapenta fishing increased. Chali et al. (2014: 112) undertook a study of kapenta operators in Siavonga and noted: 'The majority of the indigenous Zambians are increasingly becoming aware of the need to invest and own their own companies, ... today, more and more indigenous Zambians had improved standards of living compared to the past when the kapenta fishing industry was mainly run by foreign entrepreneurs'. G's engagement exemplifies how certain urban elites benefited from economic development and were able to diversify their investments.

On the other hand, people working at government and parastatal companies appeared to engage in kapenta fishing because it offered opportunities to supplement their salaries or safeguard their futures rather than the chance to engage in active investment. Especially since the introduction of the SAPs, wages have fallen significantly in the Zambian public sector. Informalisation of labour within the urban economy has extended to include civil servants, obliging them to seek out secondary employment in other fields in a manner similar to that commonly undertaken by rural people (Cliggett and Wyssmann 2009). In such a situation, although they have more stable salaries than other urban low-income residents, such individuals are driven to seek extra income to educate their children to a higher level or to prepare for their retirement.

These urban elites tend to search for opportunities to engage in profitable economic activities. For example, EC used to operate buses in a town before he started working in the kapenta fishery, and HD had engaged in chicken farming. Kapenta fishing had emerged as a key option for certain individuals to secure their present and future needs.

However, it was also apparent that these individuals were refraining from further investment in kapenta fishing because they were reluctant to increase the amount of work associated with managing employees and fishing rigs, and they were always looking for other business opportunities. The average number of rigs that those in this category were responsible for was 2.1, which was lower than the overall operator average, as shown in Table 1, indicating a lack of desire to increase their number of rigs.

The second category, rural residents, refers to those people who lived in rural areas or who had strong connections with the surrounding rural areas. Those belonging to this category were most often found in Sinazongwe because, while the operators who fished in Siavonga were based in Siavonga town, those who fished in Sinazongwe generally lived in the surrounding rural areas. Many people in this category had experience working as fish traders and fishers within the kapenta fishing industry before starting their own businesses. They saved the necessary money through working in those trades as well as through farming or raising livestock. For example, FZ had previously worked as a fisher at a kapenta fishing company and saw that it was potentially a profitable activity. He stopped working as a fisher, started a grocery store and tried other business ventures, which allowed him to save enough money to build a rig. PK had also engaged in trading fish in the villages around Siavonga and gradually earned enough money to start kapenta fishing. He was based in Siavonga town, but his family lived and farmed in rural areas, and he also travelled to and from Siavonga. In this way, such individuals were able to enter the kapenta fishing industry through funds obtained from occupations connected with fishing as well as engaging in agricultural and non-agricultural economic activities in rural areas.

Although the number of rigs owned by rural residents varied widely, one such operator had 30 fishing rigs, which was equivalent in scale to the number owned by the white operators. This was a remarkable phenomenon, showing what could be achieved by rural residents within the commercial fishery sector, which had otherwise been dominated by white people. The commercial and economic success of this operator contributes an additional perspective to the livelihood diversification debates that have become popular in African rural studies.

Livelihood diversification has been defined as 'the process by which rural households construct an increasingly diverse portfolio of activities and assets in order to survive and to improve their standard of living' (Ellis 2000: 15). It has been reported that people living in rural areas of Africa have become increasingly engaged in complex livelihoods, such as diversifying cultivated crops and combining farming and livestock raising. However, the distinctive feature of recent livelihood diversification has been that it has included not only the agricultural sector but also economic activities in other fields. The proportion of non-agricultural income in rural areas was reported to be about 35 per cent in sub-Saharan Africa (Haggblade et al. 2010). Prior researchers have claimed that SAPs, which have had a significant effect on the socio-economic conditions in most African countries, have accelerated this diversification (Bryceson 1996; Haggblade et al. 2007).

It has been argued that livelihood diversification contributes to reducing the risks and vulnerability associated with agricultural production for the poor, but at the same time, when applied to wealthier households, it functions not as a 'survival strategy' but instead as an 'accumulation strategy'. (Iliya and Swindell 1997; Oya 2007). In the case of Zambia, Ito (2014) reported that wealthy rural households were increasingly engaging in commercial and service sector businesses in rural areas, and some were investing in businesses in neighbouring small towns. Those operators categorised as rural residents represent a similar phenomenon as they also engaged in varying economic activities within agriculture and in running shops or hammer mills in addition to working in the kapenta fishery.

Finally, one retiree was found in Siavonga. For Zambian urban residents for whom social security is insufficient to address their needs, where and how they will make a living after retirement is a major issue. For example, having worked in a parastatal company in Siavonga for many years, M started kapenta fishing in order to continue living in Siavonga after retirement. Since his pension could not support him, he needed another source of income to enable him to continue living in town.

Previous studies have pointed out that retirees often start businesses in small and medium-sized cities. For example, in a survey in Eastern Province in Zambia, Ogura (2009) reported that those who retired after working in Lusaka did not return to their home villages but rather tended to live in small and medium-sized towns nearby where there were better social services and business opportunities. In a non-Zambian context, Peli (1995) showed that retirees prefer small and medium-sized towns where they have access to better medical services, there is no need for agricultural labour and there are relatively better business opportunities. Therefore, M's case can be considered representative of those people who have worked all their lives and have taken up further opportunities, for example, kapenta fishing, to allow them to continue living in town without having to return to their original village.

Thus, various reasons and means have been identified as the catalysts for recent black operators to enter the kapenta fishing industry. These economic activities have varying purposes depending on the situation and intentions of the operator, including active investment or functioning as a supplementary income source for urban elites, livelihood diversification for rural residents and a means of living for retirees. Therefore, those engaged in kapenta fishing are not driven by a single factor; understanding their involvement requires understanding their diverse situations and needs.

5. The Emergence of Rig Builders and the Influx of Cheap Fishing Equipment

Another recent change in the kapenta fishing industry is the emergence of easy access to rig builders. In their interviews, operators who started fishing after 2000 in Siavonga explained that when they started kapenta fishing, there were limited ways to obtain rigs, including ordering from established white operators, purchasing existing rigs from white operators in Zimbabwe or ordering from local rig builders in Zimbabwe. In Siavonga, there was only one local black rig builder, K. Since K was working in another job and rig building was a side business, he did not accept many orders. One of the operators who had a rig made in 2009 reported that, rather than having the work done in Zambia, he had turned to a builder living in Kariba, the base of Zimbabwe's kapenta fishing industry. Although ordering rigs in Zimbabwe incurred considerable costs due to the necessary requirements in relation to police, customs and immigration, he did it because there were many good local builders in Zimbabwe.

However, in more recent years, four major groups of black rig builders have become established, making it easier for black operators to undertake shipbuilding in Siavonga. For example, another operator who started fishing in 2006 reported that he went to Kariba in Zimbabwe for his first rig and purchased it from a white operator. However, when he wanted a second rig in 2014, he ordered it from a local rig builder in Siavonga. He claimed that only white operators had known how to build rigs in 2006, but by 2014, there were many local rig builders on the Zambian side as well, so he ordered it in Zambia.

In their interviews, the four major local rig builders reported that they started their businesses between 2006 and 2014. There was no one originally born in Siavonga; one was from a rural area in the Siavonga District, two were from other districts within Southern Province and one was from Northern Province. Before migrating to Siavonga, they had lived in other cities such as Lusaka, Choma and Mazabuka. They all had experience working in white-owned fisheries in Siavonga or Sinazongwe, where they acquired the knowledge and skills to build a fishing rig before starting their own rig-building businesses. Builder F said that building rigs was very profitable from 2010 onwards because of the increased local demand. Builder F also owned a fishing rig, had a permit and was involved in fishing.

In addition to the emergence of local rig builders, the availability of cheap Chinese-made engines and fishing gear also contributed to easier rig building. China has become an increasingly important business partner of many African countries (Taylor 2006; Tull 2006), including Zambia, where China has established a strong partnership with the government because of opportunities in the copper mining sector (Davies et al. 2008). China's engagement has had a significant effect not only on the mining sector but also within various aspects of the Zambian economy in terms of infrastructure development, the inflow of Chinese workers and traders and the influx of Chinese-made commodities.

A kapenta fishing rig has an engine to facilitate movement and provide lighting. Previously, European-made engines were predominant among white operators, but in recent years many black operators have begun to use Chinese-made engines. Concerning fishing gear such as lights and nets, it has become easier to obtain inexpensive Chinese-made commodities even within Siavonga or at Lusaka. Therefore, the strong relationship with China and the arrival of cheap Chinese commodities, including fishing equipment and engines, have encouraged black operators to venture into the kapenta fishing industry because start-up costs have declined.

In summary, a combination of local black rig builders with prior experience in white operators' companies, increasing demand for rig building among black operators and the readier availability of engines and gear have contributed to greater numbers of black operators running their own rigs, as costs have reduced and rig building has become more feasible.

6. Challenges Faced by the Kapenta Operators

The kapenta operators indicated that they faced a variety of problems. Specifically, 'theft' and 'operating rigs without a permit' were reported as serious issues.

First, 'theft' refers to the act of approaching a rig on the lake on a small boat and purchasing kapenta from the fishers at a lower price than the normal transaction price. While not technically a 'theft' as the kapenta had been paid for, the catch that should have belonged to the business owner was sold on the side at a lower price. The operators referred to this situation as 'theft' and anyone engaged in it as a 'thief'.

According to the companies that have been involved in the industry since the 1980s, this activity, in which fishers sell parts of their catch to others without an owner's knowledge, has always occurred to some extent. However, at the time of the interviews, the situation had become worse and was having an increasingly serious effect on business.

The operators sought to prevent this activity through multiple means. For example, they introduced a system whereby a bonus was given to fishers when they obtained a certain quantity of catch to reduce the incentive to sell on the lake because money could be made legitimately through retaining the catch. Additionally, the operators aimed to deploy more reliable employees on their rigs and organised patrol boats to make 'theft' more difficult.

However, many operators complained that the situation had not improved. Some long-established white operators had withdrawn. Black operators faced the same issues, and M and ED, for example, had stopped their operations. The remaining companies had begun diversifying their businesses since the catch was not as profitable as before.

'Operating rigs without a permit' was a particularly serious problem in Sinazongwe where there were many rigs. Some people engaged in fishing without permits or with expired permits. Others mistakenly believed they had a right to fish because their rigs had undergone a safety inspection. It appeared that certain people engaged in kapenta fishing lacked sufficient awareness of the regulatory laws, which require an annually renewed permit.

The interviews highlighted various issues regarding the fishing regulations. For example, operators with commercial fishing permits were required to report their monthly catches to the DoF, but this requirement was not being enforced effectively. When the author participated in a meeting between the DoF and the operators in Sinazongwe, some operators who appeared to have entered the industry more recently were not aware that they were required to update their permits every year and to report their catch every month. Kinadjian et al. (2014) also reported that 40 per cent of their sample operators did not provide records of their catch.

While fully aware of these issues, the DoF had not been able to find a solution due to a lack of funds and human resources. For example, the DoF office in Sinazongwe did not have a vehicle; therefore, a large number of operators could not be readily checked to ensure compliance with the regulations nor could reports of catches be easily obtained.

This situation, involving 'theft', operators without permits, and under-reporting of catches, indicated that a large proportion of caught kapenta was not appearing in official catch statistics but was nevertheless being traded on the market.

7. Conclusion

Kapenta were transplanted from Lake Tanganyika to Lake Kariba in the 1960s, but commercial fishing only started in Zambia in the 1980s once the negative effects of war in Zimbabwe no longer discouraged such activity. In the early stage of this commercial fishing industry, white entrepreneurs from Zambia, Zimbabwe and South Africa predominated, and they remain at the core of the formal commercial fishing sector.

In the 1990s, recommendations from an international resource management project were followed to keep the number of operators and fishing rigs within certain limits. However, after 2000, many black operators entered the kapenta fishing industry and the number of operators and fishing rigs increased substantially. Although commercial fisheries in Zambia are required to obtain permits, interviews revealed that many operators did not have permits. Commercial fishing in this context appeared to operate more in a state of open access (Kinadjian et al. 2014).

This situation arose because of weak regulation enforcement by the government due to a lack of financial and human resources (Shula and Mofya-Mukuka 2015). However, this chapter also indicated that urban and rural dwellers had entered the kapenta fishing industry in response to various changing macro-political and economic developments, such as economic liberalisation in the 1990s, economic growth after 2000 and strengthening relations with China.

The more recent black operators included members of urban elites seeking active investment or wanting to run side businesses, rural residents seeking livelihood diversification and retirees seeking a means of living in towns. Their intentions in taking up kapenta fishing differed in each case, indicating that the black operators were highly diverse and heterogeneous.

As the demand for rig building increased, local rig builders simultaneously became more independent, and it became easier to obtain relatively cheap engines and gear. It would appear that the combination of these factors further facilitated a dramatic increase in the number of operators and fishing vessels.

While there were producer associations operating in Siavonga and Sinazongwe, many recent operators did not belong to them. Given that knowledge of regulations was demonstrated to be poor among new operators, the lack of effective associations with wide ranging membership does not readily allow the operators to collectively confront and overcome the issues they face.

In Zambia, it is expected that the consumption demand for fish will increase with the increase in the urban population (Tran et al. 2019). Therefore, in recent years, the Zambian government has begun to focus on expanding the aquaculture industry (Kaminski et al. 2018), which may lead to conflicts over water and lakeside lands. For effective development, there will need to be appropriate coordination among the concerned parties and with the relevant government authorities to ensure the sustainable use of lake-related resources.

This chapter clarified the complex socio-economic conditions that have characterised the development of the kapenta fishing industry in Zambia. However, the effect of these human activities on the environment itself requires further clarification since it remains unclear how the increase in operators and fishing rigs, which has led to 'overfishing' (Paulet 2014), has affected the total catch and CPUE.

As this chapter highlighted, the official catch statistics are problematic and not likely to represent an accurate amount. Therefore, it would be necessary to reconsider whether the catch and the CPUE had actually decreased, and such an investigation would require an interdisciplinary approach that links assessment of the relevant social dynamics with a more detailed and precise understanding of the lake environment.

Finally, the dynamics of kapenta fishing presented in this chapter include the agencies expressed in this book by the phrase 'African Potentials', such as flexibility, mobility, innovativeness or networking (Gebre et al. 2017). In this respect, this chapter confirms the existence of 'African Potentials' among the individuals in commercial fishing. However, if we examine the situation from the perspective of the broader political and economic environment and resulting institutional changes at different geographical scales, 'African Potentials' may cause national and ecological problems. This chapter indicates the importance of understanding livelihood and resource management problems not only from a local level but also from a contextual and relational level, including regional, national and global perspectives.

Additionally, the development of side jobs by urban elites and diversification of economic activities by rural residents can be considered either positive responses to various opportunities or coping strategies for uncertain situations. For many, the choice to enter the kapenta fishing industry is a reaction to changing economic circumstances. Therefore, this decision may change or be modified in the future due to either external or internal factors, and it is necessary to understand the human–environmental relationships occurring in African countries from a flexible and chronological perspective.

Endnotes

[1] The surface area of the lake is 5,400 km²; the maximum water depth is 78 metres; the average water depth is 31 metres. Approximately 55 per cent of the lake belongs to Zimbabwe and 45 per cent to Zambia.

[2] The construction of the Kariba Dam and Lake Kariba was decided in 1955 by the then Rhodesian Nyasaland federal government. The dam was planned to supply electricity for mining in Northern Rhodesia (Zambia) and to industries such as manufacturing that were developing in Southern Rhodesia (Zimbabwe).

[3] In this chapter, the words 'black' and 'white' are used from an analytical perspective. This is because, in Zambia and in other Southern African societies, there have been distinctive economic disparities and diverging political interests between the 'white' people, that is, European immigrants who settled during the colonial period and their descendants, and the 'black' people who have a history of being colonised, which must be considered especially when discussing commercial fisheries that were started and have been dominated by 'white' people.

[4] The origin of one operator could not be determined.

[5] The World Bank 'World Development Indicators'.

Acknowledgements

I am grateful for the assistance of all the kapenta operators in my research. I would like to thank the DoF for their support. This work was supported by JSPS KAKENHI: Grant Number JP26760007, JP15H02601 and JP16H06318.

References

Adger, W. N., Benjaminsen, Tor. A., Brown, K., and Svarstad, H. (2001) 'Advancing a political ecology of global environmental discourses', *Development and Change*, Vol. 32, Issue 4, pp. 681–715.

Blaikie, P. and Brookfield, H. (1987a) 'Defining and debating the problem', in P. Blaikie and H. Brookfield (eds) *Land Degradation and Society*, London and New York: Methuen, pp. 1–26.

———— (1987b) *Land Degradation and Society*, London and New York: Methuen.

Bryant, R. L. (1992) 'Political ecology: An emerging research agenda in third-world studies', *Political Geography*, Vol. 11, Issue 1, pp. 12–36.

Bryceson, D. F. (1996) 'Deagrarianization and rural employment in sub-Saharan Africa: A sectoral perspective', *World Development*, Vol. 24, Issue 1, pp. 97–111.

Chali, M., Musuka, C. G. and Nyimbili, B. (2014) 'The impact of fishing pressure on kapenta (*Limnothrissa miodon*) production in Lake Kariba, Zambia: A case study of Siavonga District', *International Journal of Agriculture, Forestry and Fisheries*, Vol. 2, Issue 6, pp. 107–116.

Cheater, A.P. (1985) 'The Zimbabwean kapenta fishery', in M. F. C. Bourdillon, A. P. Cheater and M. W. Murphree (eds) *Studies of Fishing on Lake Kariba*, Harare: Mambo Press, pp. 96–132.

Cliggett, L. and Wyssmann, B. (2009) 'Crimes against the future: Zambian teachers' alternative income generation and the undermining of education', *Africa Today*, Vol. 55, Issue 3, pp. 25–43.

Cooke, S. J., Allison, E. H., Beard T. Douglas Jr., Arlinghaus, R., Arthington, Angela H., Bartley, Devin M., Cowx, Ian G., Fuentevilla, C., Leonard, Nancy J., Lorenzen, Kai, Lynch, Abigil

J., Nguyen, Vivian M., Youn, So-Jung, Taylor, William W. and Welcomme, Robin L. (2016) 'On the sustainability of inland fisheries: Finding a future for the forgotten', *Ambio*, Vol. 45, Issue 7, pp. 753–764.

CSO (Central Statistical Office) (2012) *2010 Census of Population and Housing*, Lusaka: CSO.

Davies, M., Edinger, H., Tay, N. and Naidu, S. (2008) *How China Delivers Development Assistance to Africa*, Stellenbosch: Centre for Chinese Studies, University of Stellenbosch.

De Graaf, G. and Garibaldi, L. (2014) *The Value of African Fisheries, FAO Fisheries and Aquaculture Circular No.1093*, Rome: FAO (Food And Agriculture Organization of The United Nations).

DoF (Deoartment of Fisheries) (2011) *Lake Kariba Fishery Frame Survey Report (Draft)*, Chilanga.

Ellis, F. (2000) *Rural Livelihood and Diversity in Developing Countries*, Oxford and New York: Oxford University Press.

FAO (Food and Agriculture Organization) (2014) *The State of World Fisheries and Aquaculture 2014: Opportunities and Challenge*, Rome: FAO.

Gebre, Y., Ohta, I. and Matsuda, M. (2017) 'Introduction: Achieving peace and coexistence through African potentials', in Y. Gebre, I. Ohta and M. Matsuda (eds) *African Virtues in the Pursuit of Conviviality: Exploring Local Solutions in Light of Global Prescriptions*, Bamenda: Langaa RPCIG, pp. 3–37.

Haggblade, S., Hazell, P. B. R. and Reardon, T. (2007) *Transforming the Rural Nonfarm Economy: Opportunities and Threats in the Developing World*, Baltimore: The Johns Hopkins University Press.

———— (2010) 'The rural non-farm economy: Prospects for growth and poverty reduction', *World Development*, Vol. 38, Issue 10, pp. 1429–1441.

Hesthagen, T., Sandlund, O. T. and Næsje, T. F. (1994) *The Zambia-Zimbabwe SADC Fisheries Project on Lake Kariba: Report from a Study Trip*, Trondheim: The Norwegian Institute for Nature Research.

Iliya, M. A. and Swindell, K. (1997) 'Winners and losers: Household fortunes in the urban peripheries of northern Nigeria', in D. F. Bryceson and V. Jamal (eds) *Farewell to Farms: De-agrarianisation and Employment in Africa*, Aldershot: Ashgate, pp. 85–100.

Ito, C. (2014) 'The growth of "rural business" and its impact on local society in Zambia', *MILA Special Issue: Exploring African Potentials: The Dynamics of Action, Living Strategy, and Social Order in Southern Africa*, pp. 51–60.

———— (2021) 'Development of fishing practices within commercial fisheries in Lake Kariba, Southern Africa', *African Study Monographs*, Vol. 41, No. 1, pp. 1–22.

Kaminski, A. M., Genschick, S., Kefi, A.S. and Kruijssen, F. (2018) 'Commercialization and upgrading in the aquaculture value chain in Zambia', *Aquaculture*, Vol. 493, pp. 355–364.

Kinadjian, L., Mwula, C., Nyikahadzoi, K. and Songore, N. (2014) *Report on the Bioeconomic Modelling of Kapenta Fisheries on Lake Kariba*, Ebene: SmartFish Programme of the Indian Ocean Commission, FAO Fisheries Management component.

Langerman, J. D. (1979) 'Sardine fishing methods used on Lake Kariba', *The Rhodesia Science News*, Vol. 13, Issue 4, pp. 108–110.

Magadza, C. H. D. (2011) 'Indications of the effects of climate change on the pelagic fishery of Lake Kariba, Zambia-Zimbabwe', *Lakes & Reservoirs: Research and Management*, Vol. 16, Issue 1, pp. 15–22.

Marshall, B. E. and Langerman, J. D. (1979) 'The Tanganyika sardine in Lake Kariba', *The Rhodesia Science News*, Vol. 13, Issue 4, pp. 104–105.

Ndebele-Murisa, M. R., Mashonjowa, E. and Hill, T. (2011) 'The implications of a changing climate on the Kapenta fish stocks of Lake Kariba, Zimbabwe', *Transactions of the Royal Society of South Africa*, Vol. 66, Issue 2, pp. 105–119.

Neumann, R. P. (2009) 'Political ecology', in R. Kitchin and N. Thrift (eds) *International Encyclopedia of Human Geography*, Amsterdam: Elsevier Science, pp. 228–233.

Nyikahadzoi, K. and Raakjær, J. (2009) 'Policy evolution and dynamics of governance at the Lake Kariba kapenta fishery', *Development Southern Africa*, Vol. 26, Issue 4, pp. 641–648.

Ogura, M. (2009) *One Hundred Years of Nsenga Society in Zambia: Colonial Rule, Cold War, and Market Economy*, Tokyo: University of Tokyo Press (in Japanese).

Overa, R. (2003) 'Market development and investment "bottlenecks" in the fisheries of Lake Kariba', in E. Jul-Larsen, J. Kolding, R. Overå, J. R. Nielsen and P. A. M. van Zwieten (eds) *Management, Co-management or No Management?: Major Dilemmas in Southern African Freshwater Fisheries Case Studies*, Rome: FAO, pp. 201–231.

Oya, C. (2007) 'Stories of rural accumulation in Africa: Trajectories and transitions among rural capitalists in Senegal', *Journal of Agrarian Change*, Vol. 7, Issue 4, pp. 453–493.

Paulet, G. (2014) *Kapenta Rig Survey of the Zambian Waters of Lake Kariba*, *SF/2014/45*, Ebene: Indian Ocean Commission.

Peli, M. (1995) 'The small town as a retirement center', in J. Baker and T. A. Aina (eds) *The Migration Experience in Africa*, Uppsala: Nordiska Afrikainstitutet, pp. 149–166.

Shula, A. K. and Mofya-Mukuka, R. (2015) *The Fisheries Sector in Zambia : Status, Management, and Challenges, Indaba Agriculture Policy Research Institute Technical Paper No. 3*, Lusaka: Indaba Agriculture Policy Research Institute.

Taylor, I. (2006) 'China's oil diplomacy in Africa', *International Affairs*, Vol. 82, Issue 5, pp. 937–959.

Tran, N., Chu, L., Chan, C. Y., Genschick, S., Phillips, M. J. and Kefi, A. S. (2019) 'Fish supply and demand for food security in sub-Saharan Africa: An analysis of the Zambian fish sector', *Marine Policy*, Vol. 99, pp. 343–350.

Tull, D. M. (2006) 'China's engagement in Africa: Scope, significance and consequences', *The Journal of Modern African Studies*, Vol. 44, Issue 3, pp. 459–479.

UNDP (United Nations Development Programme) (2011) *Zambia Human Development Report 2011: Service Delivery for Sustainable Human Development*, Lusaka: UNDP.

Walker, P. A. (2005) 'Political ecology: Where is the ecology?', *Progress in Human Geography*, Vol. 29, Issue 1, pp. 73–82.

Welcomme, R. L. (2011) 'An overview of global catch statistics for inland fish', *ICES Journal of Marine Science*, Vol. 68, Issue 8, pp. 1751–1756.

Wobst, P. and Thurlow, J. (2005) 'The road to pro-poor growth in Zambia: Past lessons and future challenges', in Proceedings of the German Development Economics Conference, Kiel 2005.

Chapter 11

Africa's Potential in History and in Local Initiatives: The Case of Locally Conceived Artificial Reefs (*Virundu*) for Enhancing Fisheries Production at Makanjira, Southern Lake Malawi

Bosco Rusuwa, Daud Kassam and Maxon Ngochera

1. Introduction

The history of Africa is replete with accounts of human ambition and achievement in a diversity of independent local settings across the continent. These strides were driven by a combination of optimism and self-belief inherent within the communities and, at times, by ideas introduced and adopted from other societies through budding travel and communication networks and linkages. Up to the present, the continent has had numerous cases of locally driven innovations that point to potential and hunger for utilisation of its natural resources, including human capital, for its development and progress. This chapter first explains historical examples of such innovations briefly, and then introduces a case of a fishing community in southern Lake Malawi.

2. Africa's Potential in Historical Perspective

Africa's past is not short of stories of human progress and potential for growth. In the paragraphs below, based on accounts of Butzer (1981), Ndoro (1997), Oliver and Fagan (2002), Iliffe (2007), Parker and Rathbone (2007), Conrad (2010) as well as Shuriye and Ibrahim (2013), we outline examples of such cases of mostly locally driven African achievement, spanning from the Iron Age to the 15th century, to illustrate the potential of Africa in historical times.

In the Africa of the past, we get a close glimpse of one of the first ironworkers. Dating back to before 400 BC, there already existed iron-smelting furnaces in the Great Lakes region of East Africa, in Rwanda and Burundi. Similar activities were also rampant in Katuruka in Tanzania as well as in Malawi and Zambia. These iron smelting sites were associated with a unique pottery style, the Urewe ware, whose derivatives would later spread widely throughout eastern and southern Africa. Alongside the strides in iron working and pottery were also notable advances in agriculture focused around the cultivation of sorghum and millet and as well as livestock production, mainly the keeping of goats and cattle.

From around 100 AD until the 16th century, Africa was home to powerful and prosperous states. The continent had managed to integrate itself into some of the great currents of global exchange that circulated people, merchandise and religious conceptions. Africa witnessed the development of cities where African princes had their palaces, where foreign merchants resided, where luxury products were exchanged and where notable infrastructure thrived. Africa was a major player in the exploitation of its own resources, with gold as a prominent commodity. The continent also enjoyed considerable reputation around the world, from Europe to China.

The story of Axum is that of a once powerful kingdom around the Red Sea that persisted from about 300 AD to the early 8th century and that, for some time, controlled much of northern Ethiopia, the Sudan and South Arabia. Axum had a commercial and political sophistication, its culture being a mixture of Arabian institutions and technology and East African roots. The kingdom had a well-developed local metallurgy (iron, bronze, copper) based on both local and imported ores. The kingdom was renowned for funnelling diverse resources from the continental hinterland of the Abyssinian Plateau and the Sudanese plains into a maritime exchange network which netted commodities from as far afield as India, China, the Black Sea and Spain. Axum also had a fairly advanced agriculture that was already at that time using iron-tipped, oxen-drawn ploughs, had bronze and wood-hafted sickles and practised flow irrigation from cisterns. Large herds of cattle, sheep and goats as well as camels provided meat, milk, hides or transport for the kingdom. From the

4th to the 6th centuries, Axum was a commercial and administrative centre that controlled access to resources in much of Arabia and Africa and that persistently maintained close ties with the Eastern Roman Empire.

In West Africa, records of some notable local achievements exist. For instance, the local metal-derived African style bronze artefacts that were found as part of grave-goods buried with a 9th-century ruler or ritual leader in south eastern Nigeria at Igbo-Ukwu were a display of superb technical skill, being both distinctive and perhaps unequalled elsewhere in the world at the time. The rise of urbanism and 'complex societies' in West Africa, as revealed by the archaeological findings at Jenne-Jeno, can be clearly accounted for by internal rather than external factors. The first Muslims to visit the region on the northern fringes of the savannah found already established towns and a regional trading system that were predominantly local inventions. One of such success stories is that of the kingdom of Mali. Founded by King Sundiata in 1235 as a consolidation of several small Malinké Kingdoms, Mali was one of the largest empires in West African history, stretching from the Atlantic Coast all the way to the central parts of the Sahara. The kingdom prospered in part on account of its well-organised system for collecting taxes from its citizens. All goods brought in and out of the empire were taxed. Mali traded in gold as currency together with salt and cotton cloth. At a later time, cowrie shells were also part of the currency. Its city of Timbuktu was a famous centre of learning and spectacular architecture. The Sankara Madrassa and the University of Sankore became some of the greatest centres of learning in the Islamic world, producing a great many astronomers, scholars and engineers even after the end of the empire. Mali had the greatest library in Africa since the Great Library of Alexandria, and was estimated to have housed up to 700 000 manuscripts.

Aside from being a centre of Islamic scholarship, Timbuktu was also an important market for the trans-Saharan trade in precious metal. Stories of Mali's wealth drew increasing numbers of North Africans to trading deals across the Sahara. Merchants from North Africa, the Middle East and Europe competed for Mali gold. One of its famous kings, Mansa Musa, deployed diplomats and opened an embassy in Morocco, which stimulated trade with northwest Africa. After the Musa's pilgrimage, Egyptian traders were regular visitors to Mali. On his pilgrimage to Mecca, Musa travelled with 60,000 individuals and large quantities of gold which created a massive sensation as he travelled through Egypt; he distributed so much gold in the country that a great inflation lasting a decade ensued. Apart from his 50,000 gold coins gift to the sultan of Egypt and his deputy, his entourage is said to have spent such large amounts of gold in the market that gold declined in value for several years.

A well-established trading community, the Great Zimbabwe that most likely regulated the thriving medieval gold trade was in existence between the Zambezi and the Limpopo rivers by the 14th century. The ruins of Great Zimbabwe attest to the presence of a once thriving city that may have dominated trade and culture throughout southern Africa. Its unique architecture and sculpture speak of a rich history. Although the architecture was suspected to be of Phoenician or Arabian art because of the prejudice that the continent had no sophistication and its people and tribes were culturally barren and unable to develop, it is now settled that it is, indeed, native Africans that built Great Zimbabwe. The story of Great Zimbabwe is ultimately that of early Shona culture, the African Iron Age and interactions with Arabs and Portuguese traders. It is a story of a display of wealth and a method for efficiently organising an existing labour force.

3. Africa's Potential through Local Initiatives: Fisheries Management Using Artificial Reefs at Makanjira Fishing Community

Like in historical times, extant local communities in many parts of Africa have the ability for analysing their own problems and the requisite zeal for tackling them. In this section, we present a case story of a local community in the southern part of Lake Malawi that independently initiated a system of artificial submerged reefs for managing their fish stocks.

The fisheries of Lake Malawi are probably one of the most diverse in the world; some surveys have recorded more than 200 species

270

from single fishing localities in the southern part of the water body (Weyl et al. 2005, 2010). This multispecies fishery is one of the most economically important in Malawi, providing employment to thousands of rural poor Malawians (over 200,000 people), and supporting about 14 per cent of Malawi's population along the lakeshore through fishing, processing, marketing, fishing gear construction, boat building and other fisheries-related activities (Malawi Government 2016). While commercial fishermen mostly use bottom trawlers and mid-water trawlers, small-scale fisherfolks largely use gill nets, long lines, hand lines, cast nets and various forms of open seine nets.

Total annual fish catches have historically slowly increased since the 1940s, reaching ranges of from 20,000 tonnes to 84,000 tonnes in the mid-1960s and early 1970s. The total annual catch has rather stabilised since the mid-1980s and presently fluctuates around 31,000 tonnes, most of it (±80 per cent) from the artisanal fishers (Weyl 2003). Species composition of the catches has, however, drastically changed. In some cases, high value species have disappeared from the catch. This has been attributed to the extensive use of illegal fishing gear that resulted in the destruction of nesting and feeding habitats and, eventually, recruitment and growth over-fishing (Seisay et al. 1992; Hara and Banda 1994). Inefficient enforcement of existing fisheries regulations chiefly due to budgetary constraints has also left the fishery resource ill-managed or unmanaged (FAO 1993; Hara 1996). In the early 1990s, the Government of Malawi pushed for a bottom-up fisheries co-management approach; responsibility for managing the collapsing fishery was to be shared between the Fisheries Department and the local communities so that communities would identify their own needs, set their own objectives and monitor and evaluate the fish stocks (Hara 1996; Dobson and Lynch 2003).

Despite the participatory fisheries management framework introduced in the early 1990s, the dwindling of fish stocks that began in the mid-1980s has continued. In the nearby Lake Malombe, for instance, record *Oreochromis* (*chambo*) annual catches of more than 6,000 tonnes of the 1980s are now at less than 200 tonnes. Access to the fishery is still largely unlimited and in some cases fishing effort has continued to rise together with illegal gears (Ngochera et al. 2002). The need to find means for sustainably managing the country's fisheries stocks will remain a top priority for some time. In light of the fisheries' co-management approach and the devolution of some hitherto strictly central government functions to local authorities, any locally conceived fisheries management techniques must be fully encouraged and nurtured. One such approach is the use of artificial submerged reefs (locally called, and herein after referred to as, *virundu* for plural or *chirundu* for singular) in Makanjira, in the southeastern part of Lake Malawi (Figure 1).

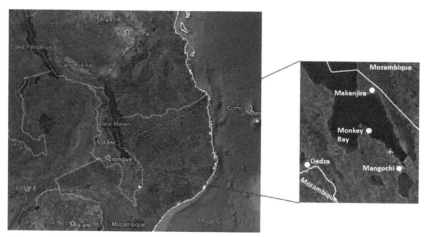

Figure 1. Map of southern part of Lake Malawi, showing the location of Makanjira

In order to understand the history of *virundu*, the (original) rationale for their establishment, their design, construction as well as their management and governance, we conducted focus group discussions (FGD) involving 51 participants (each group with 6.4 ±1.2 individuals) and centred around 25 questions at villages of Matola, Mtondo, Silimanji, Mchangani, Selemani and Mpangama in the area of Traditional Authority Makanjira in Mangochi District, southeastern shore of Lake Malawi, southern Africa (Figure 1). The FGD participants were mostly village heads, fisherfolks, *virundu* owners and the chairpersons of Beach Village Committees (BVCs): local assemblages of people in charge of fisheries matters in their areas). We also undertook short exploratory surveys of the catch from *virundu* to empirically test the claims from the FGD sessions. We narrate below a case of a local community that was able to discover an opportunity and rose up to grab it to deal with its immediate challenge related the management of fisheries stocks and their livelihood.

4. Origins of *Virundu* for Managing Fisheries at Makanjira

The construction of *virundu* at Makanjira started in the 1980s and peaked in the early 2000s. It did not result from any formal training, but had its origins in the observations of natural phenomena undertaken by local people. Fisherfolks claim to have picked up this technique from their own parents. Lilole River, the main river that drains into the lake in the area, swells and floods a lot at the start of the rainy season. This annual flooding episode results in a lot of fallen trees and logs (wood debris) being washed and deposited into the lake close to the river mouth. In the past, local people had observed that fishing adjacent to these piles of tree debris consistently yielded higher catches relative to fishing away from the debris. As these piles of debris were unstable over time, becoming scattered and often drifting along from place to place by the action of water waves, this fishing advantage tended to diminish. To ensure more control over the existence of the piles of debris and to sustain the increased fisheries benefits, local people conceived of artificially creating their own submerged reefs, *virundu* and thus reducing their dependence on the flood-made reefs. Local fisherfolks in Malawi are highly migratory, changing their fishing grounds based on reported good catches. Immigrant fishermen from Nkhotakota who settled at Makanjira reportedly talked about how this idea had already been implemented in their area, northeast of Makanjira. Knowledge sharing between local fishermen and these immigrant fishermen from Nkhotakota may also have played a part.

4-1. *The Construction of* Virundu

The *virundu* are essentially made of freshly pruned bundles of shrubs and small tree branches (mostly *Mangifera indica* and *Ficus sycomorus*) that are fastened together at their base using nylon ropes and sank down into the lake bottom with the aid of sand bags (weighing about 25–50 kg). The structures are generally constructed onshore and later transported to their respective sites by boat. In some instances, however, the raw materials (tree branches) are ferried by boat to the designated offshore sites where construction of the brush piles takes place on-site before setting them (Figure 2). Another design of *virundu* which was popular in the past, comprises a collection of used giant woven fish traps (locally called *mono*) and used traditional-style granaries made of woven bamboo and shrub twigs. These are also bundled together and anchored to a weight before being sunk to the bottom to create an aggregation of underwater 'caves'. This design is no longer popular because of its limited durability.

Figure 2. A team of fisher folks assisting each other in assembling a *chirundu*, **ready for installation on the lake**

The specific depths at which the brush parks are set are not uniform, but in any case, these structures are dropped to a depth of at least 14 m. While some fishermen alluded to the depth ranges of 15–20 m, others recalled that they set their brush parks at between 38 and 40 m deep, at between 50 and 56 m, at 56 m deep and at between 30 and 80 m deep. The guiding principle is that the brush parks are not generally installed in shallower waters because the Utaka fish (*Copadichromis* spp.), which is the main target for the *virundu*, breeds in shallow areas and the fisherfolks do not want to disturb breeding fish. The virundu are mostly installed about 1 km away from the shore and tend to be shifted into deeper waters further offshore when the lake level drops.

The choice of location where to set *virundu* (typically at least 50 m apart) is rather indiscriminate, although in some cases, the locations of the brush parks were pre-determined by their grandparents who had identified areas of the lake with high productivity and descriptively demarcated these areas of the lake. Once established, the *virundu* sites are identified again by using shoreline physical features and landmarks like mountains and specific trees. Bottles are also used as marker buoys in the water. Usually only a few people master the art of tracing exactly where the brush parks are (out of a 10-person crew, it is typically only the two lead fishermen who can remember the exact site).

An individual fisherfolk usually owns between three and fifteen *virundu*s, each consisting of two or three piles of tree branches. Normally one or two *virundu* are harvested at a time, casting the seine nets around each brush park five or six times. While some fishermen add nothing to the *virundu* structures, such as nutrients, to promote growth of algal food sources, others add about 100 kg of maize bran (in sacks or sunken old used canoes) to the brush parks during construction and periodically every six months thereafter (during routine rehabilitation) as a source of food for the fish.

4-2. The Governance of Virundu

The *virundu* structures are initially set up in September and left for at least a month, but in many cases for three to four months before any harvesting takes place. Open water seines are mostly used to harvest the fish, with the nets being pulled up-current across the brush park to trap fish. The brush parks are either surrounded with a net or a seine net is towed in between the reefs to collect fish. Depending on water temperature and currents, sometimes the catch can range from as much as 30 to 50 basins while at other times the catch can be quite dismal. A basin of fresh fish is on average equivalent to nine 5-litre pails (a standard measure for selling fish on most Malawian beaches), each costing about 3,000 Malawian kwacha or 4 US dollars (Sungani pers.com.).

Each fisherman has the responsibility of managing and looking after his reefs. In some instances, the structures are never repaired, but other new artificial reefs are instead erected to replace or add to the pre-existing ones. In most cases, however, some form of maintenance is undertaken (within two–three months of initial construction) especially when fish catches in the brush parks begin to decline or when the initial tree branches have perceptibly begun to decompose. More tree branches and/or old broken boats are added on top of the existing structures and a bag of maize bran (50 kg) is also supplied to the rehabilitated structure to attract fish.

Ownership and utilisation of *virundu* are defined by the identity of the one who sets up the structure, either as an individual or a group. Although there is little or no formal security for *virundu*, fisherfolks from one village would rarely go fishing at another village's *virundu* because they know the boundaries of their village's jurisdiction within a lake (These boundaries, however do not extend to and are no longer applicable or existent in the deeper areas of the lake). Only the owner of the *virundu* is expected to harvest from the structure. In certain circumstances, non-owners of *virundu* ask for permission to fish at these structures. When allowed, no fee is charged, but the non-owners are expected to give a token of appreciation in the form of part of the catch at the level of their own determination. BVCs mediate in *virundu* fishing conflicts and are generally the first line of recourse before matters are taken to the chief. Although there are no formally laid down punishments, when the offender is caught, the matter is brought to the village chief who customarily handles the case in accordance with the local traditional justice system, sometimes enforcing the confiscation of the encroacher's fishing gear. If it is established that a fisherman accidentally fished at someone else's *virundu*, there is no punishment given; this is commonly understood as an innocent mistake.

4-3. *Limnological Aspects of* Virundu *Sites and Their Fish Species Composition*

We conducted a comparative exploratory sampling of basic limnological aspects as well as fish catches from areas adjacent to *virundu* and those from non-adjacent areas within the same general

276

area. The concentration of soluble reactive phosphorus (SRP), the type of nutrient that limits phytoplankton growth was higher at *virundu* sites than the control sites. Concentration of chlorophyll *a* was characteristic of moderate productive waters ranging from 0.78 ± 0.03 to $1.88\pm0.83\mu gL^{-1}$ but did not significantly differ between *virundu* sites and non-*virundu* sites ($F = 1.11$, $F_{crit} = 18.51$, $p = 0.402$). However, the sites within the vicinity of *virundu* had higher zooplankton numbers than the control site. More species of fish (n = 10) were caught close to the *virundu* structures than away from these structures (n = 2). Species composition of the main catch in *virundu* as reported by fishermen closely resembled that of the actually sampled hauls. Catches from areas adjacent to *virundu* were more diverse (Shannon biodiversity index = 1.83) than away from these structures (Shannon index = 0.69). The length-frequency distribution of the shared major target species, *Copadichromis* juveniles, was different between the *virundu* areas and the control sites (Kolmogorov-Smirnov two-sample test, p = 0.0062). Juvenile *Copadichromis* in the vicinity of the *virundu* were generally bigger (32.90 $\pm$ 0.37 mm) than those fished from the control areas (31.24 $\pm$ 0.50 mm) ($F_{1,211} = 7.45$, p = 0.0069). This may indicate that the fisherfolks' venturing into *virundu* construction is empirically grounded.

5. Discussion

Fish ecologists have for long known that fish utilise woody structures and vegetated areas in the aquatic environment for breeding, feeding and refuge (Welcomme 2002). For instance, studies by Poe et al. (1986) and Bryan and Scarnecchia (1992) documented the role of near-shore aquatic vegetation as nursery grounds for fish while Lowe-McConnell (1964, 1975) reported the use of large woody debris as a refuge by fish in the main channels of some South American rivers. Fish abundance, thus tends to be greater in vegetated habitats than in unvegetated ones (Dibble et al. 1997; Valley et al. 2004).

The knowledge of the relationship between aquatic vegetation on the one hand and fish behaviour and abundance on the other has led to the development of artificial structures that are known as fish parks; essentially living vegetation or dead tree branches placed in rivers, shallow lakes and coastal lagoons to serve as fish aggregating devices (FADs) and largely to ease fish capture (Welcomme 2002). Fish parks are classified into two categories: brush parks that consist of dead tree branches as well as shrubs; and vegetation parks that consist of living, soft, floating vegetation (Welcomme 2002; Gomna 2015).

In this chapter, after some historical stories, we have presented a case of local innovation of fisheries management using *virundu*. It is a traditional form of low-technology aquaculture, which is also practised in coastal lagoons and brackish waters in many areas of the world. Zooplankton and fish production seem to have benefited from the *virundu* structures, with the fish species count and fish diversity being higher in their vicinity. Reported fish species composition of the main catch in *virundu* closely mirrored that of the actual sampled hauls. This stands in fair agreement with several studies that have also reported the potential of brush parks to contribute to the overall production of water bodies by increasing reproduction, fry survival, shelter for adults and, when properly managed, overall recruitment to the fishery in general (Lalèyè et al. 1995; Welcomme 2002; Uddin et al. 2015). Welcomme and Kapetsky (1981) observed that most mature fish within the confines of brush parks were in breeding condition and further report the presence of numerous juveniles and an 'overflow' of fingerlings into the open water from brush parks, providing further evidence of the role of brush parks as seed production sites for surrounding waters. This study may be the basis for the introduction of *virundu* in fisheries rebuilding programmes in the country's water bodies where fish stocks have been heavily depleted.

Across modern Africa, we continue to witness local initiatives that again point to the unearthing of massive hunger and potential for progress. The case study of Makanjira fisherfolks reflects similar aspects of the idea of 'African Potentials' such as the innovativeness of 'indigenous knowledge'. Modern African states would play their role of further catalysing these local initiatives better by deliberately creating conducive environments that promote mobility in space to network local initiatives so that their overall contribution to the

278

macro-economic fabric of society is harnessed and well valued for human progress.

Acknowledgements

This work was supported by JSPS KAKENHI Grant Number JP16H06318 and the Fisheries Integration of Society and Habitats (FISH) Project under the Cooperative Agreement AID-612-A-14-00004.

References

Bryan, M. D. and Scarnecchia, D. L. (1992) 'Species richness, composition, and abundance of fish larvae and juveniles inhabiting natural and developed shorelines of a glacial Iowa lake', *Environmental Biology of Fishes*, Vol. 35, Issue 4, pp. 329–341.

Butzer, K. W. (1981) 'Rise and fall of Axum, Ethiopia: A geo-archaeological interpretation', *American Antiquity*, Vol. 46, Issue 3, pp. 471–495.

Conrad, D. C. (2010) *Empires of Medieval West Africa: Ghana, Mali, and Songhay*, New York: Infobase Publishing.

Dibble, E. D., Killgore, K. J. and Harrel, S. L. (1997) 'Assessment of fish-plant interactions', *American Fisheries Society Symposium*, No. 16, pp. 357–372.

Dobson, T. A., and Lynch, K. D. (2003) 'As nearshore stocks drop, Malawi begins a return to local fisheries management', *Journal of Great Lakes Research*, Vol. 29, pp. 232–242.

FAO (Food and Agriculture Organization of the United Nations) (1993) *Fisheries Management in South East Lake Malawi, the Upper Shire River and Lake Malombe, CIFA Technical Report, No. 21*, Rome: FAO.

Gomna, A. (2015) 'A comparative study of the profitability of brush parks in two states in Nigeria', *International Journal of Fisheries and Aquaculture*, Vol. 7, No. 10, pp. 160–166.

Hara, M. (1996) *Problems of Introducing Community Participation in Fisheries Management: Lessons from The Lake Malombe and Upper Shire*

River (Malawi) Participatory Fisheries Management Programme, Southern African Perspectives, A Working Paper Series, Issue 59, Cape Town: Centre for Southern African Studies, University of the Western Cape.

Hara, M. and Banda, M. (1994) 'Seine nets and habitat degradation: How they have caused collapse of the chambo (*Oreochromis* spp.) fishery of Lake Malombe', paper presented at the Conference for Inland Fisheries of Africa, Harare.

Iliffe J. (2007) *Africans, The history of a Continent*, New York: Cambridge University Press.

Lalèyè, A. P., Philippart, J. C. and Heymans, J. C. (1995) 'Cycle annuel de l'indice gonadosomatique et de la condition chez deux espèces de Chrysichthys (Siluriformes, Bagridae) au lac Nokoué et à la lagune de Porto-Novo au Bénin', *Cybium*, Vol. 19, No. 2, pp. 131–142.

Lowe-McConnell, R. H. (1964) 'The fishes of the Rupunini savanna district of British Guiana, South America: Part 1. Ecological groupings of fish species and effects of the seasonal cycles on the fish', *Journal of the Linnean Society (Zoology)*, Vol. 45, Issue 304, pp. 103–144.

———— (1975) *Fish Communities in Tropical Freshwaters: Their Distribution, Ecology and Evolution*, London: Longman.

Malawi Government (2016) *National Fisheries and Aquaculture Policy*, Lilongwe: Department of Fisheries, Ministry of Natural Resources and Environmental Affairs.

Ndoro, W. (1997) 'Great Zimbabwe', *Scientific American*, Vol. 277, No. 5, pp. 94–99.

Ngochera, M., Weyl, O. L. F., Namoto, W., Mponda, O. C. and Mhango, T. (2002) *Mangochi District Frame Survey 2002*, Lilongwe: National Aquatic Resource Management Programme (NARMAP) Fisheries Department.

Oliver, R. and Fagan, B. M. (2002) 'The emergence of Bantu Africa', in J. D. Fage (ed.) *The Cambridge History of Africa, Volume 2*, Cambridge: Cambridge University Press, pp. 342–409.

Parker, J. and Rathbone, R. (2007) *African History: A Very Short Introduction*, New York: Oxford University Press.

Poe, T. P., Hatcher, C. O., Brown, C. L. and Schloesser, D. W. (1986) 'Comparison of species composition and richness of fish assemblages in altered and unaltered littoral habitats', *Journal of Freshwater Ecology*, Vol. 3, Issue 4, pp. 525–536.

Seisay, M. B. D., Van Zalinge, N. P. and Turner, G. F. (1992) *Population Dynamics and Stock Estimates of Chambo* (Oreochromis *spp.) in the South East Arm of Lake Malawi and Malombe: Length-Based Approach, GOM/FAO/UNDP Chambo Fisheries Research Project (FI: DP/MLW/86/013), Field Document 19*, Lilongwe: GOM/FAO/UNDP/Chambo Fisheries Research Project.

Shuriye, A. O. and Ibrahim, D. S. (2013) 'Timbuktu civilization and its significance in Islamic history', *Mediterranean Journal of Social Sciences*, Vol. 4, Issue 11, pp. 696–704.

Uddin, K. B., Basak, S. S., Moniruzzaman, M., Islam, A. K. M. S. and Mahmud, Y. (2015) 'Impact of brush shelter: A fish aggregating device (FAD) on the production potentiality of Kaptai Lake in Bangladesh', *World Journal of Fish and Marine Sciences*, Vol. 7, Issue 4, pp. 288–294.

Valley, R. D., Cross, T. K. and Radomski, P. (2004) *The Role of Submersed Aquatic Vegetation as Habitat for Fish in Minnesota Lakes, Including the Implications of Non-Native Plant Invasions and Their Management, Minnesota Department of Natural Resources Special Publication 160*, Saint Paul: Minnesota Department of Natural Resources.

Welcomme, R. L. (2002) 'An evaluation of tropical brush and vegetation park fisheries', *Fisheries Management and Ecology*, Vol. 9, Issue 3, pp. 175–188.

Welcomme, R. L. and Kapetsky, S. (1981) 'Acadjas: The brush park fisheries of Benin, West Africa', *The International Center for Living Aquatic Resources Management (ICLARM) Newsletter*, Vol. 4, No. 4, pp. 3–4.

Weyl, O. L. F. (2003) *Capture Fisheries in Malawi and Their Contribution to National Fish Supply, Aquaculture Development in Malawi (ADIM) Report*, Lilongwe: Japanese International Cooperation Agency (JICA), Malawi.

Weyl, O. L. F., Nyasulu, T. E. and Rusuwa, B. (2005) 'Assessment of catch, effort and species changes in the pair-trawl fishery of southern Lake Malawi, Malawi, Africa', *Fisheries Management and Ecology*, Vol. 12, Issue 6, pp. 395–402.

Weyl, O. L. F., Ribbink, A. J. and Tweddle, D. (2010) 'Lake Malawi: Fishes, fisheries, biodiversity, health and habitat', *Aquatic Ecosystem Health and Management*, Vol. 13, Issue 3, pp. 241–254.

Chapter 12

Sustainability in Developing Societies: Changes in Commodity Prices and Population over a Quarter of a Century in a Fishing Village in Southwestern Madagascar

Taku Iida

1. Introduction

Sustainability is one of the most important considerations with respect to the living conditions of individuals and societies in both urban and rural areas. This concept is so pervasive that we often overlook the fact that it is applicable only in certain conditions. How can one sustain, for example, things which move rapidly and unpredictably? We may talk of sustainability of resources, population, institutions and the world overall, but not necessarily of individual free markets. Sustainability is applicable to the elements of a system that is changing gradually, but not to phenomena showing rapid changes.

We must regulate phenomena showing rapid changes, including individual and entrepreneurial economic activities, as well as the behaviour of markets (Agrawal 2002). Such phenomena are difficult to discuss within a framework of sustainability and can also affect other elements. According to the concept of sustainable development, we must control rapid and radical changes in societies. If the rate of change is constant, sustainable change (and thus stability) can be achieved. However, whether such control is possible in practice is not clear. Indexes of economic growth provide a summary of myriad interrelated changes occurring simultaneously, which cannot be tracked by a single individual, entrepreneur or government. The term 'sustainable development' may thus be rhetorically, but not empirically, effective.

For this reason, in rapidly changing African societies, the concept of sustainability is often ambiguous in terms of the elements that should be sustained. Even if they all agree that a population or resource should be maintained, people may have different ideas of the degree to which such maintenance should be pursued. If an innovation of some kind was to be introduced and a new balance thus achieved – for example, if a vaccine for infection prophylaxis was introduced such that more humans or animals could coexist in the same environment – people may nevertheless differ in their opinion of whether this is actually advantageous.

The same may be said of the balance among population size, resource level and economic conditions. The fishing village in Madagascar in which I conducted my anthropological field research (on the Vezo people) over more than a quarter of a century[1] experienced significant population growth and socioeconomic changes. Unfortunately, no quantitative dataset covering this entire period is available. If resources become severely depleted, asking fishermen to cease exploitative environmental practices or prohibiting outside poaching is difficult because free fishing may promote economic stability in this area, and sustaining a resource base is not necessarily analogous to people's welfare. To further the discussion of the limitations of sustainability, this chapter describes the socioeconomic changes that occurred in the village over a quarter of a century, particularly with respect to commodity prices and population. In the concluding section, I discuss the concept of 'our common future' without the false assumption of a static system.

2. Changes in Commodity Prices over a Quarter of a Century: 1969–1994

I first visited the village of Ampasilava in 1994. The capital of Madagascar had experienced a political crisis in 1991 that was settled through the adoption of a new Constitution in 1992, ushering in the age of the Third Republic (1993–2009) (Moriyama 1996). In 1994, some intellectuals expected the country's new president, Albert Zafy (in office during the period 1993–1997), to lift the country out of the economic depression that began during the period of socialist government. In fact, the subsequent president, Didier Ratsiraka (in office during the period 1975–1993 and 1997–2002), was not willing to achieve this as the former President during the regime of the Second Republic (1975–1993). His reappointment was viewed as increasingly likely in October 1996, towards the end of my second long stay in Madagascar. At the time of writing this in 2020, more than a quarter of a century has passed since my first research visit to Ampasilava.

Several decades earlier, the French ethnographer Bernard Koechlin conducted more extensive research in this region in 1968 and 1969 (Koechlin 1971, 1975).[2] Having achieved independence in 1960, the Malagasy government pursued a pro-French policy under the First Republic regime (1960–1975) of Philibert Tsiranana (in office during the period 1959–1972) during Koechlin's fieldwork. The exchange rate of Malagasy francs (FMG) to French francs (FF) was fixed at 50 FMG/FF.[3] At the time of Koechlin's research, dried cassava and maize grains both cost 15 FMG/kg, while rice was priced at 35 FMG/kg (Koechlin 1975: 111). However, Koechlin did not describe the unit price of fresh fish, which is the best index of commodity prices for comparison with later periods. Few fresh fish must have been transacted during this period. Rather, he described only that a large, dried octopus cost 40 FMG, while a smaller one was priced at 20 FMG (Koechlin 1975: 101). A bulk order of opercula comprising striped fox conches (*Pleuroploca trapezium* or *Fasciolaria trapezium*) and branched murexes (*Chicoreus ramosus* or *Murex ramosus*), which was exported and processed to derive incense, sold for 400 FMG/kg (Koechlin 1975: 64–65). Regarding luxury food commodities, the price of sugar (70 FMG/kg) is a good index. A small canoe with a small turning circle, used to hunt sea turtles, cost 1,500 FMG, while a larger canoe (four to five fathoms in length) cost 5,000 FMG (Koechlin 1975: 109–110).

Madagascar underwent a coup d'état in 1972 and established good relations with socialist countries under the regime of the Second Republic. Meanwhile, commodity prices gradually rose. According to an Ampasilava elder, the price of rice rose to 90 FMG/kg after Prime Minister Richard Ratsimandrava was assassinated in 1975. Fresh fish transactions became more widespread in the 1980s. One man in the village reported buying and salt-drying fresh fish immediately before he got married in 1984. He claimed that he was born in 1961, but this date is not reliable since birth registration was not precise at that time. The fresh fish was purchased from fishermen for 75 FMG/kg and sold as salted fish for 200–300 FMG/kg (Iida 2008: 203). I obtained further information about commodity prices in the First and Second Republic periods, but do not include it herein as it may be unreliable.

At the beginning of the Third Republic, when I began my field research, the cost of rice had risen to 1,800–2,200 FMG/kg. Dry cassava cost 650 FMG/kg; fresh fish at the beach cost 1,000 FMG/kg; salt-dried fish sold for 3,000 FMG/kg; and larger canoes cost 1,000,000 FMG/kg. The cost of rice increased 60-fold over a quarter of a century, while the price of larger canoes increased up to 200-fold. One of the reasons for this is that the variance in canoe prices is generally greater than that in rice prices, depending on the skill of the craftsman. I speculate that the increasing labour time and material costs associated with more intricate canoe decorations may also have been a factor in the high prices.

Although the canoe price increase is an extreme case, a 60-fold price increase is relatively high for a period of a quarter of a century, indicating rapid infiltration of the monetary economy into the rural area. In the 1970s, the collection of sea cucumbers as ingredients for Chinese food, as well as the opercula of conchs and murexes for incense production, had already begun in waters near the village. At the same time, nylon nets were being introduced to catch spiny lobsters near the town, which had a significant Indian population (Iida 2008: 202–204). Although business activity declined in the 1980s, the market for shark fins in Southeast Asia and China, as well as sea cucumbers, grew at the beginning of the 1990s. As the sea cucumber population had already been depleted, Ampasilava fishermen travelled to an uninhabited island 100 km from their village to obtain shark fins and sea cucumbers (Iida 2008: 52–73). Shark fins have been an export commodity ever since, along with sea cucumbers.

3. Changes in Commodity Prices over a Quarter of a Century: 1994–2019

In the quarter-century from the end of the 1960s to the beginning of my field research, commodity prices increased severalfold. During the quarter-century period thereafter, rice, which had cost 2,000 FMG/kg in 1995, rose in price to 8,500 FMG/kg (converted from MGA, see endnote 3) by 2020; dry cassava, which had previously cost 650 FMG/kg, rose in price to 4,000–6,000 FMG/kg, while fish rose in price from 1,000 to 15,000 FMG/kg.

I occasionally recorded some of the prices referred to above in 1995, during my third stay in Ampasilava. The values may not be representative, because actual prices fluctuate according to the quality of the goods and the season. However, the values most frequently used in previous transactions are the most important ones. The maximum and minimum values may be far removed from these values. The prices that I recorded in Ampasilava were relatively stable over at least two years, although the range of values was narrow. However, the 2020 prices were reported to me by a young associate in Ampasilava via a social networking site. Therefore, I am uncertain regarding the extent to which they reflect actual transaction values, but they seemed plausible based on field research carried out in 2019.

The data showed that staple crop prices during the quarter-century increased no more than fivefold, while the price of fish increased more than tenfold. In comparison to the increase in the previous quarter-century, the increase in prices of both commodities was less steep. In the quarter-century since the late 1960s, especially in rural areas during the Second Republic era, dependency on the cash economy became so high that people began to suffer (Iida 2008: 202–209). By contrast, the increase in commodity prices after the mid-1990s was more gradual. Under such conditions, as long as the total size of fish catches is maintained, life will be stable. As the rate of increase in fish prices surpassed that of rice, fishermen's socioeconomic status improved.

Table 1 presents the sea product prices that I noted on each visit to Ampasilava.

Table 1. Change in sea-product prices during a quarter-century
(Unit: FMG/kg)

	Rabbit fish (cheap)	White fish (expensive)	Octopus	Squid	Spiny lobster
January 1995	1,000	1,000	1,000	-	-
December 1995	1,000	1,000	1,000	-	-
September 1996	1,000	1,000	-	-	-
December 2001	-	1,500	-	-	-
January 2002	1,000	1,500	1,500	-	-
March 2003	1,500	2,500	2,500	5,000	-
November 2003	1,500	2,000	3,000	4,000	12,500
October 2005	2,500	2,500	5,500	7,500	15,000
January 2010	3,000	3,000	4,000	5,000	50,000
February 2014	6,000	6,000	6,000	10,000	50,000
September 2014	7,000	7,000	8,000	15,000	50,000
November 2015	10,000	10,000	-	-	-
November 2016	11,000	11,000	10,000	15,000	60,000
July 2017	-	-	10,000	20,000	-
November 2019	12,500	15,000	20,000	47,500	122,500
June 2020	-	15,000	-	-	-

The first remarkable increase in fish prices occurred at the beginning of the 2000s. One reason for this increase was that a luxury hotel near Ampasilava began to accept foreign tourists from around 2000. Because this hotel expanded its business gradually, it is difficult to determine when this became a critical factor. In 2001, several women in their 20s and 30s were employed as housekeeping staff in the hotel. In 2003, at least four Ampasilava villagers, including three housekeepers and one boat driver, were commuting to the hotel for work (Iida 2008: 236–237). The hotel was also profitable for fishermen, because the cook bought large fish at better prices than those received when selling on the beach.

However, the hotel was not the only contributor to the increase in fish prices. In January 1999, before the hotel had opened, a man from the district capital of Morombe, around 50 km to the north, opened the first grocery and general goods store in Ampasilava. Unlike the houses of food merchants, from which food had previously been sold there, this shop had a counter to separate the clerk's area from that for visitors, to facilitate exchange of cash and goods. It also sold various goods and commodities that had been difficult to find in the village, such as medicines and stationery. This kind of shop, which was more typical of larger towns, appeared for the first time in Ampasilava in this period in response to the greater purchasing power of the fishermen and their families. The fishermen's disposable income increased due to the availability of gill nets for shark netting and sea cucumber spearing, which began in the 1990s in remote areas (Iida 2005, 2008: 47–73), and to the invention of spear guns for use in waters close to the village (Iida 2008: 210–214; Iida 2019). It is regrettable that I did not continue to collect quantitative data on household incomes at that time, so cannot fully demonstrate the income increase.

I began to take notes on anecdotes relating to income increases in early 2002, when I first noticed the change in household income. Aside from the hotel's opening, the most noteworthy event was the proliferation of small 'sidewalk cafés', the owners of which serve baked cakes, coffee and tea. Such cafés are typically situated in shady bowers close to the owner's homes and kitchens, and have a few long benches for customers. These establishments are often managed by women. Young divers returning from the sea would gather in these cafés and typically purchase three cakes and a cup of tea or coffee with their daily earnings, as a means of relaxing. I usually ordered one or two cakes and a cup of tea or coffee for breakfast. Owing to the small amount of capital required to open such cafés, they increased rapidly in number in response to rising demand.

The cafés require more fuel than typical households. Moreover, coastal regions have so little rainfall that few trees and shrubs grow, so village residents must walk for several kilometres to get fuel. For these reasons, the new cafés had already begun to hire fuel collectors by 2002. Over the following years, more villagers began to visit these cafés to buy cakes and beverages to take away in thermos flasks. Therefore, the owners required more fuel and asked their acquaintances living several kilometres away to transport fuel to Ampasilava via cattle carts. The demand for water also increased. Because it was necessary to fetch water from wells outside the village – even if only several hundred metres away – most café owners hired waged labourers to transport water to them. These cafés continue to generally increase in size and number in Ampasilava, although not linearly.

Another significant factor in the increase in fish prices is the demand for fresh or chilled fish, and associated development of transport systems (Iida 2005, 2008: 234–236). At the beginning of 2003, the crew of a large boat with freezing equipment began to buy fresh fish from several villages, including Ampasilava, with the help of a small boat with an outboard engine. Before then, most of fish was dried or salted for sale. At the same time, squid, which had no commodity value in the village, commenced to be purchased for a high price (Iida 2008: 214–216).[4] Spiny lobsters, which had only been sold in Morombe, where people of European origin lived, began to be transacted in the village. Fish and seafood purchased in Ampasilava were frozen on board the ship and exported to other countries.

By 2005, the freezer boat ceased visiting the villages to buy seafood, but several trucks with large cooler boxes and ice continued to collect food. The trucks usually provided 'sub-collectors' in the village with ice before the spring tide, when the fishermen's catches were larger. The trucks did not return to the town immediately, but instead visited several neighbouring villages in the evening (when the tide flows) to buy sea products from sub-collectors before being fully loaded and returning to the town. The sub-collectors immediately chilled the seafood with ice and recorded the weight of the harvest every time they sold it to the truck crew who brought the money when the truck returned from town. This means of collection required a much smaller initial investment than the freezer boat, although the former carries a slightly greater risk of damage to the cargo.

Entrepreneurs operating seafood collection trucks continued to increase the price of their cargo, as Figure 1 illustrates. The price of fish varies according to species in the rainy season, when there is less traffic and the demand for fish is lower. Figure 1 shows the price of *fiam-poty*, or white fish, the demand for which is comparatively high (as is the proportion of cash transactions). *Fiam-poty* is a large group that includes species from the *Lutjanidae* (snapper) and *Lethrinidae* (emperor) families.

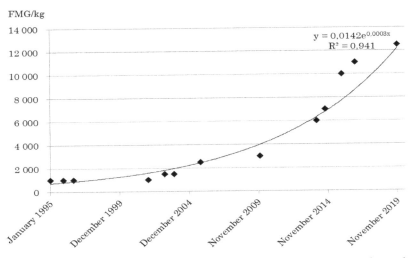

Figure 1. Changes in fish prices during the quarter-century since the mid-1990s

As Figure 1 shows, fish prices showed a geometric progression. The same trend can be assumed for rice, although empirical data are lacking. In this case, rice prices would eventually reach current fish prices, since the latter – now 15,000 FMG/kg – had been half the current price only five years ago. However, within a five-year period, fish prices can be expected to increase even more sharply, and the difference between the two will be even greater. Moreover, people's perspectives and behaviours can change significantly within five years; industrial practices may also change and stimulate demand for fish. In the following section, we will see how economic changes influenced social conditions and people's behaviour. Thus,

Ampasilava fishermen enjoyed superiority of their products, fish, in comparison to the staple food to be purchased.

I wish to conclude this section by examining how people changed their consumption behaviour after their income increased. Fishermen did not reduce their working hours, despite receiving more income. While they continue fishing from their base in Ampasilava (Iida 2008: 264), they also engage in camp fishing in other locations for several months, to catch sharks or sea cucumbers, which have high unit prices and thus provide large incomes. Young fishermen, who are expected to provide a substantial dowry to their future wives and relatives, engage in camp fishing almost without exception. They spend most of their large cash income before returning. They prefer to buy non-perishable consumer goods, such as audio-visual sets comprising a generator, loudspeakers, TV monitor and DVD player, lounge suites including a table and sofa, fishing equipment such as nets and diving fins and communication devices like cellular or smartphones (cf. Muttenzer 2020: 38–42). They bring some of the cash back to the village where they use it to build houses and canoes. As standards of education and medicine are now higher, significant amounts of money are also invested in these areas.

4. Population Movements during a Quarter-Century

To understand social changes from a non-economic perspective, let us examine population change. Table 2 shows the changes that occurred in the population of Ampasilava village over 23 years. The data collection for this population analysis was initiated during my fourth stay in Ampasilava in 1995. I listed the names and sexes of all residents, regardless of whether or not I knew them personally. I recorded the year of birth where possible, and listed them according to parent–child relationships. Thereafter, every time I arrived in Ampasilava from Japan, I visited all of the houses in the village with this list to confirm who lived there and determine where those who were absent were now residing,[5] and why they had left. New-born babies, newly settled immigrants and deceased individuals were also recorded. Thus, the list grew over the years.

Table 2. Population changes over 23 years in Ampasilava

Year	1996	2003	2009	2014	2019
Population	223	352	385	441	462
Crude birth rate		+77	+56	+72	+48
No. of immigrants		+78	+64	+71	+69
Crude death rate		−5	−4	−16	−12
No. of emigrants		−21	−83	−71	−84
Net increase		+129	+33	+56	+21

Table 2 shows that the population increased steadily although, unlike commodity prices, the rate did not show a geometric progression. Furthermore, the increase in the final year was small. Also noteworthy is that the crude birth rate was relatively high for the population size, as was the rate of immigration – the latter may even have been higher than the former.

The high immigration rate also relates to the high proportion of emigrants. Generally, in Vezo society, the populations of residential areas tend to be fluid. A newly married couple need not follow specific rules when selecting their place of residence (Iida 2008: 102–104); they can build houses in the areas of residence of both the husband's and wife's families, such that they can travel back and forth (seasonally or otherwise). Alternatively, they can choose a separate location and begin a new life there. This situation affected the methodology and data analysis of this research, because identification of a person's address can be difficult if they travel back and forth between two villages (see endnote 5).

The numbers of immigrants and emigrants are important indexes of change over the quarter-century. However, migration due to marriage must also be considered and distinguished from other types. Some inhabitants of farming villages, for example, are attracted to Ampasilava not by farming but by fishing. Farming is not particularly popular in this region, where the annual rainfall does not exceed 500 millimetres and there is only one harvest per year, or a few at most, even if multiple types of crops are planted. By contrast, fishermen can get catches every day, so have greater income opportunities. As the price of catches stabilised, farmers in this region gradually increased their dependence on fishing. For example, in the village of Ankilimalinike, located four kilometres inland of Ampasilava, several people travelled to the coast on foot to fish using simple tools at low tide, particularly those free from farm work (Iida 2001). For the quarter-century after the mid-1990s, such individuals increasingly made trips to the coast and were followed by many other people. Some even built huts in Ampasilava, such that catches could easily be exchanged for cash, and to fish during the spring tide without the need to return to Ankilimalinike. However, I did not include such 'single-day fishers' or spring-tide inhabitants in the Ampasilava population data shown in Table 2.

For the same reason, I included some people migrating from Ankilimalinike to Ampasilava in Table 2. For example, G1 migrated from Ankilimalinike to Ampasilava with his wife and two children, as well as his younger brother, G2, and his wife and two children, and their younger sister, G3, and her younger brothers, G4, G5, and G6. Among these six, the latter four were unmarried.[6] G1's wife divorced him and left in 2010. G6 also left, in 2012 or 2013, while the others remained in Ampasilava as I discovered during my last visit in 2019. New family members included four of G1's children with his first wife, his new wife from another village, the couple's three children, three children of G2 and his wife, G3's five children (although G3 remained single), and two children of G3's daughter, who married an Ampasilava youth. G4 and G5 also married Ampasilava girls, and G4 had a child with his wife. Consequently, G1's family of 12 (in 2002) grew to 29 by 2019, not including those who had lived in Ampasilava prior to 2002.

G1 had acquired fishing skills in a fishing village where he lived with his ex-wife before they came to Ampasilava. Although his younger brothers had little experience of fishing before they came to Ampasilava, they learned while earning an income by raising cattle and driving cargo carts, activities to which they were accustomed. G3 not only speared octopuses, as is the norm for Ampasilava women, but also baked cakes to sell to fishermen and returning workers. One of the merits of living in Ampasilava is the many opportunities to earn a daily cash income by fishing, as well as by providing various services to people who have comparatively high disposable incomes.

While G1 migrated to Ampasilava after acquiring fishing skills, others did so without previously acquiring such skills; still others even expressed no interest in fishing up to then. Farmer A came from Befandefa, the capital of the commune that includes Ampasilava village, located seven kilometres away. He never fished, but drove cattle carts to transport cargo. After settling in Ampasilava with his wife and nine children in 2004 or 2005, he started to accommodate his acquaintances from Befandefa, as this was convenient for business purposes. One of his children remained in Befandefa, while the other nine – all of whom were single at the time – settled in Ampasilava. Two of his daughters married Ampasilava youths. One of the two daughters later left the village due to her husband's work, while the other gave birth to three children before 2019. Another daughter gave birth to two children whom she left with her parents; she herself began her new life in another village. Two sons left Ampasilava when they got married. A's family, which comprised eleven members when they settled, had increased only to twelve in 2019 because many sons and daughters had left the village. Life in Ampasilava may not be as attractive for them as it is for those with fishing skills.

Some new inhabitants migrated to Ampasilava from other fishing villages. Mr and Mrs R and their three children came from Lamboara, five kilometres from Ampasilava, around 2015. The composition of the family did not change until 2019. Although it was typically only the husband who went fishing, during the spring tide period, the entire family fished at Nosao Island, located five kilometres offshore, where the wide rocky beach dries out and women and children can easily spear octopuses and sea cucumbers. Mr and Mrs S arrived from Andravoñe, 40 kilometres south of Ampasilava, and began a new life with their six unmarried children as well as the husband's sister, her husband and their daughter (total of eleven family members) in 2012 or 2013. One of his sons married a girl from Ampasilava, and they were expecting a child in 2019. Mr and Mrs S built a relatively large house in Ampasilava that could not be left empty in the long term. In 2019, however, they appeared to have left the house to Mr S's sister, her husband, and their daughter. However, S did not abandon his house completely: during my short stay in Ampasilava, he happened to visit there while carrying cargo en route from Andravoñe to Morombe. It appeared that he still occasionally stayed at his former home. For S and his family, Ampasilava seems to have been important not only for fishing, but also as a place in which to take refuge while waiting for a favourable wind during adverse weather. The house could also be used for storage, which would have been risky if the villagers had been poor.

All of the immigrants mentioned above had never lived in Ampasilava, or had no close relatives there before their arrival. Such distantly related immigrants (DRIs) can be distinguished from 'closely related immigrants', who return to Ampasilava after living outside the village, or shelter in Ampasilava with their spouses. DRIs, in principle, avoided conflicts with native villagers by fishing in distant waters like around the island or doing jobs other than fishing. G1 and his brothers were exceptionally engaged in fishing near the village because they and the people of their native village, Ankilimalinike, share the ancestors of four generations with Ampasilava villagers. G1 and his brothers were tolerated by native villagers because of their distant relation.

The relative proportions of DRIs and closely related immigrants are thought to indicate the degree to which outsiders settle comfortably in Ampasilava. To understand this, Table 3 was compiled, excluding the DRIs in Table 2.

Table 3. Population changes over 23 years (excluding distantly related immigrants)

Year	1996	2003	2009	2014	2019
Population	223	327	352	391	376
Crude birth rate		+77	+52	+66	+30
No. of immigrants		+53	+46	+50	+39
Crude death rate		−5	−4	−15	−12
No. of emigrants		−21	−69	−62	−72
Net increase		+104	+15	+39	−15

Table 3 does not include immigrants not born (nor their spouses) in Ampasilava, such as schoolteachers, non-government organisation (NGO) workers and shop owners and their employees. Single persons and children were not counted when they had no parent native to Ampasilava. However, such DRIs may become intimately connected with Ampasilava society through *post facto* marriage. For example, G4 and G5, who both married native residents, were counted as inhabitants after their marriage. Likewise, the status of the children in Table 3 born outside of Ampasilava and brought there by their parent(s) may differ: if their parent was not married to a native of Ampasilava when they arrived, they were not included in the table; however, they were counted as soon as their parent married a native.

The number of DRIs would have been relatively small if the Ampasilava people had been poor, because the immigrants would have obtained money independent of their friends or relatives (with the exceptions of schoolteachers and NGO workers, who receive their salaries from the headquarters of their employers). The number of DRIs provides an index of Ampasilava's wealth. To illustrate this visually, the populations in Tables 2 and 3 (with the DRIs subtracted in the latter case) are both shown in Figure 2.

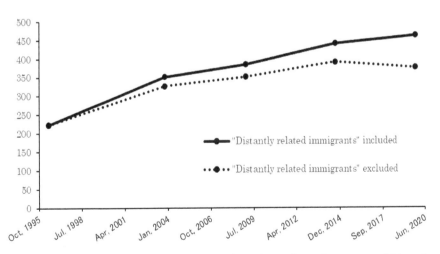

Figure 2. Population changes over time, based on data sets with and without 'distantly related immigrants'

The number of DRIs clearly contributed to Ampasilava's population increase, although the data must be interpreted cautiously because no datasets from other villages are available for comparison. The average rate of population increase over the 23 years was 3.2 per cent per annum;[7] the adjusted rate was 2.3. Neither the unadjusted nor adjusted rate reflected a geometric increase. Indeed, the adjusted value indicates that the population size became relatively stable. Nevertheless, the absolute size continues to increase, apparently because the disposable income of the villagers continues to grow, in line with the demand for services and commodities (paid for in cash), thus attracting DIRs from outside the village.

5. Conclusion: Sustainability Predicated on Maturity

As mentioned at the beginning of this chapter, the term sustainability is applicable only in certain conditions. It is not applicable to rapidly or unpredictably changing phenomena, such as the society in a developing village. In Ampasilava, people experience the same needs and wants as those in urban societies worldwide. Basic facilities, such as medical services, were largely insufficient until recently. The infant mortality rate remains high, and mothers may also die during childbirth. In such situations, change is required whether or not it is sustainable.

However, neither human nor economic development is desirable if the Earth's ecosystem is damaged in the process. Therefore, let us now turn from economic sustainability to environmental sustainability and 'carrying capacity.' In classic ecology, the latter term has been used when analysing ecosystems as separate entities. As an ecosystem consists of multiple interdependent species, the growth of one population affects the others, sometimes resulting in the collapse of the whole system. In the context of this process, carrying capacity refers to the value that an ecosystem places on the population of a certain species; this is the classic conception for ecologists. However, a complex system consisting of diverse species may have multiple points of balance. In the case of Ampasilava, the commoditisation of squid increased dependency on this species, which was instrumental for absorbing the impact of human population growth. As alluded to

298

at the beginning of this chapter, exploiting an unfamiliar species can lead to a new balance among multiple elements.[8] Against this background, we can no longer say that an ecosystem has a fixed carrying capacity for a population of any particular species.

Distinct from the concept of carrying capacity, environmental sustainability does not assume a point of balance: sustainability is a dynamic process of exploitation, conservation, release and re-organisation (Holling and Gunderson 2002). Sustainability is not achieved in a single way: rather, there are multiple routes to increasing a system's resilience. On this basis, the concept of 'adaptive management' was introduced (Allen et al. 2011). According to this idea, management is a provisional step; further modifications occur as learning progresses through monitoring. Sustainability may be more amenable to modification than carrying capacity.

Given the above, is the 'Only one Earth' concept, which emphasises that all species and environments on the earth are connected, still relevant? I believe so; an ecosystem – fishing grounds used by Ampasilava fishermen, for example – is more resilient than may initially be expected because it is actually a sub-ecosystem dependent on other systems, such that any adverse impacts are widely dispersed and absorbed. When the impact is small, the influence on other sub-ecosystems is typically negligible. With greater impacts, however, multiple sub-ecosystems may be affected. When Ampasilava fishermen reduce the fishing stress on the local water off their own village by seasonal migration, they may put more stress on remote waters off the camp fishing locations. Not only fishermen's but also farmers' behaviour affects the marine ecosystem. Therefore, even if the impacts of human activities in a sub-ecosystem can be mitigated in many ways, the entire ecosystem, or 'Only one Earth,' might collapse if activity increases simultaneously at multiple sites.

We should abandon narrow perspectives based only on population, environmental or economic growth, admitting that outsiders do not have the right to compel Ampasilava's people to reduce their fishing activities; instead, we should share a common vision of the future. Issues particular to a given society must be resolved on an individual basis; outsiders must be tolerant of this. This idea of tailoring goals for individual societies is in line with the

Sustainable Development Goals introduced at the United Nations' General Assembly in 2015. The goals were intended to reduce the vulnerability of individual societies, which have their own ways of achieving resilience in the face of crisis. Then, if it is difficult for a single individual or entrepreneur, or even for a single society, to achieve the seventeen Sustainable Development Goals simultaneously, synergetic effects are expected by interlinked plans based on each situation. Greater tolerance of others in this era of environmental conscientiousness is needed. Excessive goals are not a means of self-affirmation for narrow-scoped economic animals.

Endnotes

[1] For the research I stayed in Ampasilava 23 times: (1) 12 November 1994; (2) 19–30 December 1994; (3) 30 January–20 February 1995; (4) 26 October 1995–5 April 1996; (5) 1–3 May 1996; (6) 16 May–5 October 1996; (7) 7 January–21 February 1998; (8) 9–18 March 1998; (9) 31 December 2001–6 January 2002; (10) 30 January–14 February 2002; (11) 21 March–1 April 2003; (12) 28 October–10 November 2003; (13) 27 September–21 October 2005; (14) 20–22 January 2009; (15) 20 January–7 February 2010; (16) 5–11 February 2011; (17) 20 February–7 March 2014; (18) 30 August–15 September 2014; (19) 17–22 February 2015; (20) 9–30 November 2015; (21) 28 October–14 November 2016; (22) 30 June–18 July 2017; (23) 30 October–4 November 2019. During each stay, I sometimes left the village temporarily but for less than a week. That is, when I left the village and returned there after more than I week, I regarded that I stayed twice even if I was not in Japan in the meanwhile.

[2] However, one of Koechlin's records in the Musée de l'Homme in Paris is believed to date from 1967 (Mallet 2009: 69). He might have begun his research before 1967. I do not know whether the Musée de l'Homme still holds this record, because part of its collection was succeeded by the Musée du Quai Branly.

[3] In southwestern Madagascar, 5 FMG, referred to as *drala* (the word for money), was the basic unit of currency. This unit of currency is equivalent to *ariary* (MGA), which was formally introduced in 1961 after independence had been achieved. The value of all banknotes issued before 2003 was given

in both FMG and MGA. Malagasy currencies were unified as MGA in 2004, before which FMG was used more often by tourists and immigrants from urban areas in France, South Asia and China, whereas MGA was used mostly by descendants of rural Malagasy people residing there since before the 19th century. For inhabitants in urban areas, the issue of new banknotes in 2003/2004 had the same effect as redenomination.

4 In contrast to squids, octopuses were sometimes sold before the freezer boat arrived, albeit in small quantities. This is perhaps because they are difficult to damage when dried and are amenable to preservation. Nevertheless, they were generally purchased as food for self-consumption rather than as a commodity.

5 I included the following people in the 'Ampasilava inhabitants' group, regardless of how long they had been away from the village during the year: 1) students staying with relatives in towns within a day's distance (to attend school there); 2) people – especially fishermen – who leave their spouses or children in Ampasilava on a seasonal basis (the fishermen return home between December and March, when the climate is unstable and fishing becomes difficult); and 3) people who have not moved for more than five years. To determine whether a subject met the criteria for either or both 2) and 3), I did not analyse all of the census datasets; rather, I analysed only those showing people's movements throughout the year (e.g. 1996) or when I could conduct another census within a year before another (e.g. 2003). Despite this rigid selection process, over the lengthy study period of more than twenty years, I encountered several subjects who I could not definitively classify as inhabitants or non-inhabitants. I excluded such cases from the analysis, since the number thereof was sufficiently small to be insignificant.

6 G1 had an elder brother who farmed with his wife and children in Ankilimalinike. One of their younger brothers also lived in Ankilimalinike, as well as their mother, who lived with her grandchildren (nephews and nieces to G1 and his siblings).

7 Based on the population change from 1996 to 2003, I estimated the rate of population increase in Ampasilava as 5.9 per cent per annum (Iida 2008: 100). In this calculation, I did not exclude DRIs. Comparing this rate with that of 3.2 per cent per annum, based on the change through 2019, it is evident that the increase slowed after 2003.

8 I analysed the innovation in fishing techniques of Ampasilava residents

through bricolage of secondhand materials and factory products (Iida 2019). Their innovations appear to have reduced fishing pressure by expanding the number of target species.

Acknowledgements

The field research for this chapter was supported by JSPS Grant-in-Aid for the research fellows in FY 1994–1996 and 1999–2000; and KAKENHI Grants Numbers JP13710191, JP14251004, JP14251011, JP15255007, JP17401031, JP19401041, JP21242034, JP23251010, JP25244043, JP15H02601, JP15H01910 and JP19H01400; whereas the analysis and writing were supported by KAKENHI Grant Number JP16H06318. The author appreciates to those concerned, as well as people in Ampasilava.

References

Agrawal, A (2002) 'Common resources and institutional sustainability', in National Research Council (ed.) *The Drama of the Commons*, Washington DC: National Academy Press, pp. 41–85.

Allen, C. R., Fontaine, J. J., Pope, K. L. and Garmestani A. S. (2011) 'Adaptive management for turbulent future', *Journal of Environmental Management*, Vol. 92, No. 5, pp. 1339–1345.

Holling, C. S. and Gunderson, L. H. (2002) 'Resilience and adaptive cycle', in L. H. Gunderson and C. S. Holling (eds) *Panarchy: Understanding Transformations in Human and Natural Systems*, Washington DC: Island Press.

Iida, T. (2001) 'Fishing and farming economies in the Southwestern coastal area of Madagascar: An analysis of production and diet', *Journal of African Studies (Africa-Kenkyu)*, Vol. 57, pp. 37–54 (in Japanese).

———— (2005) 'The past and present of the coral reef fishing economy in Madagascar: Implications for self-determination in resource use', in N. Kishigami and J. Savelle (eds) *Indigenous Use and Management of Marine Resources (Senri Ethnological Studies 67)*, Suita: National Museum of Ethnology, pp. 237–258.

————— (2008) *Know-How to Survive on the Coast: An Eco-Anthropological Study in a Madagascar Fishing Village*, Kyoto: Sekaishisosha (in Japanese).

————— (2019) 'Traveling and indwelling knowledge: Learning and technological exchange among Vezo fishermen in Madagascar', in K. Omura, S. Satsuka, G. J. Otsuki and A. Morita (eds) *The World Multiple: The Quotidian Politics of Knowing and Generating Entangled Worlds*, London and New York: Routledge, pp. 190–204.

Koechlin, B. (1971) 'Vuru-bē: Un conte malgache en langue Sakalava-Vezo', *L'Homme,* Vol. 11, No. 4, pp. 31–60.

————— (1975) *Les Vezo du sud-ouest de Madagascar: Contribution à l'étude de l'éco-système de semi-nomades marins*, Paris: Mouton.

Mallet, J. (2009) *Le tsapiky, une jeune musique de Madagascar: Ancêtres, cassettes et bals*, Paris: Karthala.

Moriyama, T. (1996) *Tombs and Social Practice among the Sihanaka of Madagascar: An Ethnographic Study*, Tokyo: The University of Tokyo Press (in Japanese).

Muttenzer, F. (2020) *Being Ethical among Vezo People: Fisheries, Livelihoods, and Conservation in Madagascar*, Lanham: Lexington Books.

Chapter 13

Factors Influencing Physical and Psychological Distance between Wildlife and People in Kenya

Yumi Yamane

1. History of Wildlife and People in Kenya

From the late 1890s to the early 1900s, Kenya was little known to the Western world. It was perceived as a land of adventure; a fascinating part of the Dark Continent. Wild animals, both small and large, dangerous and harmless, teemed in the thousands. Every journey, adventure and the very lives of enterprising pioneers were characterised by the excitement of big game (Cowie 1963). Theodore Roosevelt visited the African continent in 1909 and described 'a land teeming with beasts of the chase, infinite in number and incredible in variety. The plains are alive with droves of strange and beautiful animals whose like is not known elsewhere; and with others even stranger that show both in form and temper something of the fantastic and the grotesque. There are no words that can tell the hidden spirit of the wilderness, that can reveal its mystery, its melancholy, and its charm' (Roosevelt 1910). Since the day Roosevelt reported about African wildlife and sport hunting, wildlife populations began to decline. Wildlife losses increased as land was cleared for expanding European settlements, human–wildlife conflicts increased and local people were marginalised by colonial policies.

Distinct from the West, the African continent developed under coexistence with wildlife species. In the pre-colonial era, wildlife populations were abundant. Although many Kenyans profess a distaste for game meant, and others believe that eating the meat of wild animals will bring disaster to their domestic cattle or goats, most men, and some women, have taken up arms – catapults, knives, swords, spears, nets, snares and, most frequently, bows and arrows – to kill wild animals (Steinhart 1989).

Between 1895 and 1944, formal wildlife policy established by the British government guided the country under colonial rule. During this period, ordinances regulated wildlife harvesting, controlled the ivory trade and facilitated game hunting among white settlers (De Leeuw et al. 2001). Hunting concessions were maintained for the privileged elite, including the archetypal explorer, the pioneer and the trader, almost all of whom were focused on big game (Cockerill and Hagerman 2020). This was followed by the establishment of the National Park System in 1945. Nairobi National Park was the first park established in Kenya, in 1946, on former Nairobi Commonage lands that Cowie had first recommended as a park site in 1938 (Steinhart 1989). In the process of colonialism, some African hunters assumed new roles as ancillaries to white hunters, finding employment as guides and trackers. When Captain A. T. A Ritchie became a game warden in 1923, he began to shape the Game Department in ways that would persist until independence. The specific task of the Game Department was game management, and the Department concerned itself with humane sporting behaviour and animal welfare. In 1939, Mervyn Cowie relieved the Game Department of the burden of being the sole institutional home of game conservation.

The historical relationship between Kenyans and Kenyan wildlife is interesting. Present-day Kenyans have their own perceptions and ideas of coexistence with wildlife, which are distinct from colonial concepts. Further, wildlife conservation in Kenya has become more diverse and complex in the years since colonisation.

2. The End of a Wildlife Paradise

Africa is still regarded as a wildlife paradise, and there is a long history of successful coexistence between wildlife and people on the continent. However, in many ways, this perception does not align with present realities. The human population in Kenya is increasing annually and has grown significantly since the early years of the national parks system, from six million in 1950 to 53 million in 2020

(United Nations Population Fund 2020). The growth rate between 2015 and 2020 in Nairobi and its suburbs was 3.88 per cent (United Nations Population Fund 2020). As the human population has grown, we have seen an inverse trend of decline in wildlife populations and their habitats. Population growth, particularly around Nairobi, means that humans and wildlife come into close proximity more frequently. In particular, protected area boundaries are hotspots for human–wildlife conflicts, wherein humans inhabit these areas for residential, agricultural and pastoral purposes. This increased proximity between wildlife and people has increased the frequency of human–wildlife conflicts, which include interactions between wildlife and humans directly, or with their infrastructure, livestock or crops. Negative interactions then complicate the relationship between humans and wildlife.

I conducted interviews in 2015 and found that people in Kenya have become psychologically estranged from wildlife. Electric fencing along protected area boundaries can become faulty without regular maintenance, and carnivores are known to move across protected and non-protected areas. Over 70 per cent of Kenyan wildlife utilise both protected and non-protected areas. Approximately 8 per cent of Kenya's land area is under protection within its 23 terrestrial National Parks or 28 terrestrial National Reserves (Kenya Wildlife Service 2017, Wildlife Conservation and Management Act, No 47 of 2013). Protected areas represent varied ecosystems: forests, wetlands, savannahs, marine areas and arid and semi-arid areas. In addition, conservancies are scattered outside of protected areas, and people and wildlife share space in these areas. A conservancy is land that has been set aside by an individual landowner, corporate entity, group of owners or a community for the primary purpose of wildlife conservation (Wildlife Conservation and Management Act, No. 47 of 2013). Some conservancies allow people to collect firewood and graze livestock, among other activities. However, in general, conservancies in Maasai Mara[1] are trying to spatially separate people and wildlife within the area.

When Theodore Roosevelt visited in 1909, human settlements were scattered and herds of wildlife roamed the vast area of Kenya. It is now impossible to find places in the country that have not been invaded by human activities. In the late 1890s and early 1900s, it was already difficult to encounter wildlife in Europe (Roosevelt 1910). Rapid global changes resulting from explosive population growth and swift advancements in urbanisation and technology have pushed human beings from their place in natural systems. We are now 'foreign' in the lands in which we live, almost unable to coexist with wildlife and continue destroying ecosystems. Some people still live in close proximity, both physically and psychologically, with wildlife and natural systems, but these individuals and communities have had to make their own paths based on their own knowledge and values.

3. Physical and Psychological Distance

My research has focused on conservation ecology in Kenya; my first study in 2009 focused on the relationship between leopards and people in Nairobi. At that time, I observed leopards inhabiting Nairobi National Park and conducted semi-structured interviews with residents around the park. I also began living in the park boundary area and still reside there. Although Nairobi is recognised as an international city, more than 100 mammal species inhabit the adjacent Nairobi National Park. Among Nairobi residents, cultural background tends to dictate people's attitudes toward wildlife. For example, Maasai people inhabit the southern park boundary area. When I interviewed Maasai people about lions and leopards, commonly considered dangerous animals, none of the 20 interviewees reported fearing these animals. When I asked individuals if they liked or disliked these animals, 90 per cent responded that they were indifferent. One response summarises a typical attitude – 'I don't feel any like or hate for them. They always live around us. It's normal to have them around not more than that and not less than that. If they disappear in front of us, I start fearing that something bad might happen to our environment'.

Here, I define physical distance as scenarios wherein people live or have activities in areas that are either adjacent to or overlapping with areas inhabited by wildlife, e.g., residents of the park boundary area. I note that Maasai people who live in rural areas also share the area they inhabit with wildlife, rather than a simple overlap. This means that both Maasai people and wildlife use natural resources in the area and encounter one another. By contrast, people living in urban areas often fear wildlife, even when encounters are rare, because they lack knowledge or experience of wildlife encounters. For example, many urban residents chase wildlife from their compounds and experience fear in the process. I define this type of relationship, represented by a significant psychological distance, as estrangement. Human beings are likely to need empirical or experiential knowledge to share physical and psychological space with wildlife, which may come from the older generation or community experiences. For example, the Maasai experience daily life in concurrence with wildlife. Psychological affinity with wildlife is high among Maasai from Nairobi and Maasai Mara and Pokot people.

Many urban dwellers are fascinated by wildlife, especially lions and leopards, but this interest does not extend to their living space, e.g., a lion in their compound. The residential area where I live, which is also one of my research sites, is one of the oldest residential areas in Nairobi, having been established during the colonial era. In its early years, people in this area understood that wildlife inhabited this area and viewed the space as shared. However, the area has been more intensively developed in recent years, and new residents are often unable to accept a reality that includes lions in their garden or leopards attacking their dogs. Many of these individuals feel a lack of security and lodge complaints with the Kenya Wildlife Service (KWS). Human–wildlife encounters broaden and become more complex in these scenarios.

4. Coexistence under Urban Pressures: The Case Study of Nairobi

4-1. Nairobi National Park

Nairobi National Park is located only 7 km from the city centre. Its northern boundary is delineated by electric fencing, and the southern boundary is a natural border defined by a deep gorge. The Athi-Kapiti Plains and Kitengela migration corridors, which are important wildlife areas during the rainy season (Nazalino 2014), are

309

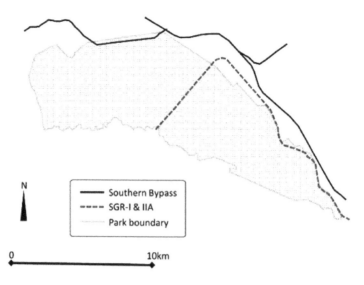

Figure 1. Nairobi National Park became smaller because of human activities

located south of the park. Residential and industrial areas are also located directly adjacent to the park boundary. Tourists landing in Nairobi quickly realise that the image of Kenya as an untouched, wild space for wildlife is an illusion; a highway and railway pass through the park, at times giving the impression of a theme park for wildlife viewing (Figure 1). In fact, some suggest that wildlife in Nairobi is not truly wild but, rather, is managed for tourism within a 'safari park'. The southern bypass highway was constructed from 2009–2016 and passes through the northern portion of the park. As of 2020, another road is being constructed within the park, encompassing an area of 61 ha. Construction on the Standard Gauge Railway (SGR), which dissects the park, began in 2016 and is ongoing. These developments were strongly opposed by local groups and individuals, and have increased public dissatisfaction with both the Kenyan government and the KWS.

The southern portion of the park, in contrast to the more developed north, experiences low development pressure. The Athi-Kapiti plain, which is inhabited by Maasai people, is often regarded as a missed opportunity, in that it is likely that it should have been

310

included in Nairobi National Park when it was established, due to its importance for wildlife migration

4-2. Leopard Behaviour in Nairobi

I fitted four wild leopards with GPS collars in Nairobi and monitored their movements to study leopard behaviour. Although it is well known that leopards move across the park boundary, quantifying the area of use, timing and motivations for movement is helpful in leopard conservation and determining areas or times of risk. The collar data indicated that leopards crossed major roads and were not deterred by electric fencing. Typically, their motivations for leaving the park appeared to be predating dogs and livestock, reproduction and avoiding the territories of other leopards. Historically, Nairobi was an important habitat for leopards, and this may be another reason why they travel within the city and its suburbs. Wildlife obviously do not observe human-made boundaries and, instead, move toward their target locations via pathways that are known or familiar to them. However, I observed that leopards avoided people when they travelled outside of Nairobi National Park. One of the four collared leopards had its core territory area in a forest reserve adjacent to Kibera slum, outside of Nairobi National Park. Reserves are not as tightly regulated as national parks, and thus people use these areas to harvest firewood, ride horses and graze livestock during the dry season. Nevertheless, the leopard was able to coexist with this level of human activity.

Leopards are typically solitary and tend to avoid other large carnivores like lions and hyenas. Lions also travel outside the park boundary into the suburban area of Nairobi, but they are more readily sighted by humans due to their size. As mentioned, many residents are not comfortable living side-by-side with wildlife, i.e., they are estranged from wildlife, and many have guard dogs to protect them from lions and leopards, among other animals. Unfortunately, leopards predate stray dogs as well as these guard animals around Nairobi. Residents may then report the loss of their dogs to police, KWS or through the media. Although KWS recognise that leopards entering residential areas are commonplace, they attempt to capture the animals to appease residents and demonstrate that they are

311

protecting citizens from wildlife. Thus, managing wildlife includes managing the physical distance between wildlife and humans.

I interviewed 26 families from urban Nairobi who did not practise pastoralism; all reported fearing carnivores. By contrast, five Samburu, Turkana and Maasai men who were pastoralists reported not fearing wildlife.

5. People and Leopards in Tourist Area: Maasai Mara Ecosystem

The Maasai Mara National Reserve began as a smaller wildlife area in 1948 and is now a famous tourist destination. In the 1990s, 25 per cent of Kenya's wildlife inhabited Maasai Mara (Western et al. 2009). Because the reserve is continuous with Serengeti National Park in Tanzania, wildlife is free to roam over an area of 25,000 km^2, of which the Greater Maasai Mara ecosystem accounts for 1,510 km^2. As of 2020, there have been 15 conservancies surrounding Maasai Mara National Reserve. Some human activities are permitted in conservancies and wheat farming has increased rapidly in conservancy lands to the north of Maasai Mara, from 5,000 ha in 1975 to 50,000 ha in 1995 (Bedelian 2014). This is a result of Maasai people leasing land to wheat cultivators. Cattle farming had a similar upward trend between 1977 and 2011 (27 per cent increase), with strong inter-annual variability and noticeable differences in stocking during the wet and dry seasons, while sheep and goat numbers increased by 210 per cent during the same period (Bedelian 2014). On average, nearly 70 per cent of Maasai household income comes from livestock, their economic and cultural mainstay, despite their involvement in tourism and ecotourism (Bedelian 2014). Typically, the financial benefits of ecotourism go to lodge and land owners who came from outside the area and bought the land, rather than to Maasai people.

My interviews at Maasai Mara revealed that the number of people who desire wildlife conservation is increasing, especially among young ones. Among Maasai people, being able to speak English is expected to generate income via tourism. For example, young English-speaking Maasai may work as safari tour guides, providing information about wildlife as well as Maasai culture. Thus, wildlife brings income to the Maasai. On the other hand, large carnivores often predate livestock that are vital to the Maasai people. Livestock are often attacked at night, especially during the rainy season, at the *boma* (a Maasai dwelling). Not only large carnivores but elephants and buffalos are also threats to people when out-grazing their livestock.

Prior to the time when Maasai children began attending school, they would typically spend their evenings listening to their elders tell stories. Because children now attend school on a daily basis, the opportunities for these experiences are disappearing. In recent years, some livestock owners have ceased grazing, fenced their lands and now keep livestock in small-scale enclosures. Therefore, due to the reduction in sharing narrative experiences and a diminished frequency of wildlife encounters, the psychological distance between wildlife and people has grown. People often fear encountering unfamiliar animals. One man reported that now that his children are in school, the manpower for grazing is diminished and it is easier to keep livestock at home. However, during holidays when children are not in school, they will typically graze livestock, leaving home around 8 a.m. and returning before six p.m. Mobile phones have also enabled people to alert one another to the presence of dangerous wildlife, and Maasai people adjust their grazing routes and locations accordingly. Although technology and education are changing the lives of Maasai people, children still know, for example, how to hide themselves among their cattle when they encounter unwelcome wildlife while grazing, and the importance of keeping a downwind position against elephants. This knowledge of wildlife has been developed historically and is likely to fade as time progresses.

6. Leopards in Rural Areas

I have been conducting a study focused on the relationship between local residents and leopards in Baringo and Marsabit, Kenya. Both counties have low population densities and no city, and are not popular tourist destinations. Baringo County is located in Rift Valley Province, which is in central Kenya. The people there are Pokot, cattle-centric nomadic pastoralists that have shifted toward sedentary and market-oriented goat keeping in recent years (Greiner et al. 2013).

Lions have not been seen in Baringo since the early 2000s, and elephant, rhino and buffalo sightings are rare. Instead, people are alert to leopards and baboons while grazing, and leopards and hyenas are the top predators in the area. Leopards are considered to be 'troublesome' and have a reputation for attacking livestock. Many of the people living in the area came there in the early 2000s because of better grazing land. The area is not densely populated, with at least 1 km between houses. For myself, as a Japanese person, it was difficult to locate houses, but walking in an area devoid of elephants, buffalo and lions was emotionally reassuring. Many of the riverbeds in this region, which are seasonally dry, had leopard prints when I visited. There are also duikers, bushbucks and hyrax in the region, which are prey for leopards. However, as the human population has increased, the number of livestock has increased, and attacking livestock is a lower energy pursuit for leopards than finding prey in the wild. Leopard attacks occur both day and night in Baringo, where the landscape is generally suitable for them, with rolling, shrubby hills, river banks and rocky gorges. During the day, when two children under the age of ten typically graze up to 200 goats and sheep, leopards typically attack silently from a hidden position before the children notice.

Many Pokot people believe that leopard populations are increasing because predation frequency has increased. This seems probable given that there are no lions in the area to prey on livestock or attack leopards. I set remote camera traps in this area in 2018 to capture photos of leopards (Figure 2). Although the KWS is active in this area, few people are aware of its role, and they often do not report livestock predation. Instead, some individuals secretly purchase poisons in an attempt to kill leopards, which often do not succeed as leopards avoid it. Generally, the physical distance between people and leopards has reduced in Baringo because of the increase in human and livestock populations and the fact that the leopard population is increasing due to successful livestock predation.

I observed similar conditions in Marsabit National Park, located in Marsabit County in northern Kenya. The human population is

Figure 2. A leopard captured by a camera trap in Baringo county, Kenya

increasing in this area due to a new road that runs to the area from Nairobi. People around Marsabit National Park and National Reserve use Mt. Marsabit Forest for animal forage, which is the main cause of human–wildlife conflicts in this area (Ouko et al. 2018). Many people in the Mt. Marsabit area are pastoralists. There has been a continuous decline in pastoral wealth since independence, which has put the livelihood of pastoralists in jeopardy. As a result, many have turned to a sedentary lifestyle and have been victims of drought and war (Witsenburg and Roba 2004). Agriculture has gained in popularity among communities who traditionally practised pastoralism, a land use practice that is traditionally compatible with wildlife conservation (Shibia 2010). Many individuals keep camels, donkeys, goats and sheep as livestock. Similar to Baringo, lions have been nearly extirpated in Marsabit, but there is a perception that leopard populations are increasing. Marsabit National Park staff reported seeing leopards at least once per week, which is very high given the typically elusive nature of these animals.

The National Park is dominated by thick forest, but the area outside its boundary is dry, sandy and grazed by livestock. Community members have set up box traps to capture leopards that have attacked their livestock, and I was able to visit one of the capture locations. Local people report that leopards come down from the surrounding hills late in the evening and early in the morning to attack livestock, often the calves of camels, goats and sheep. These attacks reportedly occur several times a week, which represents heavy predation. People therefore trap the leopards, report the capture to KWS and ask that the animal be translocated. However, leopard translocation is a controversial issue and requires extensive consideration.[1] Translocation of problem animals has been conducted in Kenya for elephants, rhinos and buffalo for many years. However, the translocation of collared carnivores has more recently been used as a mitigation measure for human–wildlife conflicts (Kenya Wildlife Service 2017). It is critical to know the mechanisms by which each carnivore species adapts to new locations prior to translocation; this information improves conservation efforts and helps to manage problem animals. For example, we know that leopards must be moved more than 200 km for translocation to be effective, as they are able to return to their original territory if they are translocated less than this distance. Furthermore, the movement of young males is the most difficult and problematic, especially when there are established leopards in the release location. Monitoring leopards in Marsabit is highly valuable not only for managing human–wildlife conflicts but also because the lack of lions in this area allows us to understand how leopards behave in their absence.

There were no data for leopard movement in northern Kenya and, thus, the KWS fitted a young male with a GPS collar in September 2019 (Figure 3). The data collected thus far indicated that the male spent most of his time inside the National Park, but moved outside the park to feed.

7. Physical and Psychological Distance and Wildlife Conservation

Wildlife habitat is being destroyed due to human population growth. However, some species show greater adaptive capacity for living in close proximity to humans or human activity. Some may even live near humans preferentially, due to resource availability or reduced predation. By contrast, long-distance migratory species like elephants that require vast amounts of space, lions, which are often killed by people during encounters, and cheetahs, which are difficult

316

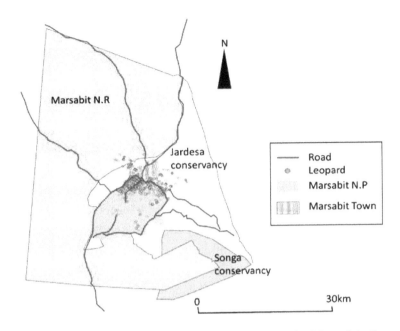

Figure 3. GPS locations of a young male leopard in Marsabit County, Kenya

to breed, are all vulnerable to increases in human populations. Specifically, cheetahs are one of the most fragile carnivores and are typically solitary in the wild. Their conservation is dependent, in part, on maintaining sufficient habitat area to reduce female–female encounters that may, in turn, lead to reduced reproductive fitness (Wielebnowski et al. 2002). They are also closely related to leopards, and the International Union for Conservation of Nature (IUCN) suggests that when one of a group of closely related species becomes endangered, the others may become so in short order. In comparison to cheetahs, leopards are relatively adaptable (Bailey 1993). They have been listed as vulnerable since 2016 by the IUCN Red List and often live in proximity to humans and utilise their property. In many cases, physical proximity between people and wildlife has a direct correlation to population size or trend for that species (Pitman 2012).

In 2009, I observed an interesting sight. One evening at dusk, three young Maasai men were grazing approximately 50 cattle in Nairobi National Park. Grazing is prohibited in the park, but these young men had chosen to risk it due to severe drought and poor forage outside the park that year. All three looked around carefully while grazing their cattle. I saw these men while driving with a KWS ranger, and observed one male and two female lions stalking their cattle. The young men were aware of the lions, but did not seem bothered by their presence. However, they were afraid of the ranger in the vehicle with me. The lions stalking the cattle appeared to be cautious of the Maasai men, but paid little attention to the ranger. Lions fear Maasai and other pastoralists because of their history; Maasai used to kill lions for cultural ceremonies to show their strength and bravery. Many Maasai men over 40 years of age reported having killed a lion, but few younger people did, and many reported that they would prefer not to kill lions. Although killing a lion is a negative conservation action, I have wondered if this Maasai ritual may be necessary in maintaining 'distance' between humans and wildlife. As knowledge about wildlife and nature diminishes and more things become unknown or unfamiliar, fear of wildlife grows. Wildlife creatures can sense fear and vanity in humans. It is possible that humans, who used to show 'strength' to wildlife, are now no longer feared by them, as wildlife are likely to sense what type of power they are facing in an opponent. This is a product of estrangement, and may lead to greater numbers of human–wildlife conflicts.

Translocation increases physical distance between humans and wildlife artificially when it is used as a mitigation measure for human–wildlife conflict. However, there are many challenges with this approach and success can be exceptionally difficult to evaluate. Translocation may cause new human–wildlife conflicts or conflicts among wildlife. I fitted three leopards with GPS collars in 2019; all three were problem animals. After collaring, two were released more than 100 km from their capture location and the third was released in the capture location. The resulting data from collaring leopards can lead the new approaches to mitigating human–wildlife conflicts. Unless we explore and adopt new methods to manage wildlife be-haviour and make use of advancing technology, conservation efforts will continue to be threatened by ongoing human–wildlife conflicts.

Over the course of a long history together, Maasai and other pastoralists have built relationships with wildlife that allow wildlife to

Table 1. Human perceptions about wildlife and physical and psychological distances between humans and wildlife in Kenya

Area	Area type	Dominant population	Physical distance	Psychological distance	Attitude toward wildlife	View on land use
	City and urban	Highly diverse	Near	Estrangement	Negative and fearful	Overlapping with wildlife
Nairobi	Maasai lands	Maasai	Near	Familiar	Negative toward human–wildlife conflict, but positive toward tourism and conservation	Shared with wildlife
Maasai Mara area	Tourism	Maasai	Near	Familiar	Negative toward human–wildlife conflict, but positive toward tourism and conservation	Shared with wildlife
Northern Baringo County	Rural	Pokot	Near	Familiar	Typically indifferent but negative toward livestock predation	Shared with wildlife
	City	Mixed ethnic groups	Near	Estrangement	Negative toward livestock predation	Overlapping with wildlife
Marsabit	Outskirts	Mixed ethnic groups and pastoralists	Near	Familiar	Strongly negative toward livestock predation	Shared with wildlife

recognise that people are dangerous or stronger than them. This represents an implicit force in the psychological distance between humans and wildlife. People tend to perceive wildlife very differently based on their background and experiences, as shown in Table 1, which summarises the results of interviews and direct observations. It is also true that pastoralists have shared space and co-existed with wildlife without unnecessary killing over a long time period. In fact, the present day distribution of many wildlife species in Kenya overlaps with that of Maasai people, and Maasai lands are recognised as being rich in wildlife (Cockerill and Hagerman 2020). The close association and coexistence demonstrated by the Maasai may be an important key to wildlife conservation in Kenya. Conservation can be promoted by reviewing historical relationships between humans and wildlife. Sustainable conservation in Kenya is likely to rely on this, in addition to ensuring the security of local communities.

Endnotes

[1] This area name was often written as 'Masai Mara', however in this chapter it is notated 'Maasai Mara', which is the same spelling as Maasai, to show respect for the Maasai people.

Acknowledgements

This work was supported by JSPS KAKENHI Grant Number JP16H06318, JP18H05728 and JP19K20925, the Japan Trust for Global Environment Fund Number 19.12, and Japan Fund for Global Environment Fund Number i-B3. I also thank to my beloved family.

References

Bailey, T. N. (1993) *The African Leopard: Ecology and Behavior of a Solitary Felid*, New York: Columbia University Press.
Bedelian, C. (2014) 'Conservation, tourism and pastoral livelihoods:

Wildlife conservancies in the Maasai Mara, Kenya', Ph.D. thesis, University College London.

Cockerill, K. A. and Hagerman, S. M. (2020) 'Historical insights for understanding the emergence of community-based conservation in Kenya: International agendas, colonial legacies, and contested worldviews', *Ecology and Society*, Vol. 25, No. 2, Article 15 (https://doi.org/10.5751/ES-11409-250215) (accessed: 22 April 2021).

Cowie, M. (1963) *I Walk with Lions: The Story of Africa's Great Animal Preserves, the Royal National Parks of Kenya, as Told by Their First Director*, New York: Macmillan.

De Leeuw, J., Waweru, M. N., Okello, O. O., Maloba, M., Nguru, P., Said, M. Y., Aligula, H. M, Hitkönig, I. M. A. and Reid, R. C. (2001) 'Distribution and diversity of wildlife in northern Kenya in relation to livestock and permanent water points', *Biological Conservation*, Vol. 100, No. 3, pp. 297–306.

Greiner, C., Alvarez, M. and Becker, M. (2013) 'From cattle to corn: Attributes of emerging farming systems of former pastoral nomads in East Pokot, Kenya', *Society and Natural Resources*, Vol. 26, Issue. 12, pp. 1478–1490.

Kenya Wildlife Service (2017) *KWS Annual Report 2017*, Nairobi: Kenya Wildlife Service.

Nazalino, J. M. (2014) 'Transport development and implications on wildlife conservation; Case study of proposed greater southern bypass (Kitengela loop)', Doctoral dissertation, University of Nairobi.

Ouko, C. A., Mulwa, R., Kibugi, R., Owuor, M. A., Zaehringer, J. G. and Oguge, N. O. (2018) 'Community perceptions of ecosystem services and the management of Mt. Marsabit forest in northern Kenya', *Environments*, Vol. 5, Issue 11, Article 121 (https://doi.org/10.3390/environments5110121) (accessed: 22 April 2021).

Pitman, R. T. (2012) 'The conservation biology and ecology of the African leopard *Panthera pardus pardus*', *The Plymouth Student Scientist*, Vol. 5, No. 2, pp. 581–600.

Roosevelt, T. (1910) *African Game Trails; An Account of the African Wanderings of an American Hunter-Naturalist*, London: Syndicate Publishing.

Shibia, M. G. (2010) 'Determinants of attitudes and perceptions on resource use and management of Marsabit National Reserve, Kenya', *Journal of Human Ecology*, Vol. 30, No. 1, pp. 55–62.

Steinhart, E. I. (1989) 'Hunters, poachers and gamekeepers: Towards a social history of hunting in colonial Kenya', *The Journal of African History*, Vol. 30, No. 2, pp. 247–264.

United Nations Population Fund (2020) World Population Dashboard, Kenya (https://www.unfpa.org/data/world-population/KE) (accessed: 23 November 2020).

Western, D., Russell, S. and Cuthill, I. (2009) 'The status of wildlife in protected areas compared to non-protected areas of Kenya', *PloS one*, Vol. 4, Issue 7, e6140.

Wielebnowski, N. C., Ziegler, K., Wildt, D. E., Lukas, J. and Brown, J. L. (2002) 'Impact of social management on reproductive, adrenal and behavioural activity in the cheetah (*Acinonyx jubatus*)', *Animal Conservation*, Vol. 5, Issue. 4, pp. 291–301.

Wildlife Conservation and Management Act, No 47 of 2013 (2013) Government of Kenya (http://www.kws.go.ke/content/wcma-act-2013-regulations) (accessed: 28 July 2021)

Witsenburg, K. M. and Roba, A. W. (2004) *Surviving Pastoral Decline : Pastoral Sedentarisation, Natural Resource Management and Livelihood Diversification in Marsabit District, Northern Kenya Deel (Vol. I)*, Amsterdam: Universiteit van Amsterdam.

Reality of 'African Potentials': Informal, Invisible and Dynamic Nature without an *Arena*

Toshio Meguro, Chihiro Ito and Kariuki Kirigia

1. Introduction

The 13 chapters that follow the Introduction discuss issues related to nature and environment in Africa. Not only the research targets – such as country, people, activity, institution and species – but also the analytical methods differ greatly from one chapter to another. Some chapters cover the same country while others focus on similar phenomena in different countries. Each chapter is in some way related to all the others. However, despite these similarities, the facts and issues emphasised in each chapter are different, making them unique and meaningful in terms of their academic, scientific or practical implications. The diverse content of the chapters means that one chapter alone is not sufficient to achieve the purpose of this book on nature or environment. This is not because of the limited content of the chapters, but because the scope of each study is inevitably limited because nature and environment can be studied from numerous and multidisciplinary perspectives (e.g. Goldman et al. [eds] 2011; Tsing et al. [eds] 2017). In view of this, this chapter considers what kind of knowledge on 'African Potentials' can be derived from these diverse chapters.

2. Two Questions Regarding 'African Potentials'

The research project that underlies this book aims to criticise the opinion that regards Africa as being in a state of 'deficiency' and takes an absolute view of modern Western knowledge. The project also seeks to pursue not only solutions for problems facing African societies today, but also a novel framework that reconstructs our understanding of 'problems' and 'solutions' by focusing on the 'potentials' that African people have cultivated.

This book focuses on two specific areas: wildlife conservation policies and projects, and the interaction between local societies and the surrounding environment. Part I comprises chapters pertaining to the main issues of wildlife conservation in Africa, with the intention of finding answers to the following questions: At the forefront of wildlife conservation, are the 'African Potentials' that were identified in the first phase of this research project recognisable? If so, do they lead to better coexistence between people-to-people and people-to-nature? Further, if better relationships have not been created despite the existence of 'African Potentials', what is hindering their realisation? In considering these questions, the concept of 'African Potentials' confirmed in the first phase of this project is used; this includes characteristics such as 'interface function', 'aspiration for pluralism', 'collective agency and networking', 'dynamism and flexibility', 'resilience and tolerance', 'innovativeness and creative expression' (Gebre et al. 2017) and also 'indigenous knowledge' (Shigeta and Kaneko 2017). In this chapter, 'indigenous knowledge' is used as a concept covering 'a manner of "not to compete" more than necessary with others and nature' (Shigeta 2016: 349) and 'something invisible and embedded in daily life' (Sato et al. 2016: 302), as well as the 'increasing opportunities for the *arena* (place for dialogue)' among stakeholders in conservation (Sato et al. 2016: 303–304).

Unlike the chapters in Part I whose central theme comprises the responses of local people to external conservation initiatives – especially for wildlife conservation – introduced to the area, the targets of the chapters in Part II are not limited to wildlife and conservation. Part II focuses on the dynamics of people's interactions with various types of natural resources while paying attention to the interrelation between people and their environments such as ecology, geography, economy, politics and society. Moreover, while the chapters in Part I basically examine whether local societies have realised 'African Potentials' defined in the first phase, the chapters of Part II explore the interrelationships between various actors and scales, and consider what, if any, 'potentials' could be recognised within them.

This chapter looks back on the discussions in Part I and Part II, and highlights the conclusions drawn from them. It also returns to the starting point of this research project and briefly, but critically, presents a few suggestions on the latest idea of environmental governance from the perspective of 'African Potentials'.

3. Reality of 'African Potentials': Limitations of Being Informal and Invisible

3-1. Forefront of Wildlife Conservation

It is said that there was a shift in wildlife conservation in Africa from the 'fortress conservation' approach, which pursues the preservation of a wilderness without human beings, to a 'community-based' paradigm at the end of the 20th century. However, the typical example of 'fortress conservation' (i.e. national parks) still exists, and none of the local societies that are studied in Part I has been compensated for the current burdens they face such as human–wildlife conflicts besides past injustices of land grabbing and forced eviction.

In general, Part I describes the difficulties faced by local societies residing adjacent to national parks. Human–elephant conflict has been intensifying around the Serengeti National Park in Tanzania, and local people are suffering not only visible damages but also invisible burdens (Chapter 1). Further, due to the increasing influence of global conservationism, anti-poaching activities around the Kruger National Park in South Africa have become more violent and suppressive, bringing negative impacts on livelihood activities and social relationships besides increasing inflicting physical pain among local residents (Chapter 2). Human–wildlife conflicts and the 'militarisation' of conservation continue to occur in various parts of Africa (see Duffy et al. 2019; Lamarque et al. 2009 as well as Chapters 4 and 13). The 'fortress conservation' approach followed by national parks continues to create problems today.

While national parks remain intact, it is also true that 'community-based' activities that are commonly referred to as either 'community-based conservation' (CBC) or 'community-based natural resource management' (CBNRM) have increased (cf. Child 2019; Hulme and Murphree [eds] 2001; Suich et al. [eds] 2009). This approach often includes the recognition of customary rights, the delegation of conservation and management authority, benefit sharing and development of local societies through tourism. It has an intention to correct the environmental injustices imposed by 'fortress conservation'. The reality is that a protected area was established around the Amboseli National Park in Kenya that once attracted acclaim as a successful example of CBC. However, it caused disparity and discord within the local community over the issues of decision making and benefit sharing (Chapter 5). Also, the project of creating a protected area around the Maasai Mara National Reserve in the same country was a source of political strife within the local community (Chapter 6). Although these protected areas claim to be 'community-based', the fact remains that they are similar to national parks in intending to conserve wildlife and its habitat by limiting human activities and to obtain economic profits from tourism. In other words, although the paradigm of conservation has changed, the same problems of the 'fortress conservation' approach continue to be reproduced by the 'community-based' approach.

Certainly, there are cases in which 'community-based' projects are approved by the majority of local people. The Maasai Olympics in the Amboseli area in Kenya, hosted by a resourceful NGO, is a good example. However, while the NGO globally promotes the event as a spectacular and successful conservation initiative, it fails in not only promoting further communication opportunities but also in strengthening mutual understanding with local people, who do not have strong conservation initiatives (Chapter 3). Although the new conservation paradigm considers dialogue among stakeholders to be as important as or even more important than benefit sharing and the recognition of rights (Berkes 2007; Brown 2003; Eriksson et al. 2019), this case reveals that the ground reality differs from the concept.

The chapters of Part I cover only a few cases of wildlife conservation efforts in Africa today. However, all of the protected areas mentioned are the most famous and popular tourist destinations in the continent. As such, a great deal of national and

326

global wildlife conservation efforts, including 'community-based' initiatives, have been launched in these protected areas. Part I confirms that even at the forefront, wildlife conservation continues to be dominated by the 'fortress' approach. While neoliberal approaches are also expanding, the 'fortress' approach is at the heart of conservation and causes locals a multitude of problems.

3-2. 'African Potentials' for Wildlife Conservation

While various problems are encountered at the forefront of wildlife conservation, it is noteworthy that the people living there are not in a state of 'deficiency' but exerting 'African Potentials'.

First of all, the knowledge and ability of the people in Serengeti about African elephants are good examples of 'African Potentials'. Based on a wealth of experience-based knowledge, or 'indigenous knowledge', about the elephants, they have the ability to notice the existence and follow the tracks of the elephants with great success, which is impossible for a foreign researcher to replicate, and to mitigate human–elephant conflicts while helping locals coexist with elephants (Chapter 1). It must be remembered that this success is not only based on their 'innovativeness and creative expression' in coming up with various countermeasures available to people with scant resources, but also their 'collective agency and networking' for cooperation in an environment where external support cannot be expected.

On the other hand, both 'dynamism and flexibility' and 'resilience and tolerance' are evident in the attitude of the Maasai people in Kenya. In the case of the Maasai Olympics (Chapter 3), the Maasai people in Amboseli believe that the NGO that hosts this 'community-based' event does not understand local culture and people's thinking. Nevertheless, they do not mind it. Even if the NGO forms a faux 'traditional' team, they continue to cooperate with it because they understand their cooperation could lead to the pleasure and satisfaction of outsiders, thereby increasing the possibility that the NGO and other outsiders will provide more benefits to them. The Maasai are not stubborn traditionalists, a typical stereotype of African people; instead, they are flexibly

327

accepting new opportunities and tolerating outsiders' lack of understanding.

In the case of Maasai Mara (Chapter 6), when the local Maasai people faced the crisis of losing their rights to land in the course of the subdivision of a group ranch, they employed various strategies. They cooperated with each other as members of the same community, showing their 'African Potentials' of 'collective agency', but what is noteworthy is that they understood the modern political, legal and juridical systems and also were well aware of the influence of NGOs and both public and social media. Not only did they demonstrate their potentials for 'networking', they also exhibited the 'interface function' of strategically and flexibly utilising both traditional and modern institutions. If one system turns out to be useful, they actively use it while simultaneously taking advantage of other means. Although the introduction of the group ranch system to Maasai societies has resulted in confusion and conflicts (cf. Rutten 1992), these facts suggest Maasai people have 'dynamism and flexibility' and their social institutions are 'resilient and tolerant'.

The existence of 'interface functions' is more explicitly argued in the case of park scouts of Ethiopia (Chapter 4). The important point in this case is that a scout tries to connect not just invisible knowledge and institutions but also two conflicting parties, namely the locals and park authorities. 'Interface function' is observed in many cases, but the case of the Ethiopian park scout differs from others in that it clearly aims for the establishment of an *arena* and of dialogue among stakeholders. As will be described later, powerful outsiders such as national institutions and NGOs have not created an *arena*. Thus, this case is remarkable because it shows the potential for African people to create it.

3-3. Challenges for 'African Potentials'

African people are collectively and actively trying to solve the problems they are facing by strategically utilising both indigenous means and new extrinsic opportunities, demonstrating the existence of what we call 'African Potentials'. However, the situations are worsening in some places and, generally speaking, problems remain unsolved. What, then, is preventing problem solving?

First, considering the knowledge and abilities of local people regarding nature, Chapter 1 praises the potentials of youth in the Serengeti area, while Chapter 4 is concerned with the loss of the younger generation's 'indigenous knowledge' in Ethiopia. As a reason for that loss, Nishizaki cites the spread of school education, which is also mentioned as one reason why the Maasai 'warriors' of Amboseli stopped their tradition of hunting lions (Chapter 3). However, as pointed out in Chapter 6, lack of school education leads to illiteracy and it is very unfavourable in claiming and protecting one's rights in today's modern system. Therefore, the impact of the modern educational system to local people is ambiguous. Then, it must be noted that apart from the influence of the enrolment of school education, the 'indigenous knowledge' is being lost as local people are banned from practising customary resource use under the philosophy of 'fortress conservation'.

The next point of argument is the side of human societies, or people-to-people interactions. Daily relationships among local people will be first examined, following which the interactions between locals and external actors will be considered.

Regarding daily relationships among local people, all chapters of this book reveal that African people act collectively. However, this does not mean that local societies are free from disharmony. For example, both the 'carrot' of CBC (Chapter 5) and the 'stick' of 'militarisation' (Chapter 2) caused discord within local societies in addition to the privatisation of communal land (Chapter 6). A CBC project that includes tourism development seemingly takes the opposite approach to 'militarisation'. However, the two approaches are similar in assuming that by giving a 'carrot/stick', one can easily control locals without understanding the kinds of damage and costs incurred by each person, and what kind and how diverse each individual's opinions are. In short, neither initiative seeks any positive potential on the ground; they simply disregard local people as suffering 'deficiency'.

Lastly, considering the forefront of wildlife conservation from the perspective of an *arena*, opportunities for dialogue between local people and external organisations are largely unguaranteed. In Serengeti (Chapter 1) and Kruger (Chapter 2), local people are the targets of unilateral and violent crackdowns; in the case of Amboseli (Chapter 5) and Maasai Mara (Chapter 6), it is not easy for the majority of local Maasai people to have an opportunity to talk to officials involved in public. Despite the success of the Maasai Olympics as an event and although there are numerous reports by various media, Maasai people in Amboseli are only represented as spectacles and have had little opportunity to discuss conservation with the NGO (Chapter 3). Further, although a park scout in Ethiopia tries to connect local people and park authorities, it remains an informal practice (Chapter 4). It is neither recognised publicly nor incorporated into national and formal systems.

One of the biggest problems is that while 'African Potentials' are existing locally and indigenously, they remain informal and invisible even after the paradigm shift in conservation because outsiders are caught up in the assumption of African societies as 'deficient' and thus pay little attention to the potentials of local people. Therefore, although today's conservation efforts are often described as 'community-based', they have failed to create an *arena* between local people, find local potentials through dialogue and visualise them in formal institutions. Of course, we do not expect too much from 'African Potentials', but it is a cause for concern that 'African Potentials' are missing from the process of dialogue, consensus making and policymaking about wildlife conservation despite much fanfare about being 'community-based'.

4. Relationships of 'African Potentials': Expansion for a Broader and Dynamic Perspective

Whereas the chapters in Part I focus on the reactions of local people to the extrinsic initiatives to conserve wildlife, those in Part II focus on the interactions between people and environments, most of which study natural resources other than wildlife. In this section, it is first confirmed whether the 'African Potentials', which were presented in the first phase of this project with small and traditional local societies in mind, can be found in each chapter of Part II. Next, we sort out the kind of environmental aspects each chapter

330

specifically focuses on and argues for the significance of focusing on relationships.

4-1. 'African Potentials' for Various Natural Resources

Among the cases in Part II, *virundu*, which was devised by a local fisherman around Lake Malawi, is a good example of 'African Potentials' for natural resource management (Chapter 11). The invention of *virundu* is the 'innovativeness and creative expression' based on 'indigenous knowledge', and its effect is scientifically demonstrated. As it is conceived based on one's own experiences and observations in an environment where external support and school education are inadequate, its effectiveness suggests the potential of 'indigenous knowledge' in a sense; modern scientific knowledge is not a necessary condition for sustainable management. Compared to *virundu*, the indigenous culture on oil palms and chimpanzees in southern Guinea explained in Chapter 7 may seem archaic, and neither innovative nor creative. However, it obviously contributes to wildlife conservation and environmental sustainability even though the human population of the area is growing. In this respect, these indigenous mechanisms exemplify a convivial relationship with nature that does not involve unnecessary conflict. In addition, there are other good examples of 'African Potentials' relating to coexistence with wildlife, such as the cultural and social customs that people in southern Madagascar have inherited concerning lemurs (Chapter 8) and the custom of the Maasai and lions coexisting while maintaining a specific distance from each other (Chapter 13). Though these relationships cannot remain intact as times change, we can confirm as a fact that African societies may have a manner of coexisting with wildlife.

On the other hand, the case of the suburbs of Kruger National Park – where competition over marula fruits increased due to commodification, but conflicts over their use were avoided under the authority of traditional leaders (Chapter 9) – is a good example of 'indigenous knowledge' of 'a manner of "not to compete" more than necessary with others'. While the abundance of the fruits is a condition that cannot be ignored, the fact remains that the presence of traditional authorities has influenced the behaviour and thinking of local people and a private company so that there have been no notable conflicts among resource users. In addition, what should not be overlooked is the realisation of social stability and coexistence between the two systems of global capitalism and traditional institution. This case reveals that novel opportunities of commodification are creating new relationships both among local people and between locals and a private corporation through the 'interface function' of 'interweav[ing] and forg[ing] connections' between Western/modern and African/traditional systems.

The above-mentioned cases show that 'African Potentials' are inherent in the context of various natural resources other than wildlife. Moreover, the sensitivity of local people to environmental changes and their proactive approach to looking for new opportunities and finding ways to make good use of them is found in many chapters of this book: the history of the coexistence of West African people and chimpanzees (Chapter 7), kapenta fishing in Lake Kariba (Chapter 10) and fishery by the Vezo people in Madagascar (Chapter 12). These results show the 'dynamism and flexibility', 'resilience and tolerance' and 'innovativeness and creative expression' of those local people; moreover, they provide evidence to refute the preconception that African societies are in a state of 'deficiency'.

In addition, a fact worthy of note about kapenta fishing in Lake Kariba is that many scholars have highlighted the problem concerning resource management here (Chapter 10). Lake Kariba is an artificial lake created by the construction of Kariba Dam in the 1950s. Kapenta was introduced after the creation of the lake, and kapenta fishing began based on a small lakeside city that is characterised by the high degree of mobility of people. The problem here is that while kapenta fisheries, whose members are highly mobile and thus easily change, have some kind of 'African Potentials' as explained above, it seems to remain a personal potential. In other words, a collective potential, like 'collective agency and networking' that are confirmed in many other chapters, appears to be missing here for natural resource management. If this understanding is correct, it raises a question of whether 'African Potentials' exist or are not effective for convivial coexistence in an urban setting or in the case of a resource that has not traditionally been used.

4-2. Perspective of Relationship with Environment

The word 'environment' refers to situations that surround a subject, and the environment of an individual includes not only the so-called natural environment but also the social environment, or human society. While each chapter of Part II deals with specific natural resources, its scope of analysis includes various social environments surrounding local people, and the interactions between people and the natural environment. Using anthropogenic West African landscapes as a case study, Chapter 7 may refer to the most diverse topics such as human culture, social institutions, wildlife ecology, interspecies interaction, landscape change, environmental politics and the historical and dynamic relationships among them. Other chapters, on the other hand, focus on their scopes and provide more detailed explanations on specific topics.

For example, Chapter 8 focuses on riparian forests in Madagascar and analyses several multifaceted ecological relationships. The analysis of the triangular relationships between humans, animals and plants clearly reveals that the survival of endangered animals is not guaranteed solely by the 'African Potentials' of the local society. When an ecosystem is a complex adaptive system comprising several diverse species, even if increased human activity is a major cause of environmental crisis, it is not appropriate to design the conservation of a certain species by merely analysing its direct relationship with human society. In fact, it has been stated in recent years that we should consider not merely an ecosystem itself but the social-ecological systems as a complex adaptive system (Colding and Barthel 2019; Levin et al. 2013).

While Chapter 8 describes the complexity of the ecosystem, Chapter 12 discusses a challenge in analysing human society. Through a case study of a fishery society in Madagascar, Chapter 12 depicts the historical relationship between the fluctuations of commodity prices and population, and the changes of the political, economic and social environment over a quarter century. In doing so, the chapter focuses on how people have changed their livelihood activities during such a dynamic chronology. The point is that a human society is so adaptable to changes that it is difficult to assume that a local society naturally maintains the status quo. It means that we cannot simply apply the concept of sustainability to social phenomena.

The dynamism of human society is very clear in other chapters: for example, people living in urban South Africa (Chapter 9) and Zambia (Chapter 10). Compared to other cases, their environment is characterised by the fluidity of residents, proximity to markets and difficulty to privately enclose natural resources under discussion (marula fruits and kapenta respectively). The two chapters depict the historical transition of the use of natural resources with an emphasis on the change of the national political and legal systems, economic and technical options available and local cultural and social contexts, revealing that both of the resource users and the use system have changed significantly due to changes such as the end of apartheid, commodification by a large company and the support through international aid.

One important result of Part II is that in many cases, such as oil palms (Chapter 7), marula fruits (Chapter 9), kapenta (Chapter 10) and Vezo fishermen (Chapter 12), drastic environmental changes have occurred and human–nature interactions have changed in just a few decades, and the people who constitute the 'resource users' have changed fluidly in the wake of environmental changes. This becomes abundantly clear because the chapters pay more attention to examining the relationship between local people and natural resources from the historical perspective. Consequently, it turns out that considering 'African Potentials' on the premise that African societies are like 'communities' that are homogeneous and geographically small groups with clear boundaries (cf. Agrawal and Gibson 1999) is not appropriate in light of the environmental dynamism. This understanding will lead to a new approach to 'African Potentials': seeking potentials for convivial coexistence in the relationships among various people, nature and environments rather than just examining whether particular subjects have 'African Potentials'. Along this line of thinking, the significance of the argument over the 'potential for commodification' (Chapter 9) becomes clear.

These findings do not immediately mean a denial of the results of Part I. It merely shows the importance of paying attention to the dynamism of environments and relationships. This also highlights the importance of remembering the reason why our project uses the word 'indigenous' instead of 'traditional' (cf. Gebre et al. 2017). The use of 'tradition' is avoided because it is commonly associated with something that is stable, unchanging and essential. Conversely, 'indigenous' is repeatedly used in this chapter because it includes the process of continuous interactions of different ideas and the emergence of novel knowledge and practice. The perspective of 'African Potentials' not only denies the idea that Africa is in a state of 'deficiency', but also focuses attention to local voices and practices, and to interactions and relationships in the changing environment.

5. Concluding Remarks

5-1. Summary of Research Results

The objective of Part I is to examine the existence and outcomes of 'African Potentials' at the forefront of wildlife conservation in Africa today. The results are as follows:

- Local societies at the forefront of wildlife conservation generally have 'African Potentials' that have been confirmed in the first phase of this research project (e.g. innovativeness, collectivity, flexibility, tolerance, interface function, and others).
- Even after the paradigm shift in the realm of conservation, 'fortress' approaches are dominant while neoliberal approaches are on the rise, and local societies are suffering from various damages and burdens despite their 'African Potentials'.
- As a result of the change in the conservation paradigm, local people have more opportunities to benefit as well as communicate, but the foundation of a public *arena*, where local people can engage in a free and equal dialogue with more powerful and resourceful stakeholders, is not confirmed.
- The conservation approaches, whether classical 'fortress' or recent neoliberal ones, presume that the best way for local people is to be governed by outside experts. In other words, they

seem to consider local societies as 'deficient' and without any 'potentials'.

- Consequently, local 'potentials' are unnoticed and suppressed by the outsiders and, therefore, remain informal and invisible.

Also, the results of Part II, which takes up more diverse natural resources and focuses on the interaction between local societies and their environment, are as follows:

- In general, local societies have 'African Potentials' for the conservation and management of various natural resources as they do for wildlife. However, there are some reservations.
- The first reservation is that even if local societies have 'African Potentials' that lead to the conservation of certain natural resources, there is a possibility that the complex relationships within the ecosystem are also contributing to that result. Therefore, the 'potentials' of local societies cannot be overly expected.
- The second reservation is that the interaction between human societies and their environment is dynamic. There is a possibility that the relationship between people and nature on a local scale will become significantly different due to changes in the natural and social environment. Thus, it is not realistic to aim for sustaining a relationship at a certain point of time for the future, even if it seems desirable.
- The third reservation is uncertainty about 'collectivity' and 'indigenousness'. While many societies demonstrate their 'collective agency' together with 'indigenous knowledge' that is a product of 'interfacing' traditional things and modern affairs, it has also become clear that 'African Potentials' for convivial coexistence may not be found in an urban society whose members are too fluid to share 'collective agency' and 'indigenous knowledge'.
- All of these reservations suggest the importance of focusing on the multifaceted relationships among and between local people

and their environment on the premise that these relationships are very complex and dynamic.

5-2. Issue of the Arena *and Philosophical Perspective of 'African Potentials'*

As summarised in the last section, African societies have been demonstrating their 'potentials' in some way or the other, and thus the attitude of assuming them first and foremost as in a state of 'deficiency' should be criticised. However, while several positive results are confirmed concerning the many examples of 'African Potentials', the results about the 'increasing opportunities for the *arena* (a place for dialogue)' are generally and exceptionally negative. We would like to offer some thoughts and arguments on this issue.

The issue of an *arena* is not limited to Part I. Many chapters of Part II develop arguments related to this as well. For example, Chapter 10 points out the lack of a formal and effective resource management system for kapenta fishery as a major problem, and Chapter 11 insists upon the necessity of public and external support for a remote society so as to unleash its 'potentials'. Also, Chapter 12 argues how outsiders should consider the opinions and rights of local people in the decision-making process of natural resource management and sustainable development. All of these concern the communication and cooperation between local people and other actors such as governmental organisations and external donors, that is to say, the issue of dialogue and interaction among stakeholders in a public *arena*. However, the case studies of wildlife conservation in this book reveal the fact that environmental conservation is based on authoritarian 'carrot-and-stick' governance rather than on an orientation towards dialogue with local people on an equal footing in an *arena*.

The one reason why the voices of local people are not listened to by outsiders or conveyed to public spaces is that experts do not have a philosophical perspective of 'African Potentials' and thus do not acknowledge the existence or effectiveness of 'African Potentials' as realistic solutions.

For example, Brian Child, who had led the CAMPFIRE (Community Areas Management Programme for Indigenous Resources) in Zimbabwe, and also has led the global debate on

337

CBC/CBNRM so far, recently published a book titled *Sustainable Governance of Wildlife and Community-Based Natural Resource Management* (Child 2019). This book refers to a number of studies on natural resource management, community development, environmental governance, and so on, and introduces a wide variety of theoretical tools for analysing and designing conservation and governance. There is no doubt that this is a practical and useful academic book.

However, there is a lack of the philosophical perspectives of 'African Potentials' such as 'incompleteness', 'collectivity' and 'conviviality'. Everything is neatly explained based on Western and scientific knowledge: the process of community participation is in conformity with Western democracy; community benefit is considered following the economic principles of proprietorship and price; and the guidelines for relationship between local people and other stakeholders are founded on the recent argument on participatory, inclusionary or adaptive governance. What is lacking in these explanations is, first of all, an awareness of the 'incompleteness' of own knowledge and of the need to 'interface' with indigenous knowledge in African societies. Second, the 'collectivity' of local societies is considered only in the context of natural resource management, meaning that people's behaviours are judged on the basis of how economically efficient, democratically just or ecologically sustainable they are. There is no notion that through dialogue and interaction with others, people will realise a 'convivial' coexistence and bring forth novel possibilities for a better life. Instead, as criteria of 'community citizenship', Child (2019: 316), for example, writes the following three things: 'Participate equally in collective action', 'Participate in a well informed way' and 'Become economic citizens, with equal rights to the benefits from collectively owned resources'.

It is true that Child (2019) discusses the 'community' from various perspectives, but there is surprisingly little mention of its 'potentials'. 'Communities' are treated as something investigated, evaluated and directed by outsiders who have scientific knowledge. The truth is that such an attitude is found in many other studies (e.g. Barnes and Child [eds] 2014; Nelson [ed.] 2010; Sowman and Wynberg [eds] 2014; Suich et al. [eds] 2009). All of these envisage only fitting local information into existing scientific theories and frameworks, with no consideration of the possibility that indigenous ideas may call for the modification or abandonment of such scientific techniques. This fact is considered to be a reflection of the strong belief in the 'completeness' of scientific knowledge held by professionals and authorities.

We think that the existence and possibility of 'African Potentials' are shown throughout this book. However, if the concept of 'African Potentials' is understood only as practical problem-solving methods with the dominant values preserved, the meaning of 'African Potentials' will be distorted – as in the case of the idea of 'community-based' – to conform with the ideology of 'completeness' together with the possibility of 'convivial' coexistence. Consideration of the idea of 'African Potentials' at a more abstract and metaphysical level, and to figure out how to incorporate the philosophy of 'incompleteness' and the essence of 'conviviality' into a timely and promising idea such as adaptive governance (cf. Chaffin et al. 2014; Cleaver and Whaley 2018; Colding and Barthel 2019; Folke et al. 2005; Van Assche et al. 2017) is an issue for the future. Either way, as a result of having been particular about fieldwork and concrete cases, we came to realise the importance of the philosophical dimension of 'African Potentials'. Thus, we felt it was worthy of discussion in concluding this book.

Acknowledgements

This work was supported by JSPS KAKENHI Grant Number JP16H06318.

References

Agrawal, A. and Gibson C. C. (1999) 'Enchantment and disenchantment: The role of community in natural resource conservation', *World Development*, Vol. 27, No. 4, pp. 629–649.

Barnes, G. and Child, B. (eds) (2014) *Adaptive Cross-Scalar Governance of Natural Resources*, Oxon: Routledge.

Berkes, F. (2007) 'Community-based conservation in a globalized world', *PNAS (The Proceedings of the National Academy of Sciences)*, Vol. 104, No. 39, pp. 15188–15193.

Brown, K. (2003) 'Three challenges for a real people-centred conservation', *Global Ecology and Biogeography*, Vol. 12, No. 2, pp. 89–92.

Chaffin, B. Gosnell, H. and Cosens, B. (2014) 'A decade of adaptive governance scholarship: Synthesis and future directions', *Ecology and Society*, Vol. 19, No. 3, Article 56 (http://dx.doi.org/10.5751/ES-06824-190356) (accessed: 26 March 2021).

Child, B. (2019) *Sustainable Governance of Wildlife and Community-Based Natural Resource Management*, Oxon: Routledge.

Cleaver, F. and Whaley, L. (2018) 'Understanding process, power, and meaning in adaptive governance: A critical institutional reading', *Ecology and Society*, Vol. 23, No. 2, Article 49 (https://doi.org/10.5751/ES-10212-230249) (accessed: 26 March 2021).

Colding, J. and Barthel, S. (2019) 'Exploring the social-ecological systems discourse 20 years later', *Ecology and Society*, Vol. 24, No. 1, Article 2 (https://doi.org/10.5751/ES-10598-240102) (accessed: 26 March 2021).

Duffy, R., Massé, F., Smibt, E., Marjinen, E., Büscher, B., Verweijen, J., Ramutsindela, M., Simlai, T., Joanny, L. and Lunstrum, E. (2019) 'Why we must question the militarisation of conservation', *Biological Conservation*, Vol. 232, pp. 66–73.

Eriksson, M., Van Riper, C. J., Leitschuh, B., Brymer, A. B., Rawluk, A., Raymond, C. M. and Kenter, J. O. (2019) 'Social learning as a link between the individual and the collective: Evaluating deliberation on social values', *Sustainability Science*, Vol. 14, pp. 1323–1332.

Folke, C., Hahn, T., Olsson, P. and Norberg, J. (2005) 'Adaptive governance of social-ecological systems', *Annual Review of Environment and Resources*, Vol. 30, pp. 441–473.

Gebre, Y., Ohta, I. and Matsuda, M. (2017) 'Introduction: Achieving peace and coexistence through African potentials', in Y. Gebre, I.

Ohta and M. Matsuda (eds) *African Virtues in the Pursuit of Conviviality: Exploring Local Solutions in Light of Global Prescriptions*, Bamenda: Langaa RPCIG, pp. 3–37.

Goldman, M. J., Nadasdy, P. and Turner, M. D. (eds) (2011) *Knowing Nature: Conservation at the Intersection of Political Ecology and Science Studies*, Chicago: The University of Chicago Press.

Hulme, D. and Murphree, M. (eds) (2001) *African Wildlife and Livelihoods: The Promise and Performance of Community Conservation*, Oxford: James Currey; Cape Town: David Philips Publishers; Harare: Weaver Press; Zomba: Kachere Press; Nairobi: E.A.E.P.; Kampala: Fountain Publishers; Portsmouth, NH: Heinemann.

Lamarque, F., Anderson, J., Fergusson, R., Lagrange, M., Osei-Owusu, Y. and Bakker, L. (2009) *Human-Wildlife Conflict in Africa: Causes, Consequences and Management Strategies*, Rome: Food and Agriculture Organization of the United Nations.

Levin, S., Xepapadeas, T., Crépin, A-S., Norberg, J., De Zeeuw, A., Folke, C., Hughes, T., Arrow, K., Barrett, S., Daily, G., Ehrlich, P., Kautsky, N., Mäler, K-G., Polasky, S., Troell, M., Vincent, J. and Walker, B. (2013) 'Socio-ecological systems as complex adaptive systems', *Environment and Development Economics*, Vol. 18, No. 2, pp. 111–132.

Nelson, F. (ed.) (2010) *Community Rights, Conservation and Contested Land: The Politics of Natural Resources Governance in Africa*, Oxon: Earthscan.

Rutten, M. (1992) *Selling Wealth to Buy Poverty: The Process of the Individualization of Landownership among the Maasai Pastoralists of Kajiado District, Kenya, 1890–1990*, Saarbrucken: Verlag Bretienbach.

Sato, T., Meguro, T. and Yamakoshi, G. (2016) 'Place and future of African Potentials in the practice of nature protection activities', in G. Yamakoshi, T. Meguro and T. Sato (eds) *Who Owns African Nature? African Perspectives on the Future of Community-Based Conservation*, Kyoto: Kyoto University Press, 295–305 (in Japanese).

Shigeta, M. (2016) 'Manner to avoid conflict: Potentials about subsistence and ecology', in M. Shigeta and J. Itani (eds) *How People Can Achieve Coexistence through the Sound Use of Ecological Resources*, Kyoto: Kyoto University Press, pp. 331–353 (in Japanese).

Shigeta, M. and Kaneko, M. (2017) '*Zairaichi* (local knowledge) as the manners of co-existence: Encounters between the Aari farmers in southwestern Ethiopia and the "Other"', in Y. Gebre, I. Ohta and M. Matsuda (eds) *African Virtues in the Pursuit of Conviviality: Exploring Local Solutions in Light of Global Prescriptions*, Bamenda: Langaa RPCIG, pp. 311–338.

Sowman, M. and Wynberg, R. (eds) (2014) *Governance for Justice and Environmental Sustainability: Lessons across Natural Resource Sectors in Sub-Saharan Africa*, Oxon: Routledge.

Suich, H., Child B. and Spenceley A. (eds) (2009) *Evolution and Innovation in Wildlife Conservation: Parks and Game Ranches to Transfrontier Conservation Areas*, London: Earthscan.

Tsing, A., Swanson, H., Gan, E. and Bubandt, N. (eds) (2017) *Arts of Living on a Damaged Planet: Ghosts and Monsters of the Anthropocene*, Minnesota: University of Minnesota Press.

Van Assche, K., Beunen, R., Duineveld, M. and Gruezmacher, M. (2017) 'Power/knowledge and natural resource management: Foucaultian foundations in the analysis of adaptive governance', *Journal of Environmental Policy and Planning*, Vol. 19, No. 3, pp. 308–322.

Index